GEOMETRY OF FOUR DIMENSIONS

THE MACMILLAN COMPANY
NEW YORK · BOSTON · CHICAGO · DALLAS
ATLANTA · SAN FRANCISCO

MACMILLAN & CO., LIMITED
LONDON · BOMBAY · CALCUTTA
MELBOURNE

THE MACMILLAN CO. OF CANADA, LTD.
TORONTO

GEOMETRY

OF FOUR DIMENSIONS

BY

HENRY PARKER MANNING, Ph.D.

ASSOCIATE PROFESSOR OF PURE MATHEMATICS
IN BROWN UNIVERSITY

New York
THE MACMILLAN COMPANY
1914

Norwood Press
J. S. Cushing Co. — Berwick & Smith Co.
Norwood, Mass., U.S.A.

PREFACE

The object and plan of this book are explained in the Introduction (page 16). I had hoped to give some account of the recent literature, but this would have delayed work that has already taken several years. I have prepared a list of technical terms as found in a few of the more familiar writings, very incomplete, and, I fear, not without errors. The list may be of service, however, to those who wish to consult the authors referred to; it will also indicate something of the confusion that exists in a subject whose nomenclature has not become fixed. It has been necessary for me to introduce a considerable number of terms, but most of these have been formed in accordance with simple or well-established principles, and no attempt has been made to distinguish them from the terms that have already been used.

I am indebted to the kindness of Mr. George A. Plimpton of New York for an opportunity to examine his copy of Rudolph's *Coss* referred to on page 2. I am also under many obligations to Mrs. Walter C. Bronson of Providence, to Mr. Albert A. Bennett, Instructor at Princeton University, and to my colleagues, Professors R. C. Archibald and R. G. D. Richardson, from all of whom I have received valuable criticisms and suggestions. Many of the references in the first four pages were found by Professor Archibald; several of these are not given in the leading bibliographies, and the reference to Ozanam I have not seen anywhere.

HENRY P. MANNING.

PROVIDENCE,
July, 1914.

CONTENTS

PAGE

INTRODUCTION I

CHAPTER I

THE FOUNDATIONS OF FOUR-DIMENSIONAL GEOMETRY

I. POINTS AND LINES 23
II. TRIANGLES 29
III. PLANES 35
IV. CONVEX POLYGONS 40
V. TETRAHEDRONS 45
VI. HYPERPLANES 50
VII. CONVEX PYRAMIDS AND PENTAHEDROIDS . . . 55
VIII. SPACE OF FOUR DIMENSIONS 59
IX. HYPERPYRAMIDS AND HYPERCONES 63

CHAPTER II

PERPENDICULARITY AND SIMPLE ANGLES

INTRODUCTORY 73
I. LINES PERPENDICULAR TO A HYPERPLANE . . . 74
II. ABSOLUTELY PERPENDICULAR PLANES 80
III. SIMPLY PERPENDICULAR PLANES 85
IV. PERPENDICULAR PLANES AND HYPERPLANES . . 90
V. HYPERPLANE ANGLES 95

vii

CHAPTER III

ANGLES OF TWO PLANES AND ANGLES OF HIGHER ORDER

PAGE
I. The Common Perpendicular of Two Lines . . 105
II. Point Geometry 112
III. The Angles of Two Planes 114
IV. Polyhedroidal Angles 126
V. Plano-polyhedral Angles 133

CHAPTER IV

SYMMETRY, ORDER, AND MOTION

I. Rotation and Translation 141
II. Symmetry 146
III. Order 153
IV. Motion in General 167
V. Rectangular Systems 179
VI. Isocline Planes 180

CHAPTER V

HYPERPYRAMIDS, HYPERCONES, AND THE HYPER-SPHERE

I. Pentahedroids and Hyperpyramids 199
II. Hypercones and Double Cones. 204
III. The Hypersphere 207

CHAPTER VI

EUCLIDEAN GEOMETRY. FIGURES WITH PARALLEL ELEMENTS

The Axiom of Parallels 221
I. Parallels 221
II. The "Hyperplane at Infinity" 230

CONTENTS

III. HYPERPRISMS 235
IV. DOUBLE PRISMS 241
V. HYPERCYLINDERS 253
VI. PRISM CYLINDERS AND DOUBLE CYLINDERS . . 256

CHAPTER VII

MEASUREMENT OF VOLUME AND HYPERVOLUME IN HYPERSPACE

I. VOLUME 265
II. HYPERVOLUME 270

CHAPTER VIII

THE REGULAR POLYHEDROIDS

I. THE FOUR SIMPLER REGULAR POLYHEDROIDS . . 289
II. THE POLYHEDROID FORMULA 300
III. RECIPROCAL POLYHEDROIDS AND RECIPROCAL NETS
OF POLYHEDROIDS 303
IV. CONSTRUCTION OF THE REGULAR 600-HEDROID AND
THE REGULAR 120-HEDROID 317

TECHNICAL TERMS 327
INDEX 335

INTRODUCTION

THE geometry of more than three dimensions is entirely a modern branch of mathematics, going no farther back than the first part of the nineteenth century. There are, however, some early references to the number of dimensions of space.

In the first book of the *Heaven* of Aristotle (384–322 B.C.) are these sentences: "The line has magnitude in one way, the plane in two ways, and the solid in three ways, and beyond these there is no other magnitude because the three are all," and "There is no transfer into another kind, like the transfer from length to area and from area to a solid."* Simplicius (sixth century, A.D.) in his *Commentaries* says, "The admirable Ptolemy in his book *On Distance* well proved that there are not more than three distances, because of the necessity that distances should be defined, and that the distances defined should be taken along perpendicular lines, and because it is possible to take only three lines that are mutually perpendicular, two by which the plane is defined and a third measuring depth; so that if there were any other distance after the third it would be entirely without measure and without definition. Thus Aristotle seemed to conclude from induction that there is no transfer into another magnitude, but Ptolemy proved it." †

---

* Aristoteles, *De Caelo*, ed. Prantl, Leipzig, 1881, 268a, 7 and 30.

† *Simplicii in Aristotelis De Caelo Commentaria*, ed. Heiberg, Berlin, 1894, 7a, 33. Ptolemy lived about 150 A.D. The book on distance, περὶ διαστάσεως, is lost, and with it Ptolemy's "proof" except so far as it may be reproduced in the above quotation from Simplicius.

There is also in the early history of algebra a use of terms analogous to those derived from the plane and solid geometry, but applicable only to geometry of more dimensions. With the Greeks, and then in general with the mathematicians that came after them, a number was thought of as a *line* (of definite length), the product of two numbers as a *rectangle* or *plane*, and the product of three numbers as a *parallelopiped* or *solid;* or, if the numbers were equal, the product of two was a *square* and of three a *cube.* When they began to study algebra, other terms were required for the higher powers, and so in Diophantus (third century) we find *square-square, square-cube*, and *cube-cube.** In later times there was a variation in the use of these terms. Thus the square-cube came to mean the square of the cube, or sixth power, while with Diophantus it means the square times the cube, or fifth power. This change required the introduction of new terms for powers of prime orders, and, in particular, for the fifth power, which was finally called a *sursolid.*† The geometrical conception of equations and the geometrical forms of their solutions‡ hindered

---

* Cantor, *Vorlesungen über Geschichte der Mathematik*, vol. I, 3d ed., Leipzig, 1907, p. 470.

† In the edition of Rudolph's *Coss* (algebra) revised by Stifel (Königsberg, 1553, described by David Eugene Smith in *Rara Arithmetica*, Boston, 1908, p. 258) *Sursolidum* denotes the fifth power, *Bsursolidum* the seventh power, and so on (Part I, chap. 5, fol. 63). Paciuolo (about 1445–1514) in his *Summa de Arithmetica Geometria Proportioni et Proportionalita*, printed in 1494, uses the terms *primo relato* and *secundo relato* (Cantor, *Vorlesungen*, etc., vol. II, 2d ed., 1900, p. 317). On the other hand, Vieta (1540–1603) follows Diophantus. He expresses all the powers above the third by compounds of *quadrato* and *cubo, cubo-cubo-cubus* being the ninth power (*Francisci Vietæ opera mathematica*, Leyden, 1646, p. 3 and elsewhere). The term sursolid occurs several times in the geometry of Descartes (1596–1650). It is to be noted, however, that a product with Descartes always means a line of definite length derived from given lengths by proportions. Problems which lead to equations of the fifth or sixth degrees require for their geometrical solution curves "one degree more complicated than conics." Conics were called by the Greeks *solid loci*, and these more complicated curves were called by Descartes *sursolid loci* (*La Géométrie*. See pp. 20 and 29 of the edition published by Hermann, Paris, 1886).

‡ Such solutions are given in the second and sixth books of Euclid's *Elements*. See Heath's edition, Cambridge University Press, 1908, vol. I, p. 383.

the progress of algebra with the ancients. Higher equations than the third were avoided as unreal,* and when the study of higher equations forced itself upon mathematicians, it meant an impossible extension of geometrical notions, which met with many protests, and only in later times gave way to a purely numerical conception of the nature of algebraic quantities. Thus Stifel (1486?–1567), in the *Algebra* of Rudolph already referred to (footnote, preceding page), speaks of "going beyond the cube just as if there were more than three dimensions," "which is," he adds, "against nature." † John Wallis (1616–1703) in his Algebra objects to the "ungeometrical" names given to the higher powers. He calls one of them a "Monster in Nature, less possible than a Chimæra or Centaure." He says: "Length, Breadth and Thickness, take up the whole of Space. Nor can Fansie imagine how there should be a Fourth Local Dimension beyond these Three." ‡ Ozanam (1640–1717), after speaking of the product of two letters as a rectangle and the product of three as a rectangular parallelopiped, says that a product of more than three letters will be a magnitude of "as many dimensions as there are letters, but it will only be imaginary because in nature we do not know of any quantity which has more than three dimensions." §

Again, we find in the writings of some philosophers references to a space of four dimensions. Thus Henry More (1614–1687), an English philosopher, in a book published in 1671, says that spirits have four dimensions,¶ and Kant (1724–1804) refers in several places to the number of dimensions of space.‖

---

* Matthiessen, *Grundzüge der antiken und modernen Algebra*, 2d ed., Leipzig, 1896, pp. 544 and 921.   † Part I, chap. 1, fol. 9 *recto*.   ‡ London, 1685, p. 126.
§ *Dictionaire mathematique*, Amsterdam, 1691, p. 62.
¶ *Enchiridion metaphysicum*, Pt. I, chap. 28, § 7, p. 384.
‖ For example, he says in the *Critique of Pure Reason*, "For if the intuition

Finally, there is a suggestion made by certain writers that mechanics can be considered a geometry of four dimensions with time as the fourth dimension (see below, p. 11). This idea is usually credited to Lagrange (1736–1813), who advanced it in his *Théorie des fonctions analytiques*, first published in 1797.* It is expressed, however, in an article on "Dimension" published in 1754 by d'Alembert (1717–1783) in the *Encyclopédie* edited by Diderot and himself. D'Alembert attributes the suggestion to "un homme d'esprit de ma connaissance."†

These are the only ways in which we have found our subject referred to before 1827.

In the period beginning with 1827 we may distinguish those writings which deal with the higher synthetic geometry from those whose point of view is that of analysis. In synthetic geometry our attention is confined at first chiefly to the case of four dimensions, while in analysis we are ready for *n* variables by the time we have considered two and three.

So far as we know, the first contribution to the synthetic geometry of four dimensions is made by Möbius, who points out that symmetrical figures could be made to coincide if there were a space of four dimensions.‡ In 1846 Cayley

---

were a concept gained a posteriori . . . we should not be able to say any more than that, so far as hitherto observed, no space has yet been found having more than three dimensions" (translation by F. Max Müller, 2d ed. revised, Macmillan, 1905, p. 19).

C. H. Hinton finds in four-dimensional space illustration and interpretation of the ideas of Plato, Aristotle, and other Greek philosophers (see *Fourth Dimension*, London, 1904, chap. iv).

* p. 223; *Œuvres*, vol. IX, Paris, 1881, p. 337.

† See paper by R. C. Archibald, "Time as a Fourth Dimension," *Bulletin of the American Mathematical Society*, vol. 20, 1914, pp. 409–412.

‡ He states very clearly the analogy with symmetrical figures in a plane and symmetrical groups of points on a line. Reasoning from this analogy, he says that the coincidence of two symmetrical figures in space would require that we should be able to let one of them make a rotation in space of four dimensions. Then he adds, "Da aber ein solcher Raum nicht gedacht werden kann, so ist auch die Coin-

makes use of geometry of four dimensions to investigate certain configurations of points, suggesting a method that is systematically developed by Veronese.* Cayley had already published a paper with the title "Chapters in the Analytical Geometry of (n) Dimensions," † but as this paper contains no actual reference to such a geometry, we may think of the paper of 1846 as the beginning of his published writings on this subject. Some of the most interesting examples of the direct study of these geometries were given by Sylvester. In 1851, in a paper on homogeneous functions,‡ he discusses tangent and polar forms in n-dimensional geometry; in 1859, in some lectures on partitions,§ he makes an application of hyperspace; and in 1863, in a memoir "On the Centre of Gravity of a Truncated Triangular Pyramid,"¶ he takes up the corresponding figures in four and n dimensions and proves his theorems for all of these figures, using analytic methods to some extent, but appealing freely to synthetic conceptions. Clifford also, about this time, makes a very interesting application of the higher geometry to a problem in probability. ‖

cidenz in diesem Falle unmöglich " (Der barycentrische Calcul, Leipzig, 1827, § 140, p. 184).

* "Sur quelques théorèmes de la géométrie de position," Crelle's Journal, vol. 31, pp. 213–226 (in particular, pp. 217–218); Collected Mathematical Papers, Cambridge, vol. I, 1889, No. 50. See also Veronese, Fondamenti, etc. (the full title is given below on p. 9), p. 690 of the German translation, and Veronese's memoir (mentioned on p. 8). In introducing this method of reasoning, Cayley says: "On peut en effet, sans recourir à aucune notion métaphysique à l'égard de la possibilité de l'espace à quatre dimensions, raisonner comme suit (tout cela pourra aussi être traduit facilement en langue purement analytique)." . . .

✓† Cambridge Mathematical Journal, vol. 4, 1844; Math. Papers, vol. I, No. 11.

‡ Cambridge and Dublin Mathematical Journal, vol. 6, p. 1; Collected Mathematical Papers, Cambridge, vol. I, 1904, No. 30.

§ Outlines of these lectures are published in the Proceedings of the London Mathematical Society, vol. 28, 1896, p. 33; Mathematical Papers, vol. II, 1908, No. 26.

¶ Philosophical Magazine, fourth series, vol. 26, Sept., 1863, pp. 167–183; Mathematical Papers, vol. II, No. 65.

‖ Educational Times, Jan., 1866; Mathematical Reprints, vol. 6, pp. 83–87; Mathematical Papers, Macmillan, 1882, p. 601.

Quite independently of this beginning of its synthetic development, we find a notion of a higher geometry springing out of the applications of analysis. Certain geometrical problems lead to equations which can be expressed with any number of variables as well as with two or three. Thus, in 1833, Green reduces the problem of the attraction of ellipsoids to analysis, and then solves it for any number of variables, saying, "It is no longer confined as it were to the three dimensions of space."* Other writers make the same kind of generalization, though not always pointing out so directly its geometrical significance. † It was but a step farther to apply the language of geometry to all the forms and processes of algebra and analysis. This principle is clearly announced by Cauchy in 1847, in a memoir on analytical loci, where he says, "We shall call a set of n variables an analytical point, an equation or system of equations an analytical locus," etc. ‡

The most important paper of this period is that of Riemann, "On the Hypotheses which Lie at the Foundations of Geometry." § In this paper Riemann builds up the notion of multiply-extended manifolds and their measure-relations. He discusses the nature of the line-element ds when the manifold is expressed by means of n variables. When ds is equal to the square root of the sum

---

* *Mathematical Papers of George Green*, edited by N. M. Ferrers, Macmillan, 1871, p. 188.

† C. G. J. Jacobi, "De binis quibuslibet functionibus homogeneis," etc., *Crelle's Journal*, vol. 12, 1834, p. 1 ; Cayley, two papers published in the *Cambridge Mathematical Journal*, vol. 3, 1841 ; *Mathematical Papers*, vol. I, Nos. 2 and 3 ; Schläfli, "Ueber das Minimum des Integrals $\int(\sqrt{dx_1^2 + dx_2^2 + \ldots + dx_n^2})$," etc., *Crelle's Journal*, vol. 43, 1852, pp. 23–36 ; "On the Integral $\int^n dx\, dy \ldots dz$," etc., *Quarterly Journal*, vols. 2 and 3, 1858–1860.

‡ "Mémoir sur les lieux analytiques," *Comptes Rendus*, vol. 24, p. 885.

§ "Ueber die Hypothesen, welche der Geometrie zu Grunde liegen," presented to the philosophical faculty at Göttingen in 1854, but not published till 1866; *Gesammelte Werke*, Leipzig, 1892, No. xiii, pp. 272–287; translated by Clifford in *Nature*, vol. 8, 1873, pp. 14 and 36; *Mathematical Papers*, No. 9, pp. 55–69.

of the squares of the quantities dx, as in the ordinary plane and space, the manifold is *flat*. In general there is a *deviation from flatness*, or *curvature;* and the simplest cases are those in which the curvature is constant. Riemann points out that space may be unbounded without being infinite — that, in fact, it cannot be infinite if it has a constant positive curvature differing at all from zero. We therefore attribute to Riemann the Elliptic Non-Euclidean Geometry, which from this time on takes its place beside that other discovered by Bolyai and Lobachevsky. His paper has a bearing on our subject in two ways: in the first place, his manifold of n dimensions is a space of n dimensions, and geometrical conceptions are clearly before the mind throughout the discussion; and then the notion of a curvature of space suggests at once a space of four dimensions in which the curved three-dimensional space may lie. Soon after, it was shown by Beltrami that the planimetry of Lobachevsky could be represented upon real surfaces of constant negative curvature just as the Elliptic Two-dimensional Geometry is represented upon the sphere, and the way was fully opened for the study of spaces of constant curvature and of curvature in general.*

Another work that has an important influence on recent developments of hypergeometry, especially in its application to physical theories, is the *Ausdehnungslehre* of Grassmann, first published in 1844, though little noticed at the

* Beltrami, "Saggio di interpretazione della geometria non-euclidea," *Giornale di matematiche*, vol. 6, 1868; *Opere*, Milan, vol. I, 1902, pp. 374–405.

Another memoir by Beltrami, "Teoria fondamentale degli spazii di curvatura costante," *Annali di matematica pura ed applicata*, Ser. 2, vol. 2, 1868–1869; *Opere*, vol. I, pp. 406–429, develops and explains much in Riemann's paper that is difficult to understand. There are French translations of both memoirs by Hoüel, *Annales Scientifiques de l'École Normale Supérieure*, vol. 6, 1869.

Beltrami considers the representations of the three-dimensional geometries upon curved spaces as only analytic, while the representations of the two-dimensional geometries upon surfaces of constant curvature are real. See *Opere*, vol. I, p. 396 and p. 427.

time. His theory of extensive magnitudes is a vector analysis, and the applications which he makes to plane geometry and to geometry of three dimensions can be made in the same way to geometry of any number of dimensions.

The number of memoirs and books relating to geometry of four or more dimensions has increased enormously in recent years. We can mention only a few. In 1870, Cayley published his "Memoir on Abstract Geometry," in which he lays down the general principles of n-dimensional geometry.* Another important contribution to the science was an unfinished paper "On the Classification of Loci" by Clifford.† An important paper by Nöther on birational transformations was published in 1870.‡ Other papers were published by Halphen in 1873 and by Jordan in 1875,§ the latter giving a methodical generalization of metrical geometry by means of Cartesian coördinates. Perhaps the most important of all was a memoir by Veronese published in 1882,¶ in which he takes up a study of the properties of configurations, the quadratic in any number of variables, the characteristics of curves, correspondence of spaces, etc.: he employed synthetic, not analytic methods, and inaugurated a purely synthetic method of studying these geometries. Veronese's *Fondamenti di geometria* contains an elementary synthetic treatment of the geometry of four dimensions and the geometry of n dimensions; and the *Mehrdimensionale Geometrie* of

* *Philosophical Transactions*, vol. 160; *Mathematical Papers*, vol. VI, 1893, No. 413.

† *Philosophical Transactions*, vol. 169, 1878; *Mathematical Papers*, No. 33, pp. 305–331.

‡ "Zur Theorie des eindeutigen Entsprechens algebraischer Gebilde von beliebig vielen Dimensionen," *Mathematische Annalen*, vol. 2, pp. 293–316.

§ Halphen, "Recherches de géométrie à n dimensions," *Bulletin de la Société Mathématique de France*, vol. 2, pp. 34–52; Jordan, "Essai sur la géométrie à n dimensions," id. vol. 3, pp. 103–174.

¶ "Behandlung der projectivischen Verhältnisse der Räume von verschiedenen Dimensionen durch das Princip des Projicirens und Schneidens," *Mathematische Annalen*, vol. 19, pp. 161–234.

Schoute, employing a variety of methods, makes these subjects very clear and interesting.* A bibliography with nearly six hundred titles, up to 1907, is to be found in Loria's *Il passato ed il presente delle principali teorie geometriche.* † The latest bibliography is that of Sommerville, ‡ which contains 1832 references on n dimensions up to 1911: about one-third of these are Italian, one-third German, and the rest mostly French, English, and Dutch.§

We see that the geometries of more than three dimensions were slow in gaining recognition. The general notion that geometry is concerned only with objective external space made the existence of any kind of geometry seem to depend upon the existence of the same kind of space. Consequently some of our leading mathematicians hesitated to use the higher geometry, ¶ although the work-

* Veronese, *Fondamenti di geometria a più dimensioni ed a più spezie di unita rettilinee esposti in forma elementare*, Padua, 1891; German translation by Schepp, *Grundzüge der Geometrie von mehreren Dimensionem*, etc., Leipzig, 1894. Schoute, *Mehrdimensionale Geometrie, Sammlung Schubert*, XXXV and XXXVI, Leipzig, 1902 and 1905. Another elementary treatment of the subject is by Jouffret, *Géométrie à quatre dimensions*, Paris, 1903.

† 3d ed., Turin, 1907.

‡ *Bibliography of Non-Euclidean Geometry, Including the Theory of Parallels, the Foundations of Geometry, and Space of n Dimensions*, University of St. Andrews, Scotland, 1911.

§ There is now a considerable popular interest in the four-dimensional geometry, because of the many curious things about it, and because of attempts which have been made to explain certain mysterious phenomena by means of it. This interest has produced numerous articles and books written to describe the fourth dimension in a non-mathematical way. In 1908 a prize of $500 was offered through the *Scientific American* for the best non-mathematical essay on the fourth dimension. Two hundred and forty-five essays were submitted in this competition. Some of these have been published in a book, whose Introduction, by the present writer, gives quite a full discussion of the various questions connected with the subject (*The Fourth Dimension Simply Explained*, Munn and Company, New York, 1910).

¶ Thus Darboux, in a memoir presented in 1869 at the Academy of Sciences and published in 1873, speaks of a *lacune* in geometry of space as compared with plane geometry, for certain plane curves can be studied with advantage as projections from space, but "Comme on n'a pas d'espace à quatre dimensions, les méthodes de projection ne s'étendent pas à la géométrie de l'espace" (*Sur une classe remarquable de courbes et de surfaces algébriques*, Paris, p. 164). Even in 1903, in his Report at

ing out of its details presented comparatively little difficulty to them. This objection has led some writers to
emphasize those applications of four-dimensional geometry
that can be made in three-dimensional space, interpreting
it as a geometry four-dimensional in some other element
than the point — just as we have interpretations of the
non-Euclidean geometries, which cannot, however, take
the place of their ordinary interpretation.* As long ago as
1846 it was pointed out by Plücker that four variables

the Congress at St. Louis, he says, "Une seule objection pouvait être faite . . .
l'absence de toute base réele, de tout substratum," etc. (*Bulletin des sciences mathématiques*, ser. 2, vol. 28, p. 261, *Congress of Arts and Sciences*, edited by H. J. Rogers,
Houghton, Mifflin and Co., Boston, vol. I, 1905, p. 557). But Darboux himself has
made important contributions to the geometry of *n* dimensions: see, for example, his
Leçons sur les systèmes orthogonaux, 2d ed., Paris, 1910; in particular, Bk. I, chap. 6,
and Bk. II, chap. 1.

Poincaré, in speaking of the representation of two complex variables in space of
four dimensions, says, "On est exposé à rebuter la plupart des lecteurs et de plus
on ne possède que l'avantage d'un langage commode, mais incapable de parler aux
sens." *Acta Mathematica*, vol. 9, 1886–1887, p. 324.

On the other hand, we have the following from Sylvester: "There are many who
regard the alleged notion of a generalized space as only a disguised form of algebraic
formulization; but the same might be said with equal truth of our notion of infinity,
or of impossible lines, or lines making a zero angle in geometry, the utility of dealing
with which no one will be found to dispute. Dr. Salmon in his extension of Chasles'
theory of characteristics to surfaces, Mr. Clifford in a question of probability, and
myself in my theory of partitions, and also in my paper on barycentric projection,
have all felt and given evidence of the practical utility of handling space of four
dimensions as if it were conceivable space" ("A Plea for the Mathematician,"
Nature, vol. 1, 1869, p. 237; *Mathematical Papers*, vol. II, p. 716).

A statement of Cayley's has been given in a previous footnote (p. 5). For
other expressions of his views we may refer to the first paragraph of the "Memoir
on Abstract Geometry" mentioned above, and to a statement quoted by Forsyth
in his "Biographical Notice," Cayley's *Mathematical Papers*, vol. VIII, 1895, p. xxxv.

As to the existence of a higher space, Gauss also is said to have considered it
a possibility (W. Sartorius von Waltershausen, "Gauss zum Gedächtniss," *Gauss
Werke*, Göttingen, vol. VIII, 1900, p. 267).

Segre, referring to the first of the two remarks that we have quoted from Darboux,
says, "Maintenant nous faisons usage de l'espace à quatre dimensions sans nous
préoccuper de la question de son existence, que nous regardons comme une question
tout-à-fait secondaire, et personne ne pense qu'on vienne ainsi à perdre de la rigueur."
Mathematische Annalen, vol. 24, 1884, p. 318.

* See Emory McClintock, "On the Non-Euclidean Geometry," *Bulletin of the
New York Mathematical Society*, vol. 2, 1892, pp. 21–33.

can be regarded as the coördinates of a line in space.*
Another four-dimensional geometry that has been sug-
gested is that of spheres.†

But this higher geometry is now recognized as an indis-
pensable part of mathematics, intimately related to many
other branches, and with direct applications in mathematical physics. The most important application for
the mathematician is the application as analytic geometry
to algebra and analysis: it furnishes concise terms and
expressions, and by its concrete conceptions enables him
to grasp the meanings of complicated formulae and in-
tricate relations. This is true of all the geometries as well
as the geometry of four dimensions. The latter is of special
use in connection with two complex variables, both in the
study of one as a function of the other, and when it is
desired to study functions of both considered as independent variables.‡ Another very important application of geometry of four dimensions is that mentioned by
d'Alembert, making time the fourth dimension: within
a few years this idea has been developed very fully, and
has been found to furnish the simplest statement of the
new physical principle of relativity.§

* *System der Geometrie des Raumes*, Düsseldorf, p. 322.

† See article by Professor Keyser, "A Sensuous Representation of Paths that
Lead from the Inside to the Outside of a Sphere in Space of Four Dimensions,"
Bulletin of the American Mathematical Society, vol. 18, 1911, pp. 18–22.

‡ See reference given on the preceding page to Poincaré's memoir in the *Acta
Mathematica*; also Kwietnewski, *Ueber Flächen des vierdimensionalen Raumes,
deren sämtliche Tangentialebenen untereinander gleichwinklig sind, und ihre Beziehung
zu den ebenen Kurven*, Zürich, 1902.

§ The theory has been developed somewhat as follows: If time is represented by
a coördinate *t* measured on an axis perpendicular to the hyperplane of the space-
axes, the *t*-axis itself or any parallel line will represent a stationary point, and uniform motion will be represented by lines oblique to the *t*-axis, forming an angle with
the *t*-axis which depends on the rate of the motion. A certain velocity (the velocity
of light) is taken as the greatest possible velocity and the same for all systems of
measurement. The lines through the origin, or through any point, representing
this velocity are the elements of a conical hypersurface. All lines not parallel to

With these various applications have been developed many methods of studying the higher geometries, besides the ordinary synthetic and analytic methods. We now have the synthetic and analytic projective geometries, including the projective theories of measurement; we have the theories of transformations and transformation groups; the geometry of algebraic curves and algebraic functions; the geometry associated with the representation of two complex variables; differential geometry and the transformation of differential expressions; analysis situs, enumerative geometry, kinematics, and descriptive geometry; the extensive magnitudes of Grassmann and different kinds of vector geometry; the application of quaternions to four dimensions; and the very recent application of four-dimensional vector analysis to the principles of relativity.*

these elements are divided into two classes: the lines of one class, less inclined to the t-axis, represent possible motions, while the lines of the other class can represent only imaginary motions. The system may be regarded as a non-Euclidean geometry in which the conical hypersurface plays the part of absolute for angles, while distances along lines of the two classes are independent and cannot be compared. Now a point moving uniformly may be regarded as stationary, and the points which are really stationary as moving uniformly in the opposite space-direction. This change of view is represented by a transformation of coördinates, the new t-axis being the line representing the given uniform motion. In this theory the angles of planes play an important part, and line and plane vectors are freely used.

This application of four-dimensional geometry was developed by Minkowski. For further elaboration see article by E. B. Wilson and G. N. Lewis, "The Space-time Manifold of Relativity. The Non-Euclidean Geometry of Mechanics and Electromagnetics," *Proceedings of the American Academy of Arts and Sciences*, vol. 48, No. 11, Nov., 1912.

* On the projective theory of measurement see d'Ovidio, "Le funzione metriche fondamentali negli spazii di quantesivogliano dimensioni e di curvatura costante," *Atti della Accademia de Lincei*, ser. 3, vol. 1, 1876, pp. 133–193; abstract in the *Mathematische Annalen*, vol. 12, 1877, pp. 403–418.

On analysis situs there is an important series of memoirs by Poincaré: *Journal de l'École Polytechnique*, vol. 100, 1894; *Rendiconti del Circolo Matematico di Palermo*, vol. 13, 1899; *Proceedings of the London Mathematical Society*, vol. 32, 1900; *Bulletin de la Société Mathématique de France*, vol. 30, 1902; *Journal de mathématiques pures et appliquées*, ser. 5, vol. 8, 1902; *Rendiconti di Palermo*, vol. 18, 1904; *Comptes Rendus*, vol. 133, 1901.

The enumerative geometry has been developed chiefly by Schubert. He has

All these interpretations and methods that have been applied to the study of the higher geometries, and all these uses to which they have been put, are interesting and valuable to a greater or less degree; but the greatest advantage to be derived from the study of geometry of more than three dimensions is a real understanding of the great science of geometry. Our plane and solid geometries are but the beginnings of this science. The four-dimensional geometry is far more extensive than the three-dimensional, and all the higher geometries are more extensive than the lower. The number and variety of figures increases more and more rapidly as we mount to higher and higher spaces, each space extending in a direction not existing in the lower spaces, each space only one of an infinite number of such spaces in the next higher.

A study of the four-dimensional geometry, with its hyperplanes like our three-dimensional space, enables us to prove theorems in geometry of three dimensions, just as a consideration of the latter enables us to prove theorems in plane geometry. Such theorems may come from much simpler theorems relating to the four-dimensional figures of which the given figures are sections or projections.*

articles in the *Mathematische Annalen*, vols. 26, 38, and 45, 1886, 1891 and 1894; in the *Acta Mathematica*, vol. 8, 1886; and elsewhere.

In kinematics we may mention: Clifford, "On the Free Motion under No Forces of a Rigid System in an *N*-fold Homaloid," *Proceedings of the London Mathematical Society*, vol. 7, 1876, *Mathematical Papers*, No. 26, pp. 236–240; Beltrami, "Formules fondamentales de cinématique dans les espaces de courbure constante," *Bulletin des science mathématiques*, vol. 11, 1876, pp. 233–240, *Opere*, vol. III, 1911, pp. 23–29; see also articles by Craig and Hatzidakis in the *American Journal of Mathematics*, vols. 20 and 22, 1898, and 1900.

Quaternions have been applied to geometry of four dimensions by Hathaway, *Bulletin of the American Mathematical Society*, vol. 4, 1897, pp. 54–57; *Transactions of the American Mathematical Society*, vol. 3, 1902, pp. 46–59; and by Stringham, *Transactions*, vol. 2, 1901, pp. 183–214; *Bulletin*, vol. 11, 1905, pp. 437–439.

Other methods are illustrated in memoirs already referred to.

* See Cayley's article in *Crelle's Journal*, vol. 31, and the articles of Veronese and Segre in the *Mathematische Annalen*. to which we have already referred.

Indeed, many theorems and processes are seen only partially or not at all in the lower geometries, their true nature and extent appearing in the higher spaces. Thus in space of four dimensions is found the first illustration of figures which have two independent angles, and of different kinds of parallelism and different kinds of perpendicularity. Another example is the general theorem of which a particular case is given in Art 31, namely, that a section of a simplex of n dimensions is one of the two parts into which a simplex of $n - 1$ dimensions (that is, its interior) may be divided by a section.* There are also many properties in which spaces of an even number of dimensions differ from spaces of an odd number of dimensions, and these differences would hardly be recognized if we had only the ordinary geometries. Thus in spaces of an even number of dimensions rotation takes place around a point, a plane, or some other axis-space of an even number of dimensions, while in spaces of an odd number of dimensions the axis of a rotation is always of an odd number of dimensions (see chap. IV).

The study of these geometries gives us a truer view of the nature of geometrical reasoning, and enables us to break away from intuition. This is especially true if we adopt the synthetic method. The analytic geometry may seem to be free from difficulty, and many feel a higher degree of certainty in the results of their algebraic processes. But we are apt to attach the terms of geometry to our algebraic forms without any attempt at a realization of their significance. There is, indeed, an abstract geometry in which the terms are regarded as meaningless symbols; but the interest and usefulness of geometry depend on the clearness of our perception of the figures to which it may be applied, and so we prefer to study some concrete geometry,

* See Schoute, *Mehrdimensionale Geometrie,* vol. II, § 1, Nr. 6.

some interpretation of the abstract geometry which we could have obtained by giving a particular interpretation to its terms. And then the abstract geometry and other interpretations can all be obtained from the concrete geometry.* There is really the same absolute certainty to synthetic geometry if it is developed logically from the axioms, and in the synthetic study of four-dimensional geometry we are forced to give up intuition and rely entirely on our logic.†

Although it is doubtful whether we can ever picture to ourselves the figures of hyperspace in the sense that we can picture to ourselves the figures of ordinary space, yet we can reason about them, and, knowing that the validity of our geometry depends only on the logical accuracy of our reasoning, we can proceed to build it up without waiting for a realization of it; and then we may in time acquire such facility in handling the geometrical proofs of the theorems and in stating precisely the forms and properties of the figures that it is almost as if we could see them. For

---

* Some portions of our study are treated by themselves as new interpretations of geometries already studied. As soon as the fundamental propositions which correspond to the axioms of some such geometry have been established, so as to justify this mode of procedure, we have only to translate its theorems in accordance with these propositions to have in our possession a complete development of the particular subject considered. Examples are, the three-dimensional Point Geometry (Art. 64), the two-dimensional Edge Geometry (Art. 78), and the theory of systems of isocline planes at a point (Art. 112).

† We do not seek to know which of several geometries is the true geometry, and in laying the foundations we do not seek for the true system of axioms, or even the true system of elements and relations. All geometries are equally true, and sometimes a particular geometry may be built up equally well in several different ways. A complete treatise on geometry should consider not only the different geometries, but different methods of building up each geometry. An example of such a treatment is the first volume of *Fragen der Elementargeometrie*, edited by Enriques (Leipzig, 1911, German translation by H. Thieme of *Questioni riguardanti la geometria elementare*, Bologna, 1900). See also the chapters on this subject by Enriques and others in the *French* and *German Encyclopedias* (*Encyklopädie der math. Wiss.*, vol. III₁, Leipzig, 1907; *Encyclopédie des sci. math.*, vol. III₁, Leipzig, 1911). A list of different systems of fundamental elements and relations is given in a footnote at the beginning of Coolidge's *Non-Euclidean Geometry*, Oxford, 1909.

in studying the geometry synthetically our attention is fixed upon the figures themselves, and this takes us directly to the heart of the difficulty and keeps it before us until we have mastered it. Thus in its results this geometry greatly increases our power of intuition and our imagination.*

The following pages have been written with the object of meeting as far as possible the difficulties of the subject. No knowledge of higher mathematics is necessary; yet we do not believe that the simplest way is to avoid a mathematical treatment. The confidence gained from a study of the proofs, if they can be made clear and precise, will do more for the student than a mere description of four-dimensional space. We will indicate how this purpose has influenced us in our choice of subject-matter and the form of presentation.

We have adopted the synthetic method and made no use of analytic proofs, feeling, as we have already explained, that this study of the figures themselves will serve best to help us understand them.

We have confined ourselves to the fourth dimension, although it would have been easy to cover a much wider field. † We hope that in this way the four-dimensional space will be made to appear as a concrete matter to be studied by itself, and not as one of an indefinite series of spaces, each understood only in a vague general way.

We have wished to give to these pages a familiar appearance, and so have endeavored to follow the popular text-books and build up a structure that will rest on the foundations laid in the schools. Our geometry might have been adapted to the axioms of some modern investigation, or

---

* See C. J. Keyser, "Mathematical Emancipations," *Monist*, vol. 16, 1906, pp. 65–83, particularly pp. 81–82.

† See, for example, the *Mehrdimensionale Geometrie* of Schoute.

have attempted to establish a system of axioms, but either course would have raised questions quite different from those of four-dimensional geometry. The methods employed in this book are methods which the student has used freely in the past, even though he may be ignorant of their true significance and justification: there is nothing new in their application here, and their employment without question leaves him free to fix his attention upon the difficulties inherent in the subject.

There is, however, one part of the foundations which has been presented with considerable care, namely, that which relates to the definitions and the intersections of certain elementary figures. It is here that the four-dimensional geometry begins to contradict our experience, declaring, for example, that two complete planes may have only a point in common, and that a line can pass through a point of the interior of a solid without passing through any other of its points. It is true that these facts and many others not easy to realize are easily proved, and require only a few of the theorems given in this connection. On the other hand, the theorems for which most of these details are needed are so "evident" that they are usually ignored altogether. Now a statement of these theorems, with a realization of what is assumed and of what is to be proved, and a logical working out of the proofs themselves, will give the student more confidence in all the results of his study. Similar considerations have led us in the fourth chapter to take up symmetry, order, and motion in space of two dimensions and in space of three dimensions.

Great assistance comes from the analogies that exist in geometry, and so we have gone back in some cases and given proofs which are not well known, and to which more difficult proofs that follow are analogous;* and we have

* See, for example, the theorems of Arts. 61 and 62.

c

tried to facilitate the comparison of chapters and sections analogous to one another by adopting in them the same arrangement of paragraphs and the same phraseology.

Not much use can be made of diagrams, and so far as they are given they must be regarded as indicating the relations of different parts of a figure rather than as showing in any way its appearance. A figure can be accurately determined by its projections, and the descriptive geometry of four dimensions will be helpful to those who are familar with the methods of descriptive geometry.* Much can also be learned by studying the *sections* of a figure. A section of a four-dimensional figure is that part which lies in a three-dimensional space or hyperplane, and is, therefore, like the figures of our space. We can suppose that we are able to place ourselves in any hyperplane, and so to examine any hyperplane section : in connection with the diagrams we shall sometimes call attention to those parts which lie in any one section, speaking of them as "what we can see in a hyperplane." One way of studying a figure is to let it pass across our space, giving us a continuously varying section, as if time were the fourth dimension. Another way is to let it turn, or our section of it, so that the direction of our view changes. It is along these lines, if at all, that we are to acquire a perception of hyperspace and its figures.

Some explanation should be made in regard to the arrangement, the particular form chosen for the foundations so far as they are considered, and the fundamental conceptions as we have presented them.

We have given only the Euclidean Geometry, except that the geometry of the hypersphere, and of the hyperplane at infinity, and the geometry in a few less important cases,

* See Schoute, *Mehrdimensionale Geometrie*, vol. I, § 5.

are themselves non-Euclidean. It has been found, however, that several chapters can be completed before we make any hypothesis in regard to parallels, and that, too, without much variation from the usual treatment. Perpendiculars and all kinds of angles, symmetry and order, and those hypersurfaces (the hyperpyramid, the hypercone, and the hypersphere) which do not involve parallels — in fact, all of "restricted" geometry — can be taken up before the introduction of parallels.* In the chapter on the hypersphere, its geometry, being elliptic, is stated as such, and a group of theorems is given from the non-Euclidean geometry; and in the last chapter the non-Euclidean properties of the hypersphere are used quite freely. Although these portions of the book may be omitted, the student will find it an advantage to make himself familiar with the Hyperbolic and Elliptic geometries. †

We have started with points only as elements, regarding all figures as classes of points, and so defining a figure simply by stating what points constitute the class. To do this we assume first a relation by which with any two points certain points are said to be collinear. Then for line we take two points and the class of points collinear with them, add to the group all points collinear with any two that we now have, and thus continue, at each step adding to our class of points all that are collinear with any two already in the group, so that the line includes every point which it is possible to get in this way. Thus any two points determine a class consisting of the points which are collinear with them, and any two points determine a class of the kind which we call a line.‡ By the axioms of Art. 3 the

* See the author's *Non-Euclidean Geometry*, Ginn and Co., Boston, 1901, chap. I; in particular, p. 6.

† The Hyperbolic and Elliptic geometries are the only non-Euclidean geometries that we have referred to at all.

‡ That two points determine a line does not mean, as in some of our text-books,

two classes are identical : the line consists only of the points collinear with the two given points, and there are no additional points to be obtained by taking any two of these points. In fact, any two points of a line determine the same class of points as collinear with them, and the same line. But until we have adopted these axioms we must suppose that the line might be a much more extended class : that, if we have the points collinear with two given points, the class of points collinear with any two of these might be quite different; and that, while a line must contain every point of the line determined by any two of its points, the latter might not contain every point of the former. Thus we make a distinction at the beginning between the notion of collinear points and the notion of points of a line, and this distinction makes line analogous to plane and hyperplane, and to spaces of more than three dimensions. But after we have adopted our first two axioms we are able to employ the word collinear in its commonly accepted sense, and thus to avoid the introduction of a new term for one of these two relations.

A careful distinction has been made between the points of a closed figure and the points of its interior. Thus a triangle is made to consist of three vertices and the points of its sides, a tetrahedron of its vertices and the points of its edges and faces, and so on. This is only carrying to the limit the tendency to regard a circle as a curve rather than as the portion of the plane enclosed by the curve, and a sphere as a surface. The figure of one-dimensional geometry corresponding to the triangle and tetrahedron, the *one-dimensional simplex*, is the *segment*. Therefore, we have defined segment as consisting of two points, and let

that the line contains the two points, or that no other line contains them. A figure may be determined in various ways. Thus a line in the ordinary plane geometry may be determined by two points as the locus of points equidistant from them.

the points between them constitute the interior of the segment.* On the other hand, a side of a polygon or an edge of a polyhedron is the interior of a segment, consisting of the points between two vertices and not including the vertices themselves; a face consists of the interior of a triangle or polygon; a half-line is defined so as not to include its extremity, a half-plane so as not to include its edge; and so on. We speak, indeed, of the sides and vertices of a face, of the length of a segment, and of the area of a triangle, just as, in general, we have used the terms of ordinary geometry without definition, and employed freely all the words and phrases of its everyday language. But the distinction between the points of a closed figure and the points of its interior is of great importance, and has been carefully observed.

* Hilbert defines segment (Strecke) as a "system of two points," but he speaks of the points between A and B as "points of the segment AB," although he also speaks of them as points "situated within the segment" (*Grundlagen der Geometrie*, Leipzig, 1899, p. 6, 4th ed., 1913, p. 5).

In the *Encyclopédie des sciences mathématiques*, vol. III₁, p. 23, Enriques defines segment upon a line as "having its extreme points at two given points A and B of the line and containing the intermediate points." More definitely, in the *Elementi di geometria* of Enriques and Amaldi (Bologna, 1911), half-line is defined so as to include its extremity, and then the segment AB is the part common to the half-lines AB and BA (p. 3).

E. H. Moore defines the segment AB as consisting of points "distinct from A and B," etc.; that is, A and B are not included among the points of his segment ("On the Projective Axioms of Geometry," *Transactions of the American Mathematical Society*, vol. 3, 1902, p. 147, Axiom 2). See also Veblen, "A System of Axioms for Geometry," *Transactions*, vol. 5, 1904, p. 354, Definition 1, and "The Foundations of Geometry," *Monographs on Modern Mathematics*, edited by J. W. A. Young, New York, 1911, p. 5.

Most writers who use the word segment in this connection regard a segment as an entity, a piece of a line, without considering whether the end-points are included or not. Many writers speak of the segment as the "measure of the distance" between the two points (see Schotten, *Inhalt und Methode des Planimetrischen Unterrichts*, Leipzig, vol. II, 1893, chap. 1, § 2).

Veblen, in the "Foundations of Geometry" just referred to, defines triangle and tetrahedron in the same way that we have defined them (pp. 29 and 45).

* A remarkable memoir on geometry of n dimensions is *Theorie der vielfachen Kontinuität*, by L. Schlafli, edited by J. H. Graph, Bern, 1911. This was written in the years 1850–1852, but the author did not succeed in getting it published, apparently on account of its length, and it remained among his papers for fifty years, until after his death (see Vorbemerkung).

Among other things he works out the theory of perpendicularity and all kinds of angles, giving, in particular, a generalization of the theorems which we have given in Arts. 66 and 67 (§ 15). He proves the polyhedroid formula and the corresponding formula for any number of dimensions, and he constructs the six regular convex polyhedroids and the three regular figures which exist in each of the higher spaces, proving that these are the only regular figures of this kind (§ 17). He makes an extensive study of the hypervolume of a spherical simplex, showing the difference between the cases of an even number and of an odd number of dimensions, and giving the formula for a pentahedroid to which we have referred at the end of Art. 165 (§ 22). In the third part of the memoir he takes up quadratic hypersurfaces, the classification of these hypersurfaces, confocal hypersurfaces, etc.

The methods are analytical, but the language and conceptions are purely geometrical.

* This note was written after the rest of the Introduction was in type.

CHAPTER I

THE FOUNDATIONS OF FOUR-DIMENSIONAL GEOMETRY

I. POINTS AND LINES

1. Points. Figures regarded as classes of points.
The elements of geometry are *points*. We do not define the term point. It is impossible to build up a system of geometry without undefined terms, and if we can give different meanings to this word we shall be able hereafter to give to our geometry different interpretations (see, for example, Arts. 64 and 78 and Introduction, p. 15).

The objects which we study are to be regarded as consisting of points, that is, as classes of points selected according to various laws from the class which includes all points. Any selected class is said to constitute a *figure*, although the word figure is also used to denote a drawing or picture. The points *of* a figure may also be said to *lie in* the figure or *belong to* it. One figure is said to *lie in* another when all of its points are points of the second. It will often be convenient to speak of a figure as consisting of certain other figures, but this expression should always be understood as meaning that it consists of the points of these other figures.

Two figures *intersect* when they have a point or points in common, and their *intersection* consists of such common point or points.

2. The collinear relation. Geometries of 1, 2, 3, . . . *n*, . . . dimensions. Points have an undefined relation denoted by the term *collinear*.   Given any two points, there is a class consisting of the points *collinear with them*.

Geometries of 1, 2, 3, . . . *n*, . . . *dimensions* are geometries of figures lying in *spaces of* 1, 2, 3, . . . *n*, . . . *dimensions;* that is, in a *line*, *plane*, *hyperplane*, and in spaces of more than three dimensions.

A *line* * consists of the points that we get if we take two distinct points, all points collinear with them, and all points collinear with any two obtained by this process.

A *plane* consists of the points that we get if we take three points not points of one line, all points collinear with any two of them, and all points collinear with any two obtained by this process.

A *hyperplane* consists of the points that we get if we take four points not points of one plane, all points collinear with any two of them, and all points collinear with any two obtained by this process.

A *space of four dimensions* consists of the points that we get if we take five points not points of one hyperplane, all points collinear with any two of them, and all points collinear with any two obtained by this process.

Continuing in this way, we can define a space of $n + 1$ dimensions after we have defined a space of *n* dimensions. All spaces have this property: that the points collinear with any two points of a space belong to the space.

Two distinct points are said to be *independent*.   In general, a point is *independent of the points of a given class* if it is not included among the points that we can get by taking these points, points collinear with any two of them, and points collinear with any two obtained by this process.   The points of a given set are *absolutely in-*

* In the ordinary interpretation of these terms, *line* alone is used for *straight line*, and *the complete line* is meant, not that part of a line which we shall speak of as the interior of a segment (Art. 5).

dependent if it is impossible to obtain them all in this way from a smaller number of points.* The different kinds of space are distinguished by the number of absolutely independent points that they can contain.

3. Segments. Two axioms concerning the collinear relation. A *segment* † consists of two distinct points. Any two points are the points of a segment. The segment consisting of the points A and B will be called the *segment AB*.

A point is said to be *collinear with a segment* when it is collinear with the two points of the segment.

Concerning the collinear relation we shall now make two axioms:

AXIOM 1. *The class of points collinear with the segment AB includes the two points of this segment.*

AXIOM 2. ‡ *If a point O, not the point B, is collinear with the segment AB, then any point P collinear with the segment AB will be collinear with the segment OB.*

In other words, if O is collinear with the segment AB and is not the point B (so that there is a segment OB), then all points collinear with the segment AB will be collinear with the segment OB. In particular, A itself will be collinear with the segment OB, and therefore, conversely, all points collinear with the segment OB will be collinear

---

* If the points of a set are absolutely independent, each point will be independent of the rest; and in this geometry we shall find that the points of a set are absolutely independent if each point is independent of the rest (Art. 4, Th. 2; Art. 10, Th. 2; etc.). We may, therefore, speak of such points simply as *independent points*.

† Halsted calls this a *sect* (*Elements of Geometry*, New York, 1885, p. 9). He also uses the word *straight* for line, taking these terms from the German *Strecke* and *Gerade* (see *Rational Geometry*, New York, 1907, pp. 1 and 6).

‡ In the Elliptic Non-Euclidean Geometry this is assumed with certain restrictions. Thus on the sphere, whose geometry is the elliptic two-dimensional geometry, collinear meaning "on a great circle with," the statement given here as Axiom 2 is not true when A and B are opposite points.

with the segment AB. The class of points collinear with one segment is the same as the class of points collinear with the other segment. We can use A or O interchangeably in connection with B as one of the two points with respect to which the class is selected.

In this second axiom we do not intend to make any distinction between the points A and B. Except when O is one of these points, P will be collinear with both of the segments OA and OB; and when O is the point B, it will be collinear with the segment OA.

4. Lines. Only one line contains two given points. Given two distinct points A and B, the *line* AB is the line obtained when we start with these points and carry out the process described in the definition of line (Art. 2).

If A' and B' are two distinct points of the line AB, then all points of the line $A'B'$ will be points of the line AB; for the process of obtaining the second line is but a continuation of the process of obtaining the first. We shall now prove that all points of the line AB are points of the line $A'B'$; in other words, that the two are the same line, and that two points can both be points of only one line.

Theorem 1. *Any point O of the line AB is collinear with the segment AB.*

Proof. We shall prove this theorem by induction. We know that it is true of the points A and B (Art. 3, Ax. 1). Let O be any other point of the line.

By hypothesis, O, being a point of the line AB, is collinear with two points M and N of the line. We assume that the theorem is true of M and N. M must be distinct from one, at least, of the points A and B, since they are distinct. Let us suppose that M is not B. Then we can substitute M for A, and say that all points collinear with the segment AB are collinear with the segment MB.

Again, since N is one of these points and is not the point M, we can substitute N for B, and say that all of these points are collinear with the segment MN. Now O is collinear with the segment MN. Therefore, reversing this process of substitution, we have O collinear with the segment MB, and finally with the segment AB.

THEOREM 2. *If A' and B' are two distinct points of the line AB, then the line $A'B'$ is the same as the line AB.*

PROOF. We may suppose that A' is not B. Then, since A' is collinear with the segment AB, A will be collinear with the segment $A'B$, and the line $A'B$ will be the same as the line AB. In the same way we prove that the line $A'B'$ is the same line.

It follows from these two theorems that the class of points collinear with the segment AB constitute the line AB, and that *collinear with* means *lying on a line with*. It follows also that the two points A and B do not play any particular part among the points of the line. We can speak of a set of collinear points, or of points collinear with one another, without specifying any two particular points as special points of the class. We can also speak of two or more points as collinear with one given point.

5. Order of points on a line. Half-lines. Another relation in geometry, a relation of the points of a line, is that of *order*.* This may be explained somewhat in detail as follows:

If A and B are two distinct points, then A comes *before* B and B lies *beyond* A in one *direction along the line AB*, while B comes before A and A lies beyond B in the *opposite direction*. If A comes before B and B before C in a given direction along a line, then A comes before C in the same

---

* Veblen uses the word *order* to mean *order on a line*, "System of Axioms," p. 344; or "Foundations of Geometry," p. 5 (full references are given above, p. 21).

direction, and B is said to lie *between* A and C. Given any three points of a line, one of them lies between the other two.

This relation of order belongs to other classes of points besides those of a line. For example, it belongs to the class of points constituting what is commonly called a broken line.

The points of a line have also relations of *density* and *continuity*, but it will not be necessary to explain these terms here, nor to give the axioms and theorems by which these relations and the relations of order are established.*

The *interior of a segment* consists of the points which lie between the two points of the segment.

A *half-line* or *ray* is that portion of a line which lies in one direction along the line from a given point of it. The given point is called the *extremity of the half-line*, but this point is not itself a point of the half-line. The half-line which has the extremity A and contains B, the half-line which we can describe as drawn from A through B, is called the *half-line AB*; and that portion of this half-line which lies beyond B is itself a half-line, called the *continuation of AB*, or *AB produced*. The two half-lines into which a given point of a line divides the rest of the line are called *opposite* half-lines.

6. Cyclical order. There is another kind of order called *cyclical order*. When the points of a class are in cyclical order, two of these points A and B (unless they are consecutive points) divide the rest of them into two sub-classes, those of one sub-class lying from A towards B in one direction and those of the other sub-class lying from A towards B in the opposite direction. A and B are said to lie

* See Introduction, p. 16. For a treatment of these subjects we will refer to Veblen's "System of Axioms" or "Foundations of Geometry," and to R. L. Moore, "Sets of Metrical Hypotheses," *Transactions of the American Mathematical Society*, vol. 9, 1908, pp. 487–512.

between the points of the two sub-classes and to *separate* them. If C is a point of one sub-class and D a point of the other sub-class, that is, if we have these points in the cyclical order $ACBDA$, then we can say that the segments AB and CD separate each other. If we think of a class of points in cyclical order as cut at some point, they will then have the relations of order described in the preceding article. We shall have many illustrations of cyclical order (see Arts. 7 and 14).*

II. TRIANGLES

7. Triangles. Axiom of Pasch. Intersection of a line and a triangle. A *triangle* consists of three non-collinear points and the interiors of the three segments whose points are these points taken two at a time.

The three points are the *vertices*, and the interiors of the segments are the *sides*.

Any three non-collinear points are the vertices of a triangle. In particular, two vertices of a given triangle and a point in a side which does not lie between them are themselves the vertices of a triangle; so also are a point in each of two sides and the vertex where these two sides meet.

The points of a triangle are in cyclical order in the triangle (Art. 6).

For a complete treatment of the intersections of lines and triangles the following axiom is required: †

---

* The points of a circle are in cyclical order. Indeed, the points of a line are in cyclical order in Projective Geometry and in the Elliptic Non-Euclidean Geometry. We do not wish to exclude the Elliptic Geometry by assuming that the points of the entire line are not in cyclical order. In many cases of cyclical order there will be an "opposite" to every element, and on a line of this kind we can determine the two directions at any point by regarding the line as cut at the opposite point (see, for example, the definition of "between" and "side produced" in Art. 122); or we can suppose that we are considering only a "restricted" portion of the line; that is one of the sub-classes determined by two points suitably chosen in any given case.

† See Veblen, "System of Axioms," p. 351.

AXIOM. *A line intersecting one side of a triangle and another side produced intersects the third side.*

This will be referred to as the *Axiom of Pasch.* As stated, it is a little broader than is necessary.

THEOREM. *No line can intersect one side of a triangle and two sides produced, nor can a line intersect all three sides of a triangle.*

PROOF. The first statement follows directly from the Axiom of Pasch. To prove the second statement, let us suppose that a line could intersect the three sides of the triangle ABC, BC at A', AC at B', and AB at C', B' coming between A' and C' on the line. In the triangle $A'BC'$ we should then have the line AC intersecting one side, $A'C'$, at B', and the other two sides produced. But this is contrary to the first statement of the theorem. Therefore a line cannot intersect all three sides of a triangle.

COROLLARY. *No line can contain more than two points of a triangle unless it contains one of the sides of the triangle.*

8. Interior of a triangle. The *interior of a triangle* consists of the interiors of all segments whose points are points of the triangle, except of those segments which are collinear with two vertices of the triangle, that is, whose interiors also lie in the triangle. The interior of a triangle does not include the triangle itself; hence, whatever is in the triangle cannot be in the interior of the triangle.

THEOREM 1. *If two segments lying in a triangle separate each other in the cyclical order of the points of the triangle (Art. 6), then their interiors intersect, unless the interior of one of these segments lies in the triangle.*

PROOF. When each of the two given segments has a vertex for one of its points, each segment with the third vertex determines a triangle to which we can apply the

Axiom of Pasch and thus prove that the interior of this segment is intersected by the line containing the other segment. From this it follows that the interiors of the two segments have a point in common.

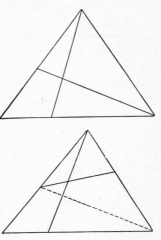

When one of the two given segments has a vertex for one of its points and the other does not, we form a triangle by taking one point of the latter and the two vertices of the given triangle which are collinear with its other point. This triangle contains also the first segment, or a segment whose interior is a part of the interior of the first segment.* We can prove the theorem, then, by proving it for this segment and the second given segment.

When neither of the two given segments contains a vertex we proceed in the same way, reducing this case first to the preceding.

THEOREM 2. *A half-line drawn from any point P of a triangle through a point O of the interior intersects the triangle in a point of PO produced.*

In proving this theorem we follow the methods of the preceding proof, taking first the case where O is between one vertex and a point of the opposite side and P is at another vertex.

COROLLARY. *If one of two opposite half-lines drawn from a point O of the interior of a triangle intersects the triangle, the other does also.*

---

* According to theorems of order referred to in Art. 5; see Veblen, "System of Axioms," p. 357, Lemma 6, or "Foundations of Geometry," p. 11, Cor. 4.

9. The relation, collinear with a triangle. A point is said to be *collinear with a triangle* when it is collinear with any two points of the triangle.

This is true, in particular, of all points of the triangle, of all points of the sides produced, and of all points of the interior.

THEOREM 1. *If a point O is collinear with a triangle ABC, and if P is any point of this triangle not a vertex and not the point O, then the line PO will intersect the triangle at least in a second point Q.*

PROOF. The line *PO* may contain one side of the triangle. Otherwise, if *O* is a point of the triangle, it will itself be the second point *Q*, and if *O* is a point of a side produced, the theorem is the same as the Axiom of Pasch. If *O* is a point of the interior, the theorem is the same as Th. 2 of the preceding article.

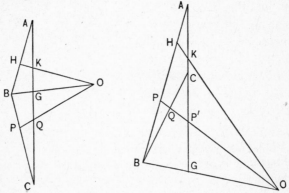

There remains, therefore, only the case where *O* is not a point of any one of the lines *AB*, *BC*, or *AC*, nor a point of the interior of the triangle. Let *H* and *K* then be the two points with which *O* is collinear, *H* a point of the side *AB*, or the vertex *B*, and *K* a point of the side *AC*, or the vertex *C*, *H* and *K*, not both vertices, however.

We may suppose also that O is a point of HK produced. Then K will lie in the interior of the triangle OAB or on the side OB, and the half-line AC, which passes through K, will intersect the interior of the segment BO in a point G. Now O is a point of BG produced. We have the triangles ABG and CBG, and in one or both of these triangles the line PO, intersecting BG produced and one other side, will intersect the third side. Therefore, in all cases this line will intersect the triangle ABC in a second point Q.

THEOREM 2. *If a point O, not a point of the line BC, is collinear with the triangle ABC, then any point P collinear with the triangle ABC will be collinear with the triangle OBC.*

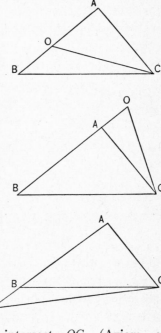

PROOF. First let O be a point of the line AB. If O is at A, the triangle OBC is the same as the triangle ABC. If P is a point of the line AB, it is collinear with O and B. Let us suppose then that P is not a point of this line, and that O is a point of the side AB, a point of BA produced, or a point of AB produced.

If O is a point of the side AB, then a line through P and a point of OB will intersect BC or will pass through C, or, intersecting AC, will intersect OC (Axiom of Pasch).

D

If O is a point of BA produced, then a line through P and a point of AB will intersect BC or will pass through C, or, intersecting AC, will intersect OC.

If O is a point of AB produced, then a line through P and a point of AB will intersect AC or will pass through C, or, intersecting BC, will intersect OC. P will be collinear with the triangle OAC, and therefore, by the first case, with the triangle OBC.

In the same way we prove the theorem when O is a point of the line AC.

If O is not a point of any one of the lines AB, BC, or AC, then a line through O and a point D of the side

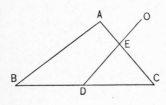

BC will pass through A or will intersect one of the sides AB or AC. Let the point of intersection be E, and let us suppose that it is the point A or a point of AC. Then P, being collinear with the triangle ABC, will be collinear with the triangle ADC, then with the triangle EDC, with the triangle ODC, and finally with the triangle OBC.

In other words, if O is collinear with the triangle ABC and is not a point of the line BC (so that there is a triangle OBC), then all points collinear with the triangle ABC will be collinear with the triangle OBC. In particular, A itself will be collinear with the triangle OBC, and therefore, conversely, all points collinear with the triangle OBC will be collinear with the triangle ABC. The class of points collinear with one triangle is the same as the class of points collinear with the other triangle. We can use A or O interchangeably in connection with the segment BC as one of the three points with respect to which the class is selected.

In this theorem we do not intend to make any distinction between the point A and the points B and C. Except when O is collinear with two of these three points, P will be collinear with all three of the triangles OBC, OAC, and OAB.

III. PLANES

10. Planes. Only one plane contains three given non-collinear points. As already stated, a *plane* consists of the points that we get if we take three points not points of one line, all points collinear with any two of them, and all points collinear with any two obtained by this process.

Given three non-collinear points, A, B, and C, the *plane* ABC is the plane obtained when we take these points and carry out the process described in the definition.

Now we can take for two of the three given points any two points of their line. That is, if B' and C' are points of the line BC, the plane $AB'C'$ is the same as the plane ABC (Art. 4, Th. 2). We can think of a line as one of the things with which we start in the process of obtaining a plane. Given the points of a line and a point not a point of the line, we take all points collinear with any two of these and all points collinear with any two obtained by this process.

If A', B', and C' are three non-collinear points of the plane ABC, then all points of the plane $A'B'C'$ will be points of the plane ABC; for the process of obtaining the second plane is but a continuation of the process of obtaining the first. We shall now prove that all points of the plane ABC are points of the plane $A'B'C'$; in other words, that the two are the same plane, and that three non-collinear points can all be points of only one plane.

THEOREM 1. *Any point of the plane ABC is collinear with the triangle ABC.**

---

* Collinear with a triangle is therefore the same as *coplanar* with the triangle, in the usual sense of the word coplanar.

PROOF. We prove this theorem just as we proved Th. 1 of Art. 4. We know that it is true of all points of the triangle and of all points of the sides produced. We let O be any other point, and prove by induction that the theorem is true for O.

This point is, by hypothesis, collinear with two points M and N of the plane ABC. We assume that the theorem is true of M and N. We can suppose also that M is not a point of the line BC and that N is not a point of the line MB. It follows (Art. 9, Th. 2) that we can substitute M for A, and say that all points collinear with the triangle ABC are collinear with the triangle MBC. Again, since N is one of these points and is not a point of the line MB, we can substitute N for C, and say that all of these points are collinear with the triangle MNB. Now O is collinear with the segment MN and so with the triangle MNB. Therefore, reversing this process of substitution, we have O collinear with the triangle MBC, and finally with the triangle ABC.

THEOREM 2. *If A', B', and C' are three non-collinear points of the plane ABC, then the plane $A'B'C'$ is the same as the plane ABC.*

PROOF. We will prove this theorem just as we proved Th. 2 of Art. 4. We can suppose that A' is not a point of the line BC, and that B' is not a point of the line $A'C$. Then, since A' is collinear with the triangle ABC, A will be collinear with the triangle $A'BC$ (Art. 9, Th. 2), and the plane $A'BC$ will be the same as the plane ABC. In the same way we prove that the plane $A'B'C$, and finally the plane $A'B'C'$, is the same plane.

11. Intersection of a line and a triangle in a plane.

THEOREM. *In the plane ABC any line intersecting a side of the triangle ABC will intersect this triangle at least*

*in a second point, and any half-line drawn from a point O
of the interior of the triangle will intersect the triangle.*

PROOF. The first statement follows directly from Art. 9,
Th. 1, since the line contains points collinear with the
triangle. To prove the second statement, let the half-line
AO intersect the side BC in a point D, a point of AO produced (Art. 8, Th. 2). Since the given plane can also be
regarded either as the plane ABD or as the plane ACD, it
follows that any line of this plane through O other than the
line AD will intersect both of these triangles again; that
is, that any line through O, whether the line AD or some
other line of the plane, will intersect the given triangle;
and, therefore, that any half-line drawn in the plane from
O, as well as its opposite half-line, will intersect the triangle (see Art. 8, Th. 2, Cor.).

12. The two parts of a plane lying on opposite sides of a line.

THEOREM 1. *Any line of a plane divides the rest of the
plane * into two parts, so that the interior of a segment lying
one point in each part intersects the line, and the interior
of a segment lying both points in the same part does not intersect the line.*

PROOF.† Let a be the given line, and A a point of the
plane which is not a point of a. We divide the points of
the plane which are not points of a into two classes, putting
A into the first class, putting a point B into the first class
if the interior of the segment AB does not contain a point
of a, and putting a point B' into the second class if the
interior of the segment AB' does contain a point of a.

---

* Or at least any restricted portion of the plane through which it passes. The
same statement applies to the first theorem of Art. 23, and to Art. 28.

† This proof is given in Halsted's *Rational Geometry*, p. 8. The point A used
for purposes of proof does not play any particular part in the actual separation of
the points into two classes, any more than do any two points play a particular part
in the class of points which we call a line.

Any line of the plane through A will contain only points of the first class, or will contain a point of a by which the rest of its points are separated into two classes, so

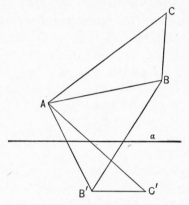

that the interior of a segment with one point in each class itself contains a point of a, and the interior of a segment with both points in the same class does not contain a point of a.*

Now in a triangle ABB', B being a point of the first class, and B' a point of the second class, the line a, intersecting the side AB' and not AB, must intersect BB' (Art. 11).

In a triangle ABC, B and C being points of the first class, the line a does not intersect either side coming to A, and therefore it cannot intersect BC (same reference).

Finally, in a triangle $AB'C'$, B' and C' being points of the second class, the line a intersects both of the sides which meet at A, and therefore it cannot intersect $B'C'$ (Art. 7).

The two parts into which any line of a plane divides the rest of the plane are said to lie *on opposite sides of the line*, and the line is said to lie *between* them.

---

* This is one of the theorems of order referred to in Art. 5.

THEOREM 2. *If two lines intersect, the opposite half-lines of each, drawn from their point of intersection, lie in their plane on opposite sides of the other.*

13. Half-planes. The three half-planes of a triangle.

That portion of a plane which lies on one side of a line of it is called a *half-plane*, and the line is the *edge* of the half-plane. The half-plane which has the line AB for its edge and contains the point C will be called the *half-plane AB–C*. The two half-planes into which any line of a plane divides the rest of the plane are called *opposite half-planes*.

THEOREM 1. *Every point of the plane ABC belongs to one, at least, of the three half-planes BC–A, AC–B, or AB–C.*

PROOF. All points of the plane which do not belong to the half-plane BC–A belong to the line BC or to the half-plane opposite to BC–A.

All points of the line BC belong to the half-line CB or to the half-line BC, or to both, and so to one, at least, of the half-planes AC–B or AB–C.

Let P be a point of the half-plane opposite to BC–A. The interior of the segment AP has a point Q in common with the line BC, a point of one or both of the half-planes AC–B and AB–C. Now the interior of the segment PQ cannot have points in common with both of the lines AC and AB; for PQ produced contains their common point A. Therefore P belongs, with Q, to one or both of these two half-planes.

That is, every point of the plane which is not a point of the half-plane BC–A belongs to one, at least, of the two half-planes AC–B and AB–C.

THEOREM 2. *Any point O of the interior of the triangle ABC belongs to all three of the half-planes BC–A, AC–B, and AB–C.*

THEOREM 3. *Conversely, if a point P belongs to all three of the half-planes BC–A, AC–B, and AB–C, then it is a point of the interior of the triangle ABC.*

PROOF. Let O be any point other than P of the interior of the triangle. Then O like P belongs to each of the half-planes BC–A, AC–B, and AB–C, and the interior of the segment PO cannot intersect the triangle (see statement of Th. 1 of Art. 12). But the opposite half-lines drawn from O, the half-line OP and the half-line PO produced, do intersect the triangle (Art. 11), intersecting it in the two points of a segment whose interior contains O, and therefore P, and lies entirely in the interior of the triangle. Therefore P lies in the interior of the triangle.

IV. CONVEX POLYGONS

14. Polygons. The half-planes of a convex polygon. A *polygon* consists of a finite number of points, three or more, taken in a definite cyclical order, and the interiors of the segments whose points are consecutive points of this order.

The points are the *vertices* of the polygon, and the interiors of the segments are its *sides*. If $A, B, C, \ldots$ are the vertices in order, the sides are the interiors of the segments AB, BC, . . ., and the polygon may be described as the polygon $ABC \ldots$ The entire class of points belonging to the polygon are in cyclical order (Art. 6).

The triangle is a particular case of the polygon.

A *diagonal* of a polygon is the interior of a segment whose points are two non-consecutive vertices of the polygon. A polygon must have at least four vertices to have a diagonal.

A *plane polygon* is a polygon which lies entirely in a plane. If two points of such a polygon are on opposite sides of a line of the plane, each of the two portions into which these points divide the rest of the polygon will intersect the line, for in each portion there will be a vertex on the line or a side that has points on both sides of the line.

A polygon is a *simple polygon* when no point occurs twice as a point of the polygon.   By *polygon* we shall always mean a simple plane polygon.

A *convex polygon* is a simple plane polygon no point of which is a point of a side produced.

THEOREM 1.   *If each pair of consecutive vertices of a polygon lie in the edge of a half-plane which contains all of the other vertices, the polygon is a convex polygon.*

THEOREM 2.   *Conversely, in a convex polygon each pair of consecutive vertices lies in the edge of a half-plane which contains all of the other vertices.*

PROOF.   Let A and B be two consecutive vertices, and let D and E be any other vertices.   If AB–D and AB–E were opposite half-planes, each of the two portions into which D and E divide the rest of the polygon would contain at least one point of the line AB.   But the side AB lies entirely in one of these two portions, and no point of the other portion can be a point of the line AB if the polygon is a convex polygon.

COROLLARY.   *If A and B are two consecutive vertices of a convex polygon, and if P is any point of the polygon not a point of the line AB, then all points of the polygon except those of the line AB will be points of the half-plane AB–P.*

15. Intersection of a line and a convex polygon.

THEOREM 1.   *No line can contain more than two points of a convex polygon unless it contains one of the sides.*

PROOF.   Let us suppose that a line a, not containing a side of the polygon, could contain the three points H, K, and M of the polygon, M coming between H and K on the line. That side of the polygon of which M is a point, or one of the two sides which meet at M if M is a vertex, is a part of a line b, the common edge of two opposite half-planes which contain the points H and K respectively.

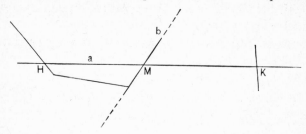

But this is contrary to the corollary of the preceding theorem. Therefore, a line cannot contain three points of the convex polygon unless it contains one of the sides.

THEOREM 2. *If H and K are two points of a convex polygon, with at least one vertex in each of the two portions into which they divide the rest of the polygon, then H and K and the interior of the segment HK will form with each of these two portions a convex polygon.*

PROOF. Let A, B, . . . be the vertices in one of these portions, taken in order from H. These points with H and K will then be the vertices of a polygon HAB . . . KH. This is a simple polygon, for no point of the interior of the segment HK is a point of the original polygon (Th. 1). It is also a convex polygon: no point of either continuation of HK can be a point of the original polygon (same reference); moreover, no point of HK can be a point of some other side produced, for the line containing such a side would be the common edge of two opposite half-planes, one containing the point H and the other the point K, which is contrary to the corollary in the last article. In the same way we prove that the other polygon is a convex polygon.

THEOREM 3. *If a line intersects a convex polygon in two points, and does not contain one of the sides of the polygon, the two portions into which these points divide the rest of the polygon lie on opposite sides of the line.*

PROOF. If either of the two points is a point of a side and not a vertex, the extremities of this side will lie on opposite sides of the given line; and as the polygon can intersect the line in only the two given points, the two portions into which these points divide the rest of the polygon must lie one entirely on one side and the other entirely on the opposite side. It only remains, therefore, to prove the theorem in the case of a diagonal.

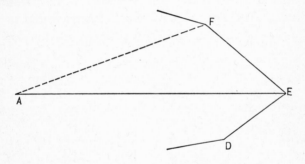

Let AE be any diagonal, D, E, and F being three consecutive vertices. No three of the points A, D, E, and F can be collinear (Th. 1).

Now D, like all the vertices except E and F, is a point of the half-plane EF–A (Art. 14, Th. 2). Again, D is a point of the half-plane AF–E; for D and E, being consecutive vertices, belong to one of the two portions into which A and F divide the rest of the polygon, and lie on the same side of the line AF. Then if D and F were on the same side of the line AE, D would be a point of the half-plane AE–F, and would therefore be in the interior of the triangle AEF (Art. 13, Th. 3). But this would put A

and F on opposite sides of the line ED (see Art. 8, Th. 2), which is contrary to the second theorem of Art. 14. It follows that D and F lie on opposite sides of the line AE; and the same must be true of the entire portions into which A and E divide the rest of the polygon.

THEOREM 4. *Any line in the plane of a convex polygon intersecting a side will intersect the polygon at least in a second point.*

If the polygon is not a triangle, a diagonal will form with it two convex polygons, each having a smaller number of vertices than the given polygon. Thus the theorem, being true of a triangle (Art. 11), can be proved by induction to be true of any convex polygon.

16. Interior of a convex polygon. The *interior of a convex polygon* consists of the interiors of all segments whose points are points of the polygon, except of those whose interiors also lie in the polygon.

THEOREM 1. *If two segments lying in a convex polygon separate each other in the cyclical order of the points of the polygon (Art. 6), then their interiors will intersect unless the interior of one of these segments lies in the polygon.*

PROOF. Let EF and HK be two segments separating each other in the cyclical order of the points of the polygon. The points H and K lie on opposite sides of the line EF, and the points E and F lie on opposite sides of the line HK, unless one of these lines contains a side of the polygon (Art. 15, Th. 3). The line of each segment therefore passes between the points of the other, and the interiors of the two segments intersect.

THEOREM 2. *Any half-line drawn in the plane of a convex polygon from a point O of the interior will intersect the polygon.*

PROOF. The point O is in the interior of a segment HK whose points are points of the polygon. It lies, then, in the side HK of two convex polygons, all of which, except this side and the points H and K, lie on opposite sides of the line HK (Art. 15, Ths. 2 and 3). The theorem can therefore be proved in the same way that the theorem of Art. 11 is proved.

THEOREM 3. *Any half-plane whose edge contains two consecutive vertices of a convex polygon, and which itself contains the other vertices* (Art. 14, Th. 2), *contains also all the points of the interior.*

THEOREM 4. *Conversely, if a point P lies in each of the half-planes whose edges contain two consecutive vertices of a convex polygon and which themselves contain the other vertices, then P is in the interior of the polygon.*

The proof is the same as that of Th. 3 of Art. 13.

V. TETRAHEDRONS

17. Tetrahedrons. Intersection of a plane and a tetrahedron. A *tetrahedron* consists of four non-coplanar points and the sides and interiors of the four triangles whose vertices are these points taken three at a time.

The four points are the *vertices* of the tetrahedron, the sides of the triangles are the *edges*, and the interiors of the triangles are the *faces*. Any four non-coplanar points are the vertices of a tetrahedron.

We shall sometimes speak of the vertices and sides of a face, but it should always be remembered that a face of a tetrahedron is the interior of a triangle and does not include the triangle itself.

THEOREM 1. *The plane of three non-collinear points of a tetrahedron, if not itself the plane of one of the faces, intersects the tetrahedron in a triangle or a convex quadrilateral.*

PROOF. Two points of the given intersection in the plane of any one face determine a line which contains a point in each of the planes of at least two other faces. If then we have another point of the given intersection in the plane of one of these faces, we have a second line; and we can sometimes continue in this way and trace the intersection completely around the tetrahedron.

This will always be the case when one of the given points is a vertex. Any plane through a vertex and two points of the tetrahedron not collinear with the vertex, if not itself the plane of one of the faces, will intersect the tetrahedron in a triangle.

The following construction, with slight modifications, will provide for all other cases:

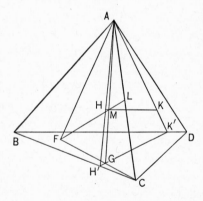

Let $ABCD$ be the given tetrahedron. Let H, F, and K be three points of the given intersection: H a point of the face ABC, F a point of the face BCD, and K a point of the edge AD or of one of the faces ABD or ACD. AH produced will meet the triangle BCD in a point H', and AK produced in a point K', H' a point of the side BC, and the interior of the segment $H'K'$ lying in the interior of this triangle.

If F is a point of the line $H'K'$, the given plane will pass through A. Let us suppose that F lies on the opposite side of this line from C. We have a point G common to the interiors of the segments CF and $H'K'$ (Art. 12, Th. 1, and Art. 8, Definition and Ths.) ; then in connection with the triangle $AH'K'$ we have a point M common to the interiors of the segments AG and HK (Art. 8, Th. 1); and finally, with M in the interior of the triangle ACF, we have in FM produced a point L of the side AC. But F and the segment HK lie in the plane of the given intersection. Therefore, the line FM lies in this plane, and L itself is a point of the given intersection.

Now assuming that the given plane does not pass through a vertex, we have the following cases:

First, if the three given points lie in three different faces, we can take any one of these points for the point H and obtain a point of the intersection in one side of this face, and then a line in which the given plane intersects the plane of this face. These lines will intersect the edges of the tetrahedron in three points or in four points, and the intersection will be a triangle or a quadrilateral. The given plane cannot intersect the three sides of a triangle (Art. 7, Th.), and therefore it cannot intersect more than four of the edges of the tetrahedron.

Again, if two of the given points lie in two different faces and the third lies in the edge which is not a side of either of these faces, there will be lines in the planes of these two faces intersecting in their common side, and intersecting two other edges of the tetrahedron in two points which, with the third given point, determine the rest of the intersection. The intersection will in this case be a quadrilateral.

In the third place, if one of the given points lies in a face and the other two in edges which are not sides of this face, let us suppose that H lies in the face ABC, F in the edge BD, and K in the edge AD. This change in the position of F will not affect the determination of the point L; there will be a line HL intersecting the edge BC, and the intersection will be a quadrilateral. The half-line LH cannot meet the edge AB, for the plane already intersects AD and BD.

Finally, if the three given points lie in three edges not all meeting at one vertex nor lying in one plane, we may suppose that H is a point of BC, F a point of BD, and K a point of AD. In the construction above, H and H' coincide, but this will not affect the determination of the point L; we still have a point of the intersection in each of four edges, and the intersection will be a quadrilateral.

All cases in which the intersection cannot be determined directly from the given points can be reduced to one of these four.

When the intersection is a quadrilateral, it is a convex quadrilateral. No point of any face of the tetrahedron lies in the plane of any other face, and no point of any edge lies in the plane of any face except of the two faces which have this edge for a common side. Therefore no point of any side of the quadrilateral can be a point of a line containing another side, and no vertex can be collinear with two other vertices.

THEOREM 2. *No line can contain more than two points of a tetrahedron unless it lies in the plane of one of the faces.*

PROOF. Let a given line a intersect the tetrahedron in two points H and F, and let A be a vertex which is not a point of a. The plane AHF will contain the line a and will intersect the tetrahedron in a triangle, if it does not contain one of the faces. The intersection of a and the tetrahedron will then be the same as its intersection with the triangle, and will consist only of the two points H and F (Art. 7, Cor.).

18. Interior of a tetrahedron. The *interior of a tetrahedron* consists of the interiors of all segments whose points are points of the tetrahedron, except of those segments whose interiors also lie in the tetrahedron.

THEOREM. *A half-line drawn from any point P of a tetrahedron through a point O of the interior intersects the tetrahedron in a point of PO produced.*

PROOF. The point O is given as in the interior of a segment whose points are points of the tetrahedron. If P is one of these points, the other will be the point in which the half-line PO intersects the tetrahedron, a point of PO produced. If P is not one of these points, these points and P will lie in a plane intersecting the tetrahedron in a triangle or convex quadrilateral, and the theorem follows as a theorem concerning this intersection (see Art. 16, Th. 2).

19. The relation, collinear with a tetrahedron. A point is said to be *collinear with a tetrahedron* when it is collinear with any two points of the tetrahedron.

This is true, in particular, of all points of the tetrahedron, of all points in the planes of its faces, and of all points of its interior.

THEOREM 1. *If a point O is collinear with a tetrahedron ABCD, and if P is any point of a face, not the point O, then the line PO will intersect the tetrahedron at least in a second point Q.*

PROOF. Let H and K be the two points with which O is collinear. Through these two points and P we can pass a plane intersecting the tetrahedron in a triangle or convex quadrilateral, or containing a face of the tetrahedron. When the intersection is a triangle or quadrilateral, P will be a point of a side, and thus in any case the line PO will

E

contain at least a second point Q of the tetrahedron (Art. 9, Th. 1, and Art. 15, Th. 4).

THEOREM 2. *If a point O, not a point of the plane BCD, is collinear with the tetrahedron ABCD, then any point P collinear with the tetrahedron ABCD will be collinear with the tetrahedron OBCD.*

PROOF. Take a point H in the face BCD, not collinear with O and P. The line HO will intersect the tetrahedron in a second point F, and the line HP in a second point K. The points H, F, and K are not collinear, and do not lie in the plane of any one face of the tetrahedron $ABCD$. The plane HFK intersects this tetrahedron in a triangle or convex quadrilateral, one side of which lies in the face BCD and contains the point H. That is, the plane intersects the triangle BCD in a segment MN, and therefore the tetrahedron $OBCD$ in a triangle OMN, with H a point of the side MN. The line HP must then intersect this triangle in a second point, and P must be collinear with it. Therefore P is collinear with the tetrahedron $OBCD$.

Remarks similar to those at the end of Art. 9 may be made at this point. The class of points collinear with the tetrahedron $OBCD$ is the same as the class of points collinear with the tetrahedron $ABCD$. We can use A and O interchangeably in this connection.

VI. HYPERPLANES

20. Hyperplanes. Only one hyperplane contains four given non-coplanar points. Our space a hyperplane. A *hyperplane* consists of the points that we get if we take four points not points of one plane, all points collinear with any two of them, and all points collinear with any two obtained by this process.

Given four non-coplanar points, A, B, C, and D, the

hyperplane ABCD is the hyperplane obtained when we take these points and carry out the process described in the definition.

THEOREM 1. *If two points of a line lie in a given hyperplane, the line lies entirely in the hyperplane; and if three non-collinear points of a plane lie in a given hyperplane, the plane lies entirely in the hyperplane.*

For the line or plane can be obtained from these points by the process used in obtaining the hyperplane.

It follows that a plane having two points in a given hyperplane, but not lying entirely in it, will intersect the hyperplane in the line which contains these two points.

THEOREM 2. *From the points of the figures given in each of the following cases we can obtain just the points of a hyperplane if we take all points collinear with any two of them and all points collinear with any two obtained by this process:*

(1) *A plane and a point not in it, or a plane and a line that intersects it but does not lie in it;*

(2) *Two lines not in one plane;*

(3) *Three lines through one point but not in one plane;*

(4) *Two planes intersecting in a line.*

We can, indeed, speak of a line or a plane as one of the things with which we start in the process of obtaining a hyperplane (compare this with Art. 10).

It follows from (1) that a line and a plane which do not lie in a hyperplane do not intersect at all, and from (4) that two planes which do not lie in a hyperplane cannot have more than one point in common.

THEOREM 3. *If A', B', C', and D' are four non-coplanar points of the hyperplane ABCD, then the hyperplane A'B'C'D' is the same as the hyperplane ABCD.*

The proof follows the lines of proof of the two theorems given in Art. 10.

In regard to Th. 2 we can now say that the hyperplane obtained in each case is the only hyperplane that contains the given figures.

Three non-collinear points can be points of two different hyperplanes. The intersection of the hyperplanes will then be the plane of the three points (see Art. 27, Th. 2).

Apparently we get all the points of ordinary space by taking four non-coplanar points, all points collinear with any two of them, and all points collinear with any two obtained by this process. The space of our experience will therefore be regarded as a hyperplane.

21. Intersection of a line or plane and a tetrahedron in a hyperplane.

THEOREM 1. *In the hyperplane ABCD, any line intersecting a face of the tetrahedron ABCD will intersect this tetrahedron at least in a second point, and any half-line drawn from a point O of the interior of the tetrahedron will intersect the tetrahedron.*

PROOF. The first statement follows directly from Art. 19, Th. 1, since the line contains points collinear with the tetrahedron. To prove the second statement, let the half-line AO intersect the face BCD in a point P, a point of AO produced (Art. 18, Th.). If we have given any other half-line drawn from O in the hyperplane, any point O' of this half-line will be collinear with the tetrahedron (see reference in connection with Art. 20, Th. 3), and the line PO' will intersect the tetrahedron at least in a second point Q not collinear with A and P (Art. 19, Th. 1). The plane APQ will intersect the tetrahedron in a triangle; and the given half-line, being drawn in this plane from a point in the interior of the triangle, will intersect the triangle, and therefore the tetrahedron.

THEOREM 2. *In the hyperplane ABCD, any plane intersecting a face of the tetrahedron ABCD (if not itself the plane of this face), or any plane containing a point O of the interior of the tetrahedron, will intersect the tetrahedron in a triangle or convex quadrilateral.*

For in either case by drawing lines in the plane we can obtain three non-collinear points of the intersection.

22. Intersection of two planes in a hyperplane.

THEOREM. *If two planes lying in a hyperplane have a point O in common, they have in common a line through O.*

PROOF. Let α and β be the two given planes. Let C and D be two points of α not collinear with O, and take P a point between C and D, B a point of PO produced, and A any point of the hyperplane not a point of α. The point O lies in the face BCD of the tetrahedron $ABCD$, and we can consider the given hyperplane as the hyperplane of this tetrahedron. The plane β, containing O, will intersect the tetrahedron in a triangle or convex quadrilateral (Art. 21, Th. 2), and α, the plane of the face BCD, in the line which contains one side of the triangle or quadrilateral, a line through O.

23. Opposite sides of a plane. Half-hyperplanes. The four half-hyperplanes of a tetrahedron.

THEOREM 1. *Any plane of a hyperplane divides the rest of the hyperplane into two parts, so that the interior of a segment lying one point in each part intersects the plane, and the interior of a segment lying both points in the same part does not intersect the plane.*

The proof of Art. 12, Th. 1, applies almost without

change, the reference to Art. 11 holding true by virtue of Art. 22.

The two parts into which any plane of a hyperplane divides the rest of the hyperplane are said to lie *on opposite sides of the plane*, and the plane is said to lie *between* them.

That portion of a hyperplane which lies on one side of a plane of it is called a *half-hyperplane*, and the plane is the *face* of the half-hyperplane. The half-hyperplane which has the plane ABC for its face and contains the point D will be called the *half-hyperplane ABC–D*. The two half-hyperplanes into which any plane of a hyperplane divides the rest of the hyperplane are called *opposite half-hyperplanes*.

THEOREM 2. *If two planes intersect in a line, the opposite half-planes of each, which have this line for a common edge, lie in their hyperplane on opposite sides of the other.*

THEOREM 3. *Every point of the hyperplane $ABCD$ belongs to one, at least, of the four half-hyperplanes BCD–A, ACD–B, ABD–C, or ABC–D.*

The proof is like that of Art. 13, Th. 1.

THEOREM 4. *Any point O of the interior of the tetrahedron $ABCD$ belongs to all four of the half-hyperplanes BCD–A, ACD–B, ABD–C, and ABC–D; and, conversely, if a point belongs to all four of these half-hyperplanes, it is a point of the interior of the tetrahedron $ABCD$.*

See Art. 13, Ths. 2 and 3.

We shall sometimes speak of a tetrahedron as a *surface* and of its interior as a *solid*. A tetrahedron divides the rest of its hyperplane into two portions, interior and exterior to the tetrahedron.

VII. CONVEX PYRAMIDS AND PENTAHEDROIDS

24. Pyramids. Intersection of a plane and a convex pyramid. A *pyramid* consists of a simple plane polygon which has an interior, and a point not in the plane of the polygon, together with the interior of the polygon and the interiors of the segments formed by taking the given point with the points of the polygon.

The point is called the *vertex* of the pyramid, and the interior of the polygon is the *base*. The interiors of the segments formed by taking the vertex and the vertices of the polygon are the *lateral edges*, and the interiors of the triangles determined by the vertex and the sides of the base are the *lateral faces*. Often the term *vertices* is applied to the vertex and the vertices of the polygon taken together, the term *edges* to the lateral edges and the sides of the polygon, and the term *faces* to the lateral faces and the base. Sometimes, also, we shall speak of the vertices and sides of the base or of a lateral face (see remark at the beginning of Art. 17).

The tetrahedron is a particular case of the pyramid.

When the polygon is convex, the pyramid is a *convex pyramid*. We shall consider only convex pyramids.

THEOREM. *The plane of any three non-collinear points of a convex pyramid, if not itself the plane of one of the faces, intersects the pyramid in a convex polygon.*[*]

PROOF. If the plane passes through the vertex, the intersection will be a triangle, as in the case of a tetrahedron (Art. 17).

Let O be the vertex, and let A, B, C, . . . be the vertices of the base.

Suppose the plane, not passing through O, intersects the base in the interior of the segment HK, H and K

---

[*] It may be a triangle, which is a particular case of the convex polygon.

being points of the polygon AB . . . , dividing the rest
of this polygon into two portions with each of which they
and the interior of the segment HK form a convex polygon
(Art. 15, Th. 2). The triangle OHK will divide the rest
of the pyramid into two portions, with each of which it
and its interior will form a convex pyramid. Now the
base and the vertex of one of these pyramids will lie on
opposite sides of the given plane, while all of the other
pyramid except the segment HK and the points of its
interior lie on the same side of this plane. The given plane
will not intersect the second pyramid except along the
line HK, and the given intersection is the same as the
intersection of the plane with a pyramid whose vertex
and base lie on opposite sides of the plane.

Let us suppose, then, that we have a plane and a pyramid
O–ABC . . . whose vertex and base lie on opposite sides
of the plane. The plane may contain one vertex of the
base, or a side and two vertices, but the base itself does
not intersect the plane, and all the rest of the intersection
lies in the lateral faces and lateral edges. In particular,
any lateral edge OA will intersect the plane in a point A' or
will meet the plane at A. Then the face OAB will intersect the plane in the interior of a segment $A'B'$, or AB',
unless (in one particular case) AB itself lies in the plane;
and the entire intersection will be a polygon $A'B'C'$ . . .
There is a one-to-one correspondence of the points of this
polygon and the points of the polygon ABC . . . , corresponding points being collinear with O. There is, indeed,
a correspondence of the entire planes of these two polygons
so far as there are points in both collinear with O. There
is also a correspondence in the order of the points of the
two polygons, and in the order of the points of any two
corresponding lines (Art. 8, Ths. 1 and 2). If, then,
a point P' were to be found twice among the points of the

polygon $A'B'C'$ . . ., the corresponding point P would be
found twice among the points of ABC . . .; or if a point
of the former polygon were also a point of some side produced, the same would be true of the corresponding point
in the plane of the base. It follows that the intersection
must be a simple convex polygon, the polygon ABC . . .
being such a polygon (Art. 14, Defs.).

**25. Pentahedroids. Intersection with a plane. In-
terior. The collinear relation.** A *pentahedroid* consists
of five points not points of one hyperplane, and the edges,
faces, and interiors of the five tetrahedrons whose vertices
are these points taken four at a time.

The five points are the *vertices*, the edges and faces of
the tetrahedrons are *edges* and *faces* of the pentahedroid,
and the interiors of the tetrahedrons are its *cells*. Any five
points, not points of one hyperplane, are the vertices of
a pentahedroid.

We shall sometimes speak of the vertices, edges, and faces
of a cell, but it should always be remembered that a cell
of the pentahedroid is the interior of a tetrahedron and does
not include the tetrahedron itself.

THEOREM. *The plane of three non-collinear points of
a pentahedroid, if it does not itself lie in the hyperplane of one
of the cells, intersects the pentahedroid in a convex polygon.*

PROOF. As in the case of a tetrahedron (Art. 17, Th. 1,
first part of the proof), we can sometimes determine the
intersection directly from the three given points, two points
in the hyperplane of one cell determining a line which
contains a point in each of the hyperplanes of at least two
other cells. In particular, this will be true when one of
the given points is a vertex.

Let $ABCDE$ be the pentahedroid, and let A be a vertex
not in the plane of the given points. If H is any point

of the pentahedroid other than A, the half-line $A H$ will meet the hyperplane of the opposite cell in a point H'. This point we shall call the projection of H from A. H' is the same as H when H itself is a point of the cell $BCDE$. In all other cases H' is a point of the tetrahedron $BCDE$ (see Art. 8, Th. 2, and Art. 18).

Let the three given points be H, F, and K, and let H', F', and K' be their projections from A. These last three points are not collinear; for, if they were, the plane determined by their common line and A would be a plane containing the three given points and the vertex A. They are not all in the plane of any one face of the tetrahedron $BCDE$; for, if they were, H, F, and K would be in the hyperplane determined by this face and A, and the given plane would lie entirely in this hyperplane. Therefore the plane $H'F'K'$ intersects the tetrahedron $BCDE$ in a triangle or convex quadrilateral (Art. 17, Th. 1). This triangle or quadrilateral is the base of a pyramid with vertex at A which lies entirely in the hyperplane $A H'F'K'$, and which is, indeed, the intersection of the hyperplane and pentahedroid (see Art. 31, Th. 1).

The points H, F, and K are points of this pyramid, and the plane HFK lies entirely in the hyperplane of this pyramid. The intersection of the plane and the pentahedroid is the same as the intersection of the plane and this pyramid: it is a convex polygon (Art. 24, Th.).

As there are only five cells, the intersection can only be a triangle, a quadrilateral, or a pentagon.

We define *interior of a pentahedroid* and *collinear with a pentahedroid* exactly as we define the corresponding expressions for the tetrahedron, and for the pentahedroid we have theorems analogous to those of Arts. 18 and 19.

In a pentahedroid each tetrahedron is adjacent to each of the other four. If we move along a line through the interior of one of the tetrahedrons until we come to a face, a continuation of our movement along this line will take us entirely away from the pentahedroid. But we can change the direction of our path so as to pass into the interior of an adjacent tetrahedron, thus following a broken line that belongs entirely to the pentahedroid. This is like what we do when we move along a line in one face of a polyhedron until we come to an edge, and then change the direction of our path so as to pass across an adjacent face.

It may not be very difficult to think of two adjacent tetrahedrons, even though they lie in different hyperplanes, but it is quite impossible for us to form any picture of the pentahedroid as a whole. All that we should try to do now is to remember in a mechanical way the numbers and relations of the different parts.

VIII. SPACE OF FOUR DIMENSIONS

26. Space of four dimensions. The hyperspace of this book. A *space of four dimensions* consists of the points that we get if we take five points not points of one hyperplane, all points collinear with any two of them, and all points collinear with any two obtained by this process.

By a series of theorems analogous to others already given for the plane and hyperplane, we can prove that any five points of a given space of four dimensions, not points of one hyperplane, determine the same space of four dimensions.

We shall limit ourselves to a discussion of space of four dimensions. We shall assume that there is such a space, and that all points lie in one such space.* The preceding theorem can, therefore, be stated as follows:

THEOREM I. *We get all points if we take any five points not points of one hyperplane, all points collinear with any*

---

* This is a mere matter of convenience, enabling us to avoid frequent repetition of the phrase "in one space of four dimensions," and to state many theorems in a simpler form.

*two of them, and all points collinear with any two obtained
by this process.*

The word *hyperspace* is used for any space of more than
three dimensions, but as the only hyperspace that we shall
consider is the space of four dimensions we shall use these
terms interchangeably.

THEOREM 2. *Any line intersecting a cell of a pentahedroid will intersect the pentahedroid at least in a second point,
and any half-line drawn from a point O of the interior of
a pentahedroid will intersect the pentahedroid.*

THEOREM 3. *Any plane intersecting a cell of a pentahedroid, if it does not itself lie in the hyperplane of this cell,
or any plane containing a point O of the interior of the pentahedroid, will intersect the pentahedroid in a convex polygon.*

These two theorems correspond to the two theorems of
Art. 21. For theorems on the intersections of pentahedroids and hyperplanes see Art. 31.

27. Intersection of a plane and a hyperplane and of two hyperplanes. The linear elements of planes.

THEOREM 1. *If a plane and a hyperplane have a point
O in common, they have in common a line through O.*

The proof is like that of the theorem of Art. 22. We
construct a pentahedroid with a cell lying in the given
hyperplane and containing O. The given plane intersects
the pentahedroid in a convex polygon and the given hyperplane in the line which contains one side of this polygon.

THEOREM 2. *If two hyperplanes have a point O in common, they have in common a plane through O.*

PROOF. Let α and β be the two hyperplanes. Any
plane of α through O will intersect β in a line through O,
by the preceding theorem; and a second plane of α through

O, drawn so as not to contain the line in which the first plane intersects β, will intersect β in a second line. We have two lines through *O* common to the two hyperplanes. The hyperplanes therefore intersect in a plane (see Art. 20).

Three hyperplanes having a point in common have in common at least one line, a line lying in one hyperplane and in the plane of intersection of the other two. Three hyperplanes may also have a plane in common.

THEOREM 3. *Two planes which do not lie in one hyperplane contain a set of lines, one and only one through each point of either plane which is not a point of the other plane, and any two of these lines coplanar.*

PROOF. Let α and β be two planes which do not lie in one hyperplane. Let *A* be any point of α which is not a point of β, and let *B* be any point of β which is not a point of α. The hyperplane determined by β and *A* intersects α in a line *a*, and the hyperplane determined by α and *B* intersects β in a line *b* (Th. 1). The lines *a* and *b*, each lying in both hyperplanes, lie in the plane of intersection of the hyperplanes.

On the other hand, no two lines lying in one of the given planes and coplanar with lines in the other can intersect in a point which is not common to the two given planes; for, if they did, both of them and the entire plane in which they lie would lie in the hyperplane determined by their point of intersection and the other given plane.

The planes α and β are covered with these lines, and might be said to consist of them. We shall call them the *linear elements* of the two planes. When the two planes have a point in common, the linear elements all pass through this point. If any plane intersects the two planes in lines, these lines are linear elements.

The student may prove the following theorem:

If two planes have only one point in common, then through any point not a point of either plane passes one and only one plane intersecting both the two planes in lines.

28. Opposite sides of a hyperplane. Half-hyperspaces.

A hyperplane divides the rest of hyperspace just as a plane in a hyperplane divides the rest of the hyperplane (Art. 23). We can speak of the *opposite sides of a hyperplane*, and of a *half-hyperspace*. We may have, for example, the *half-hyperspace ABCD–E* lying on one side of the hyperplane *ABCD*, and the *opposite half-hyperspace* lying on the opposite side of this hyperplane. The hyperplane is the *cell* of the half-hyperspace. If two hyperplanes intersect, the opposite half-hyperplanes of each which have the plane of intersection for a common face lie on opposite sides of the other.

Given a pentahedroid, each of the five tetrahedrons determines the cell of a half-hyperspace which contains the opposite vertex and all points of the interior; and, conversely, if a point lies in all five of these half-hyperspaces it will lie in the interior of the pentahedroid. Every point of hyperspace is a point of at least one of these half-hyperspaces.

We shall sometimes speak of a pentahedroid as a *hypersurface* (see Art. 33), and of its interior as a *hypersolid*. A pentahedroid divides the rest of hyperspace into two portions, interior and exterior to the pentahedroid.

As a line divides a plane into two parts, but not ordinary space (a hyperplane), so a plane divides a hyperplane, but not hyperspace. In hyperspace we can pass completely around a plane, keeping near some one point of it, without touching the plane at all. We can do this, for example, by keeping in another plane which has only one point in common with the given plane. The student should bear this in mind when he comes to consider absolutely perpendicular planes (Art. 42) and rotation around a plane (Art. 81).

IX. HYPERPYRAMIDS AND HYPERCONES

**29. Introduction. Knowledge of polyhedrons presup-
posed.** In this section will be introduced the *hyperpyramids* and *hypercones* of four-dimensional geometry,
with a few theorems analogous to those already given for
convex polygons and convex pyramids. We shall assume
that the term *polyhedron* has been defined, at least so far
as the *hyperplane polyhedron* is concerned, together with
vertices, *edges*, and *faces*, and the expressions *convex polyhedron* and *interior of a polyhedron*. We shall also speak
of *curve* and *surface*, and, in particular, of the *circle*, the
sphere, and the *circular conical surface;* and we shall use
such theorems as we need concerning these surfaces, and
concerning polyhedrons (see Introduction to chap. II).

We may find some difficulty in understanding the forms here considered, but that need not deter us from going on, as the next three
chapters do not depend on this part of our text. Indeed, the study
of hyperpyramids and hypercones could be omitted entirely until
we come again to their treatment in chap. V.

30. Hyperpyramids. Interior of a hyperpyramid. Figures in hyperspace which correspond to the polyhedrons
of geometry of three dimensions are called *polyhedroids*.
We shall not attempt to define this term, except to say that
a polyhedroid consists of *vertices*, *edges*, *faces*, and *cells*,
the cells being the interiors of certain hyperplane polyhedrons joined to one another by their faces so as to enclose
a portion of hyperspace, the *interior of the polyhedroid*.
We shall apply the term polyhedroid only to certain simple
figures which we shall define individually. The pentahedroid is the simplest polyhedroid.

A *hyperpyramid* consists of a hyperplane polyhedron
enclosing a portion of its hyperplane, and a point not a

point of this hyperplane, together with the interior of the polyhedron and the interiors of the segments formed by taking the given point with the points of the polyhedron.

The point is the *vertex*, and the interior of the polyhedron is the *base*. The meaning of other terms used in connection with the hyperpyramid may be readily inferred from the definitions of Arts. 24 and 25. The pentahedroid is the simplest hyperpyramid.

The *interior of a hyperpyramid* can be defined as consisting of the interiors of the segments formed by taking the vertex with the points of the base, but in the case of a convex hyperpyramid the interior of any segment whose points are points of the hyperpyramid will lie entirely in the interior of the hyperpyramid unless it lies entirely in the hyperpyramid itself. No line can intersect a convex hyperpyramid in more than two points unless it lies in the hyperplane of one of the cells, and any half-line drawn from a point O of the interior will intersect the hyperpyramid in one and only one point.

In the last statement is involved one of the difficulties that we have in attempting to understand geometry of four demensions. Since a half-line can be drawn from O through any point of the hyperpyramid, each point of the hyperpyramid plays a part in separating the interior from that portion of hyperspace which is exterior to the hyperpyramid. When we think of a solid as forming a part of the boundary of a figure, we are apt to think of one face of the solid as coming next to the interior and the other face as on the outside, and we think of the thickness of the solid as representing the thickness of the boundary. It is in a very different way that the cells of a polyhedroid separate the interior from the outside. Each point, no matter how far within the solid, is exposed both to the interior and to the outside, and its removal would allow free passage to a half-line from O.

31. Hyperplane sections of a hyperpyramid. A hyperpyramid or any polyhedroid can be cut by a hyperplane

in a *section** which divides the rest of the polyhedroid into two parts lying on opposite sides of the hyperplane (Art. 28).

The sections of a polyhedroid are polyhedrons whose faces are the sections of the cells of the polyhedroid made by the planes in which the hyperplane intersects the hyperplanes of the cells. Thus the following theorems in regard to the sections of a hyperpyramid or pentahedroid are proved by considering the plane sections of their cells:

THEOREM 1. *A section of a convex hyperpyramid made by a hyperplane containing the vertex, is a convex pyramid whose base is the corresponding plane section of the base of the hyperpyramid. In the case of a pentahedroid this applies to any vertex. When one vertex of a pentahedroid lies in a hyperplane and two vertices of the opposite cell lie on each side of the hyperplane, the section will be a quadrilateral pyramid. In all other cases the section of a pentahedroid by a hyperplane containing one vertex and not containing a cell will be a tetrahedron.*

THEOREM 2. *A hyperplane passing between one vertex of a pentahedroid and the opposite tetrahedron will intersect the pentahedroid in a tetrahedron.*

THEOREM 3. *If two vertices of a pentahedroid lie on one side of a hyperplane and three on the opposite side, the section will be a polyhedron in which there are two triangles separated by three quadrilaterals.*

PROOF. Let $ABCDE$ be the pentahedroid, A and B on one side of a hyperplane α, and C, D, and E on the opposite side. The hyperplanes of the tetrahedrons $ACDE$ and $BCDE$ are cut by α in planes which pass between the

---

* The word *section* is somewhat synonymous with intersection, but in general it will not be used except for an intersection which divides the rest of a figure into two parts and completely separates these parts. Thus a triangle or convex quadrilateral would be a section of a tetrahedron.

F

triangle CDE and the points A and B (Art. 28), and which therefore cut these tetrahedrons in triangles. The hyperplanes of the other three tetrahedrons are cut by α in planes which pass between their common edge AB and the opposite edges CD, DE, and CE, and which therefore cut these tetrahedrons in quadrilaterals. If we suppose the triangles to be $C'D'E'$ and $C''D''E''$, the quadrilaterals will be $C'D'C''D''$, $D'E'D''E''$, and $C'E'C''E''$, and the section of the pentahedroid will be $C'D'E'$–$C''D''E''$.

If α intersects the line AB in a point P, the three lines $C'C''$, $D'D''$, and $E'E''$ will pass through P, and the section will be a polyhedron which may be called a truncated tetrahedron. In any case the section will be a figure of this type (see Introduction, p. 14, and the exercise at the end of Art. 128).

A section of a figure in hyperspace is all that we can see in any hyperplane (see Introduction, p. 18). We can, however, see any section, and we can learn much about a figure by studying its various sections.

32. Double pyramids. A hyperpyramid whose base is the interior of a pyramid may be regarded in two ways as a hyperpyramid of this kind, the vertex of the base in one case being the vertex of the hyperpyramid in the other case.

Thus there are two pyramids having themselves a common base, and we can say that the hyperpyramid is determined by a polygon and two points neither of which is in the hyperplane containing the polygon and the other point. Looked at in this way the hyperpyramid is called a *double pyramid*.

A double pyramid consists, then, of the following classes of points:

(1) the points of a convex polygon, or of any plane

polygon which has an interior, and the points of its interior;

(2) two points not in a hyperplane with the polygon, the interior of the segment formed of these two points, and the interiors of the segments formed by taking each of these points with the points of the polygon;

(3) the interiors of the triangles formed by taking each point of the polygon with the two given points;

(4) the interiors of two pyramids each formed by taking the polygon with one of the two given points.

The interior of the segment of the two given points is called the *vertex-edge* of the double pyramid, and the interior of the polygon is the *base*. The interiors of the triangles (3) are called *elements*, and, in particular, those elements whose planes contain the vertices of the polygon are *lateral face elements* or *lateral faces* of the double pyramid. The two pyramids (4) are called the *end-pyramids*.

The vertex-edge and the sides of the base are opposite edges of a set of tetrahedrons. These tetrahedrons are in a definite cyclical order corresponding to the sides of the polygon, and are joined, each to the next, by the faces which are adjacent to the vertex-edge. They are joined to the end-pyramids by the faces which are adjacent to the sides of the base. The interiors of these tetrahedrons are the *lateral cells*, and these and the interiors of the end-pyramids are the *cells* of the double pyramid.

The pentahedroid is the simplest double pyramid.

Certain cases of intersection of double pyramids are given by the following theorems:

THEOREM 1. *A plane containing a point of the vertex-edge and intersecting the base in the interior of a segment, or a plane containing the vertex-edge and a point of the base, will intersect the double pyramid in a triangle.*

In the latter case two sides of the triangle are in the interiors of the end-pyramids.

THEOREM 2. *A hyperplane containing the base and a point of the vertex-edge will intersect the double pyramid in a pyramid.*

THEOREM 3. *A hyperplane containing the vertex-edge and intersecting the base will intersect the double pyramid in a tetrahedron.*

In this case two faces of the tetrahedron are sections of the interiors of the end-pyramids.

We have already referred to the importance of studying the sections of a figure of hyperspace (Art. 31). Another way of studying a polyhedroid is to examine its cells. These cells can be cut apart sufficiently to spread them out in a hyperplane where we can see them. They are the interiors of polyhedrons; and we can think of a polyhedroid as formed by taking a suitable set of polyhedrons, placing them upon one another, and folding them away from our hyperplane until they come together completely.

In a pentahedroid, for example, there are five tetrahedrons whose twenty faces fit together in pairs, each tetrahedron having a face in common with each of the other four. We can take any one of these tetrahedrons and place the other four upon it, all in one hyperplane, and then we can turn the four outside tetrahedrons away from this hyperplane without separating them from the fifth or distorting them in any way (Art. 81), until we have brought together every pair of corresponding faces. The five tetrahedrons together with their interiors now enclose a portion of hyperspace. This is analogous to the process of forming a tetrahedron by placing three of its faces in a plane around the fourth, turning them about the sides which lie upon the sides of the fourth, and bringing them together completely.*

Another way of constructing a pentahedroid is by means of its ten edges. Any tetrahedron will have six of these edges and will be connected with the opposite vertex by the remaining four. We can take these four and cause them to stand out from the vertices of the tetrahedron, all in one hyperplane. In hyperspace these four edges

* Other examples of this method of studying polyhedroids are given in notes in Arts. 135, 136, and 141.

can be turned so that their ends come together at a point, and with the faces of the given tetrahedron determine the other four tetrahedrons and the complete figure.

33. Hyperconical hypersurfaces. Hypercones. *Hypersurface* is the term applied to a figure in hyperspace which corresponds to the surfaces of geometry of three dimensions. We shall not attempt to define hypersurface, and we shall use the word only in connection with certain simple figures which we shall define individually. The hyperplane is the simplest hypersurface.

A *hyperconical hypersurface** consists of the lines determined by the points of a hyperplane surface and a point not in the hyperplane of this surface.

The point is the *vertex*, the surface is the *directing-surface*, and the lines are the *elements*. The hyperconical hypersurface has two nappes.

The only hyperconical hypersurfaces which we have to consider at present are those in which the directing-surface is a plane, a sphere, a circular conical surface, or a part or combination of parts of such surfaces. When the directing-surface is a plane, the hypersurface is a hyperplane or a portion of a hyperplane.

A *hypercone* consists of a hyperplane surface, or portions of hyperplane surfaces, forming a closed hyperplane figure, and a point not a point of the hyperplane of this figure, together with the interior of the latter and the interiors of the segments formed by taking the given point with the points of the hyperplane figure.

The point is the *vertex*, the interiors of the segments are *elements*, and the interior of the hyperplane figure is the *base*.

---

* See foot-note, p. 220. We shall sometimes use the word *conical* for hyperconical when there is no ambiguity.

A hypercone, or the hypersolid which we call the interior of a hypercone (see below), can be somewhat inaccurately described as cut from one nappe of a hyperconical hypersurface by the hyperplane of the directing-surface.

The hyperpyramid may be regarded as a particular case of the hypercone. The only other cases which we have to consider at present are those in which the base is the interior of a sphere or of a circular cone.

A plane containing the vertex of a hypercone and intersecting the base in the interior of a segment, will intersect the hypercone in a triangle; and a hyperplane containing the vertex and intersecting the base, will intersect the hypercone in a cone.

The *interior of a hypercone* consists of the interiors of the segments formed by taking the vertex with the points of the base, but in the case of a convex hypercone the interior of any segment whose points are points of the hypercone will lie entirely in the interior of the hypercone unless it lies entirely in the hypercone itself. No line can intersect a convex hypercone in more than two points if it passes through a point of the interior, and any half-line drawn from a point O of the interior will intersect the hypercone in one and only one point.

34. Double cones. A hypercone whose base is the interior of a cone may be regarded in two ways as a hypercone of this kind, the vertex of the base in one case being the vertex of the hypercone in the other case.

Thus there are two cones having themselves a common base, and we can say that the hypercone is determined by a closed plane curve and two points neither of which is in the hyperplane containing the curve and the other point. Looked at in this way the hypercone is called a *double cone*.

A *double cone* consists, then, of the following classes of points :

(1) the points of a closed plane curve and the points of its interior ;

(2) two points not in a hyperplane with the curve, the interior of the segment formed of these two points, and the interiors of the segments formed by taking each of these points with the points of the curve ;

(3) the interiors of the triangles formed by taking each point of the curve with the two given points ;

(4) the interiors of two cones each formed by taking the curve with one of the two given points.

The interior of the segment of the two given points is the *vertex-edge* of the double cone, and the interior of the curve is the *base*. The interiors of the triangles (3) are the *elements*, and the two cones (4) are the *end-cones*.

35. Plano-conical hypersurfaces.

A *plano-conical hypersurface* consists of the planes determined by the points of a plane curve and a line not in a hyperplane with this curve.

The line is the *vertex-edge*, the curve is the *directing-curve*, and the planes are the *elements*. Each element meets the plane of the directing-curve in only one point, the point where it meets the directing-curve itself. There are two nappes to the hypersurface.

The only case which we have to consider at present is the case where the directing-curve is a circle.

THEOREM. *A hyperplane which contains the directing-curve of a plano-conical hypersurface and a point of the vertex-edge, intersects the hypersurface in a conical surface.*

The line containing the vertex-edge of a double cone, and the curve whose interior is the base, are the vertex-edge and directing-curve of a plano-conical hypersurface.

A double cone, or the hypersolid which we call the interior of a double cone, can be somewhat inaccurately described as cut from one nappe of a plano-conical hypersurface by two hyperplanes each of which contains the directing-curve and a point of the vertex-edge.

There are theorems on certain cases of intersection of double cones corresponding to the theorems of Art. 32.

CHAPTER II

PERPENDICULARITY AND SIMPLE ANGLES

36. Introductory. From this point the theorems of ordinary geometry presupposed. We shall now take up perpendicularity and various kinds of angles in very much the same way that these subjects are taken up in the text-books. We shall find the relation of the perpendicular line and hyperplane analogous to the relation of the perpendicular line and plane of three-dimensional geometry, but a new kind of perpendicularity in the case of two planes absolutely perpendicular in hyperspace, every line of one plane through their point of intersection being perpendicular to every line of the other through this point. The relation of perpendicular planes in a hyperplane now takes a very simple form, as that of a plane intersecting in a line each of two absolutely perpendicular planes. This chapter will conclude with a treatment of perpendicular planes and hyperplanes, and of hyperplane angles, which are analogous to dihedral angles.

Chap. III will take up what may be called two-dimensional angles, and angles which correspond to polyhedral angles; and chap. IV will consider questions of order, symmetry, and motion. After finishing these chapters we shall return to the polyhedroids and other hypersurfaces already introduced.

As indicated at the beginning of the preceding section (Art. 29), the three chapters which follow do not depend on that section. Indeed, only a few simple facts are needed from the entire first chapter besides what are already familiar to the student.   These facts are easily stated and understood, and a study of their application to the theorems which follow will help us to realize their truth.

Except for the properties of points on a line referred to in Art. 5, the development of most of chap. I has been complete in itself, no theorem being based on theorems not given there.   The subjects now to be taken up belong more particularly to metrical geometry; and we shall assume the axioms of metrical geometry,* and employ its terms without special definition.   In fact we shall assume all of the theorems of the ordinary geometry, except, for the present, those which depend on the **axiom of parallels.**†

I. LINES PERPENDICULAR TO A HYPERPLANE

37. Existence of perpendicular lines and hyperplanes.

THEOREM 1.   *The lines perpendicular to a line at a given point do not all lie in one plane.*

PROOF.   Every point in hyperspace lies in a plane with the given line, and in every plane which contains the line there is a perpendicular to the line at the given point.   Now if these perpendiculars were all in one plane, that plane and the given line would determine a hyperplane containing all of the planes which contain the line (Art. 20, Th. 1), and so all points of hyperspace.   But the points of hyperspace do not all lie in one hyperplane.

THEOREM 2.   *A line perpendicular at a point to each of three non-coplanar lines, is perpendicular to every line through this point in the hyperplane which the three lines determine.*

---

* For a set of axioms of metrical geometry see R. L. Moore, "Sets of Metrical Hypotheses," referred to on p. 28, or Veblen, "Foundations of Geometry," pp. 27, ff.

† The theorems of plane geometry are true in any plane and of any plane figures, and the theorems of geometry of three dimensions are true in any hyperplane and of any hyperplane figures, for all the axioms are assumed to be true in every portion of hyperspace.

PROOF.　Let m be a line perpendicular at a point O to each of three non-coplanar lines, a, b, and c, and let d be any other line through O in the hyperplane determined by these three lines. The plane of cd will intersect the plane of ab in a line h (Art. 22, Th.). The line m, being perpendicular to a and b, is perpendicular to h lying in the plane of ab; and then, being perpendicular to c and h, it is perpendicular to d lying in the plane of ch.*

THEOREM 3. *All lines perpendicular to a given line at a given point lie in a single hyperplane.*

PROOF.　Let m be the given line and O the given point. Three non-coplanar lines perpendicular to m at O determine a hyperplane α such that m is perpendicular to every line of α through O. Now let a be any line perpendicular to m at O. The plane of am intersects α in a line b (Art. 27, Th. 1), also perpendicular to m at O. In this plane, then, we have a line m and the two lines a and b perpendicular to m at O. Therefore a must coincide with b and lie in the hyperplane α.

A line intersecting a hyperplane at a point O is *perpendicular to the hyperplane* when it is perpendicular to all lines of the hyperplane which pass through O; the hyperplane is also said to be *perpendicular to the line*. The point O is called the *foot* of the perpendicular.

38. One hyperplane through any point perpendicular to a given line.　Planes in a perpendicular hyperplane.

THEOREM 1. *At any point of a line there is one and only one hyperplane perpendicular to the line.*

This follows immediately from the theorems of the preceding article.

---

* A line m through a point O, perpendicular to each of two lines intersecting at O, is perpendicular to every line through O in the plane which the two lines determine. This is always true, for the plane and the line m lie in one hyperplane.

THEOREM 2. *Through any point outside of a line passes one and only one hyperplane perpendicular to the line.*

THEOREM 3. *A line perpendicular to a hyperplane is perpendicular to every plane of the hyperplane passing through the foot of the line; and every plane perpendicular to a line at a point lies in the hyperplane perpendicular to the line at this point.*

THEOREM 4. *If a line and plane intersect, a line perpendicular to both at their point of intersection is perpendicular to the hyperplane determined by them; or if two planes intersect in a line, a line perpendicular to both at any point of their intersection is perpendicular to the hyperplane determined by them.*

39. Lines perpendicular to a given hyperplane.

THEOREM 1. *At a given point in a hyperplane there is one and only one line perpendicular to the hyperplane.*

PROOF. Consider three non-coplanar lines lying in the hyperplane and passing through the given point. The three hyperplanes perpendicular to these lines at the point have in common at least a line (Art. 27, Th. 2 and remark), and any such line must be perpendicular to the given hyperplane because perpendicular to the three lines.

If there were two lines perpendicular to the hyperplane at the given point, they would both be perpendicular to the line in which their plane intersects the hyperplane. We should have in a plane two lines perpendicular to a third at the same point, which is impossible.

THEOREM 2. *Two lines perpendicular to a hyperplane lie in a plane.*

PROOF. Any two lines lie in a hyperplane (Art. 20, Th. 2 (2)), and a hyperplane containing the two given lines intersects the given hyperplane in a plane to which the lines are both perpendicular (Art. 38, Th. 3). Therefore, as proved in geometry of three dimensions, the two lines lie in a plane.*

THEOREM 3. *Through any point outside of a hyperplane passes one and only one line perpendicular to the hyperplane.*

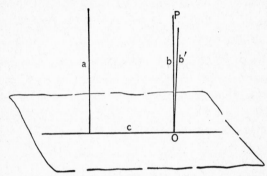

PROOF. Let *P* be the point, and *a* some line perpendicular to the hyperplane. If *a* does not pass through *P*, *a* and *P* determine a plane which intersects the hyperplane in a line *c*, and in this plane there is a line *b* through *P* perpendicular to *c*, intersecting *c* at a point *O*. Let *b'* be the line perpendicular to the hyperplane at *O*. *a* and *b'* lie in a plane (Th. 2), which is the plane containing *a* and the point *O*. But the plane determined by *a* and *P* passes through *O*. Therefore *b'* lies in the plane determined by *a* and *P*, and in this plane is perpendicular to *c* at *O*. In other words, *b'* coincides with *b*, and *b* must be perpendicular to the hyperplane.

If there were two lines through *P* perpendicular to the hyperplane, we should have two lines through *P* perpendicular to the line which passes through their feet, and this is impossible.

* Euclid proves this in connection with the theorem that two lines perpendicular to a plane are parallel (*Elements*, Bk. XI, Prop. 6). The proof does not, however, depend on the axiom of parallels.

40. Projection of a point upon a hyperplane. Distance from a hyperplane. The *projection* * *of a point upon a hyperplane* is the foot of the perpendicular from the point to the hyperplane. The perpendicular may be called the *projecting line.*

THEOREM 1.† *The distance from any point outside of a hyperplane to its projection upon the hyperplane is less than the distance from the point to any other point of the hyperplane.*

The *distance between a hyperplane and a point outside of the hyperplane* is the distance between the point and its projection upon the hyperplane.

COROLLARY.‡ *If the distance between two points is less than the distance of one of them from a hyperplane, they lie on the same side of the hyperplane in hyperspace.*

THEOREM 2. *Given any point P outside of a hyperplane, and O its projection upon the hyperplane, then any two points of the hyperplane equally distant from P will be equally distant from O, and any two points equally distant from O will be equally distant from P; and if two points of the hyperplane are unequally distant from either P or O, that point which is nearer to one of them will be nearer to the other.*

PROOF. The perpendicular PO, and the lines through P and any two points of the hyperplane, lie in a second hyperplane which intersects the given hyperplane in a plane α. The perpendicular is perpendicular to α, and the three lines intersect α in the points where they intersect the given hyperplane. The theorem is therefore a theorem in the three-dimensional geometry of the second hyperplane.

---

* That is, orthogonal projection. We sometimes have cases of projection by lines through a point (see, for example, the proof in Art. 25), but when we use the word projection alone we shall mean by it orthogonal projection.

† The two theorems of this article are true at least when the distances referred to are "restricted" (see Introduction, p. 19, and reference given there in the footnote).

‡ Used in the proof of the first theorem of Art. 96.

From any point of our three-dimensional space we can move off into hyperspace without passing through or approaching any other point of our space. A point at the centre of a sphere, for example, moving off on a line perpendicular to our space, would not approach any point of the sphere. It would, indeed, be moving farther and farther from all points of the sphere, the distances from all of these points being the same, and all increasing at the same rate. An object completely enclosed within a surface in our three-dimensional space would be entirely free if it could pass off in any direction out of this space.

41. Projection of a line upon a hyperplane. Angle of a half-line and hyperplane. The projection of any figure upon a hyperplane consists of the projections of its points.

THEOREM 1. *When a line and hyperplane are not perpendicular, the projection of the line upon the hyperplane is a line or a part of a line.*

PROOF. Let m be the line, and a the perpendicular projecting some point of m upon the hyperplane. Any other perpendicular b projecting a point of m upon the hyperplane, lies in a plane with a (Art. 39, Th. 2), and this plane, containing two points of m, is the plane determined by m and a. Therefore, all the perpendiculars projecting points of m upon the hyperplane lie in the plane determined by m and a, and the projection of m upon the hyperplane is the same as its projection upon the line in which this plane intersects the hyperplane.*

* In plane geometry, when two lines are not perpendicular, the projection of one upon the other is the latter line itself or a single connected part of it. That is, if two given points are the projections on a line a of points of another line m, any point between them will be the projection of a point of m. For the perpendiculars at the three points of a do not intersect one another, and therefore it follows that the perpendicular which lies between the other two must intersect m (Art. 12, Th. 1); that is, any point of a between the projections of two points of m is itself the projection of a point of m.

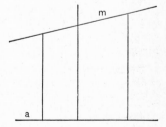

COROLLARY. *When a half-line drawn from a point O of a hyperplane does not lie in the hyperplane and is not perpendicular to it, its projection upon the hyperplane is a half-line drawn in the hyperplane from O, or the interior of a segment which has O for one of its points.*

THEOREM 2. *When a half-line drawn from a point O of a hyperplane does not lie in the hyperplane and is not perpendicular to it, the angle which it makes with the half-line drawn from O containing its projection is less than the angle which it makes with any other half-line drawn in the hyperplane from O.*

When a half-line drawn from a point O of a hyperplane does not lie in the hyperplane and is not perpendicular to it, the angle which it makes with its projection is called the *angle of the half-line and hyperplane*. A half-line drawn from a point O of a hyperplane perpendicular to the hyperplane is said to make a *right angle* with the hyperplane.

II. ABSOLUTELY PERPENDICULAR PLANES

42. Existence of absolutely perpendicular planes.

THEOREM 1. *A plane has more than one line perpendicular to it at a given point.*

For the plane is the intersection of different hyperplanes, and the lines in these hyperplanes perpendicular to the plane at the given point must be different lines (see Art. 20).

THEOREM 2. *Two lines perpendicular to a plane at a given point determine a second plane, and the two planes are so related that every line of one through the point is perpendicular to every line of the other through the point.*[*]

We cannot prove without the axiom of parallels that every point of a is the projection of a point of m, for the perpendiculars at some points of a may not intersect m at all. The projection of m may be the entire line a, but it may be only a half-line of a, or the interior of a definite segment of this line.

* See foot-note, p. 75.

THEOREM 3.   *All the lines perpendicular to a plane at a given point lie in a single plane.*

PROOF.   Let α be the given plane, and O the given point. Two lines perpendicular to α at O determine a plane β in which every line through O is a line perpendicular to α. Now let a be any line perpendicular to α at O.   The hyperplane determined by a and α intersects β in a line b (Art. 27, Th. 1), also perpendicular to α at O.   But in a hyperplane containing α only one line can be perpendicular to α at O. Therefore a coincides with b and lies in β.

Two planes having a point in common are *absolutely perpendicular* when every line of one through that point is perpendicular to every line of the other through that point.

These planes have only the point in common, and do not intersect in a line.   We can never see both planes in a single hyperplane like the space in which we live.   The most that we could see would be one plane and a single line of the other.

43.   One plane through any point absolutely perpendicular to a given plane.

THEOREM 1.   *At any point of a plane there is one and only one plane absolutely perpendicular to the given plane.*

This follows immediately from the theorems of the preceding article.

A plane and a point outside of the plane lie in one and only one hyperplane.   Through any such point, therefore, by three-dimensional geometry, passes one and only one line perpendicular to the plane; and the *projection of the point upon the plane*, as in geometry of three dimensions, is the foot of this perpendicular.   A point that lies in a given plane is its own projection upon the plane.

G

THEOREM 2. *Through any point outside of a plane passes one and only one plane absolutely perpendicular to the given plane.*

PROOF. Let P be the point, and O its projection upon the plane. The absolutely perpendicular plane at O will then contain the perpendicular line OP, and therefore P. Moreover, any absolutely perpendicular plane containing P must contain a perpendicular line through P, and there is only one such line.

44. Planes absolutely perpendicular to planes which intersect in a line.

THEOREM 1. *If two planes intersect in a line and so lie in a hyperplane, their absolutely perpendicular planes at any point of their intersection intersect in a line and lie in a hyperplane.*

PROOF. Let α and β be two planes intersecting in a line a, and let α' and β' be the planes absolutely perpendicular to α and β respectively at a point O of a. α' and β' are, then, both perpendicular to the line a at O, and lie in a hyperplane perpendicular to a at O (Art. 38, Th. 3). Therefore α' and β' intersect in a line (Art. 22, Th.).

THEOREM 2. *If three planes have a line in common, their absolutely perpendicular planes at any point of this line lie in a hyperplane; and if three planes lie in a hyperplane and have a point in common, their absolutely perpendicular planes at this point have a line in common.*

This is proved by Art. 38, Th. 3, the line being perpendicular to the hyperplane.

COROLLARY. *If three planes have a line in common and lie in a hyperplane, their absolutely perpendicular planes at any point of this line have a line in common and lie in a hyperplane.*

45. Planes absolutely perpendicular to a plane at different points.

THEOREM. *Two planes absolutely perpendicular to a third lie in a hyperplane.*

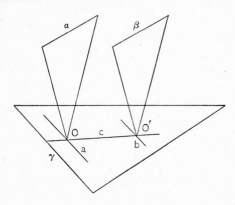

PROOF.   Let α and β be the planes absolutely perpendicular to a given plane γ at two points O and O'. Let c be the line OO', and let a and b be the lines perpendicular at O and O' to the hyperplane determined by α and c. a and b lie in a plane (Art. 39, Th. 2), and this plane is γ, for a, being perpendicular to α, must lie in γ, and only one plane can contain a and the point O'. b is then perpendicular to β; so that β lies with α in the hyperplane to which b is perpendicular (Art. 38, Th. 3), the hyperplane determined by α and c.

COROLLARY. *All the planes absolutely perpendicular to a plane at the points of any line of it, lie in a hyperplane.*

It should be noted that the figure given here is merely to serve as a diagram, and does not represent the actual appearance of two planes absolutely perpendicular to a third. The most that we could ever see in any one hyperplane would be the plane γ and a line in each of the other two planes, or the two planes α and β and the single line c of γ.

46. Projection of a line upon a plane. As in other cases of projection, the projection of any figure upon a plane consists of the projections of its points (Art. 41).

THEOREM 1. *The perpendiculars projecting the points of a line upon a plane do not lie in a single plane, unless the line itself lies in a hyperplane with the plane upon which it is projected.*

PROOF. If any two of the perpendiculars were in a plane, that plane, having two points in common with the given plane, would intersect the latter in a line and lie with it in a hyperplane (Art. 20, Th. 2 (4)). Therefore, the given line would lie in a hyperplane with the plane upon which it is projected.

When two planes are absolutely perpendicular at a point O, all the points of one project upon the other in the single point O. We may regard projection upon a plane as made by planes absolutely perpendicular to it, just as in geometry of three dimensions we may regard projection upon a line as made by planes perpendicular to the line. We shall sometimes speak of *projecting planes* and think of a point as projected upon a plane in this way.*

THEOREM 2. *The projection of a line upon a plane is a line or a part of a line, unless the given line lies in a plane absolutely perpendicular to the given plane.*

PROOF. Let m be the given line and γ the given plane. Let α be the plane absolutely perpendicular to γ which projects some point of m upon γ. Any other plane projecting a point of m upon γ lies in a hyperplane with α (Art. 45, Th.). But this hyperplane containing two

---

* In a hyperplane, on the other hand, where the perpendiculars projecting points of a line upon a plane always lie in a single plane, the latter is sometimes called the *projecting plane*, projecting the line as a whole. These two uses of the expression "projecting plane" should be carefully distinguished.

points of m, is the hyperplane determined by m and α; and the projection of m upon γ is the same as its projection upon the line in which this hyperplane intersects γ.*

The projecting lines form a curved surface which contains the given line and its projection and lies in the hyperplane of these two lines.

The student may prove the following theorem:

Given any two lines, we can pass through either a plane upon which it will be the projection of the other.

III. SIMPLY PERPENDICULAR PLANES

47. Planes intersecting in lines two absolutely perpendicular planes. Two planes are *perpendicular*, or *simply perpendicular*, when they lie in one hyperplane and in this hyperplane form right dihedral angles. Each contains a line in the other and lines perpendicular to the other.†

THEOREM 1. *A plane perpendicular to one of two absolutely perpendicular planes, and passing through the point where they meet, is perpendicular to the other.*

PROOF. Let α and α' be two absolutely perpendicular planes meeting in a point O, and let β be a plane passing through O and perpendicular to α. Two planes which are perpendicular lie in a hyperplane, and, by a theorem of geometry of three dimensions, a line in one perpendicular to their intersection is perpendicular to the other. There

---

* See foot-note, p. 79.

† In a sense two planes are perpendicular whenever one of them contains a line perpendicular to the other. Such planes have also been called *half-perpendicular*, in distinction from absolutely perpendicular planes, which are then said to be *completely perpendicular* (see Schoute, *Mehrdimensionale Geometrie*, vol. I, p. 49). Two planes in a hyperplane forming a right dihedral angle might be described as *perpendicular in a hyperplane*. We shall find that such planes are of great importance in our geometry, and we shall, at least for the present, apply to them the word perpendicular. Perpendicular, then, has with us the same meaning as in the ordinary geometry; and the only new concept with which we have to become familiar at this point is that of absolute perpendicularity.

is, then, a line in β perpendicular to α at O, that is, a line common to β and the absolutely perpendicular plane α', so that β intersects α' in a line and lies with α' in a hyperplane. Now the line in which β intersects α, like all the lines of α through O, is perpendicular to α'; so in the hyperplane of β and α' we have a line lying in β perpendicular to α'. Therefore β is perpendicular to α'.

THEOREM 2. *A plane intersecting in a line each of two absolutely perpendicular planes, is perpendicular to both.*

PROOF. Let α and α' be two absolutely perpendicular planes meeting in a point O, and let β be a plane intersecting both of these planes in lines. These two lines and the plane β pass through O; otherwise the hyperplane determined by β and O would contain both α and α', which is impossible. Now the line in which β intersects α' is that line which is perpendicular to α at O in the hyperplane determined by α and β. In this hyperplane, then, we have a line lying in β and perpendicular to α. Therefore β is perpendicular to α.

In the same way, or by Th. 1, we prove that β is perpendicular to α'.

THEOREM 3. *If two planes are perpendicular, their absolutely perpendicular planes at any point of their intersection are perpendicular.*

PROOF. Let α and β be two perpendicular planes, and let α' and β' be their absolutely perpendicular planes at a point O of their intersection. α, being perpendicular to β, is perpendicular to β'; and then β', being perpendicular to α, is perpendicular to α'.

The student may prove:

If a plane is perpendicular to one of two absolutely perpendicular planes, and contains a point of the other, it is perpendicular to both.

48. The different possible positions of two pairs of absolutely perpendicular planes at a point. Let two pairs * of absolutely perpendicular planes have their intersection point O in common. Then

(1) they may have only the point O in common;

(2) each plane of one pair may intersect in a line one plane of the other pair; or

(3) each plane of one pair may be perpendicular to both planes of the other pair.

In the last case the four lines of intersection are mutually perpendicular, and, taken two at a time, determine also a third pair of absolutely perpendicular planes. The planes of each of the three pairs are then perpendicular to all the planes of the other two pairs.

We have, in fact, four mutually perpendicular lines, any two of them determining a plane, and any three a hyperplane. Each line is perpendicular to the hyperplane determined by the other three. In each hyperplane are three of the six planes, three mutually perpendicular planes forming a trirectangular trihedral angle.

We shall call this figure a *rectangular system* (see Art. 71).

49. Common perpendicular planes of two planes intersecting in a line.

THEOREM. *Two planes which intersect in a line have at any point O of that line one and only one pair of common perpendicular planes.*

PROOF. Let α and β be the two given planes, and let α' and β' be their absolutely perpendicular planes at O. A plane which is perpendicular to α and β at O is a plane which intersects these four planes in lines. The planes

---

* In general, we shall use the word "pair" in speaking of two planes only when we have in mind two planes absolutely perpendicular to each other. Thus we shall speak in this way of a pair of planes perpendicular to a given plane, and of a pair of common perpendicular planes when we have two given planes.

α and β intersect in a line and lie in a hyperplane, and the planes α' and β' intersect in a line and lie in a hyperplane (Art. 44, Th. 1). The line of intersection of α' and β' is perpendicular to the hyperplane of α and β, and the line of intersection of α and β is perpendicular to the hyperplane of α' and β' (Art. 38, Th. 4).

In a hyperplane two intersecting planes have a common perpendicular plane at any point of their intersection, perpendicular to the intersection. Thus we have one plane perpendicular to α and β at O lying in their hyperplane. This plane cannot contain the intersection of α' and β', for the intersection of α' and β' is perpendicular to the hyperplane of α and β. The plane must therefore intersect α' and β' in separate lines, and lie also in their hyperplane. In other words, the common perpendicular plane with which we are familiar in the case of two intersecting planes, perpendicular to their intersection at a point O, is the plane of intersection of their hyperplane with the hyperplane of their absolutely perpendicular planes at O.

A second common perpendicular plane is the plane absolutely perpendicular to the plane already found (Art. 47, Th. 1). This plane contains the lines of intersection of α and β and of α' and β' and may be regarded as determined by them.

It remains to prove that these two planes are the only planes perpendicular to α and β at O.

Any plane intersecting α and β in lines must pass through their line of intersection or lie entirely in their hyperplane, and any plane intersecting α' and β' in lines must pass through their line of intersection or lie entirely in their hyperplane (Art. 20, Th. 1). But, as we have seen, a plane lying entirely in the hyperplane of two of these planes can not pass through the line of intersection of the other two. Any common perpendicular plane, therefore, must lie in both hyperplanes or pass through both lines of intersection : that is, it must be one of the two planes already found. These are therefore the only planes which can be perpendicular to α and β at O.

When the two given planes are perpendicular, the four planes have all together four lines of intersection, and there are four different hyperplanes which contain two of the four planes. The planes can be associated in two ways so that two planes shall intersect in a line and the other two planes be their absolutely perpendicular planes. But the plane determined by the two lines of intersection in one case is the plane of intersection of the two hyperplanes in the other case. Therefore we get only two planes perpendicular to the two given planes.

That is, if α and β are perpendicular, so that α is also perpendicular to β' and β to α', then the plane determined by the intersection of α and β and the intersection of α' and β' is the plane of intersection of the hyperplane determined by α and β' and the hyperplane determined by α' and β; and the plane determined by the intersection of α and β' and the intersection of α' and β is the plane of intersection of the hyperplane determined by α and β and the hyperplane determined by α' and β'. Thus we have only two planes intersecting in lines the four planes, α, β, α', β', and so perpendicular to the two given planes α and β.

The four planes and the two common perpendicular planes in this case are the six planes of a rectangular system (Art. 48).

COROLLARY. *If each of two planes having a common point O intersects in a line the plane absolutely perpendicular to the other at O, then these planes have one and only one pair of common perpendicular planes.*

The student may prove the following theorem:

Given two planes with a point O in common, through any line containing O in one of these planes can be passed a plane perpendicular to this plane and intersecting the other in a line. In other words, any line of one plane through O is the projection upon this plane of a line of the other.

If the two planes intersect in a line and the given line is this line of intersection, an infinite number of planes can be drawn satisfying the conditions of the theorem. Or, if one of the two planes lies in a hyperplane with the plane absolutely perpendicular to the other at O, and the given line is the intersection of the other given plane with this hyperplane, there will be an infinite number of these planes.

Except in these two cases there is only one plane satisfying the conditions of the theorem.

IV.   PERPENDICULAR PLANES AND HYPERPLANES

50. Perpendicular planes and hyperplanes.   The planes perpendicular or absolutely perpendicular to planes lying in the hyperplanes. A plane intersecting a hyperplane is *perpendicular to the hyperplane* at a point of their intersection, if the plane absolutely perpendicular to the given plane at this point lies in the hyperplane. The hyperplane is also said to be *perpendicular to the plane.*

THEOREM 1.   *If a plane is perpendicular to a hyperplane at one point of their intersection, it is perpendicular all along this line.*

For the line of intersection and the plane absolutely perpendicular to the given plane at the given point determine the hyperplane (Art. 20, Th. 2 (1)), which, therefore, contains the planes absolutely perpendicular to the given plane at all points of the line of intersection (Art. 45, Th. and Cor.).

THEOREM 2.   *If a plane α is perpendicular to a hyperplane along a line c, any plane in the hyperplane perpendicular to c is absolutely perpendicular to α, and any plane ab-*

*solutely perpendicular to α through a point of the hyperplane
lies entirely in the hyperplane.*

PROOF. The planes absolutely perpendicular to α at
the points of *c* lie in the hyperplane, and in the hyperplane
they are planes perpendicular to the line *c*. Now in the
hyperplane only one plane can be perpendicular to a given
line at a given point. Any plane in the hyperplane, therefore, perpendicular to the line *c*, must be one of the planes
absolutely perpendicular to α at the points of *c*.

On the other hand, if a plane α′ is given as passing through
a point of the hyperplane and absolutely perpendicular to
α, we can draw a plane β in the hyperplane through the same
point perpendicular to *c*. β is then absolutely perpendicular to α, and α′ must coincide with β and lie entirely in the
hyperplane, since we cannot have two planes through a
point absolutely perpendicular to a given plane (Art. 43,
Ths.).

THEOREM 3.   *If a plane α is perpendicular to a hyperplane
along a line c, any plane in the hyperplane passing through c
is perpendicular to α, and any plane perpendicular to α passing through c, or through any line which lies in the hyperplane and is not itself perpendicular to c, lies entirely in the
hyperplane.*

PROOF. In the first case, the given plane, passing
through *c*, intersects α in this line; and, lying in the given
hyperplane, it intersects in a line the plane absolutely perpendicular to α at any point of *c*. It is therefore perpendicular to α.

On the other hand, if the plane is given as perpendicular
to α and passing through *c*, or through any line *b* which lies
in the hyperplane and is not itself perpendicular to *c*, it
must intersect in a line the plane absolutely perpendicular
to α through any point of the given line, a plane which lies

entirely in the hyperplane (Th. 2). It must, therefore, contain two lines of the hyperplane and lie entirely in it (Art. 20, Th. 1).

THEOREM 4. *If two hyperplanes are perpendicular to a plane at a point O, they intersect in the absolutely perpendicular plane at O.*

For the absolutely perpendicular plane lies in both hyperplanes, by hypothesis.

51. Lines lying in the plane and perpendicular to the hyperplane, or in the hyperplane and perpendicular to the plane.

THEOREM 1. *If a plane is perpendicular to a hyperplane, any line in the plane perpendicular to their intersection is perpendicular to the hyperplane, and any line perpendicular to the hyperplane through a point of the plane lies entirely in the plane.*

PROOF. In the first case, the line, lying in the given plane, is perpendicular not only to the intersection, but also to the absolutely perpendicular plane at the point where it meets the intersection. The line is therefore perpendicular to the hyperplane (Art. 38, Th. 4).

On the other hand, if the line is given as passing through a point of the plane and perpendicular to the hyperplane, we can draw a line in the plane through the same point perpendicular to the intersection, and the two lines must coincide, since they are both perpendicular to the hyperplane (Art. 39, Ths. 1 and 3).

COROLLARY. *If two planes are perpendicular to a hyperplane at a point O, they intersect in a line which is perpendicular to the hyperplane at O.*

For, by the theorem, the line perpendicular to the hyperplane at *O* lies in both planes.

THEOREM 2. *If a plane is perpendicular to a hyperplane, any line in the hyperplane perpendicular to their intersection is perpendicular to the plane, and any line perpendicular to the plane through a point of the hyperplane lies entirely in the hyperplane.*

PROOF. In the first case, the line, lying in the hyperplane and perpendicular to the intersection, lies also in the plane which in the hyperplane is perpendicular to the intersection at the same point. But this plane is absolutely perpendicular to the given plane (Art. 50, Th. 2). Therefore the given line is perpendicular to the given plane.

On the other hand, if the line is given as passing through a point of the hyperplane and perpendicular to the given plane, it lies in the absolutely perpendicular plane which passes through the same point, and therefore in the hyperplane (same reference).

52. Through any line one plane perpendicular to a given hyperplane, or one hyperplane perpendicular to a given plane.

THEOREM 1. *If a line is perpendicular to a hyperplane, any plane passing through the line is perpendicular to the hyperplane.*

For the plane absolutely perpendicular to the given plane at the point where the line meets the hyperplane is perpendicular to the line, and therefore lies in the hyperplane (Art. 38, Th. 3).

THEOREM 2. *Through a line not perpendicular to a hyperplane passes one and only one plane perpendicular to the hyperplane.*

PROOF. The plane perpendicular to the hyperplane along the projection of the given line upon the hyperplane, contains the given line (Art. 51, Th. 1); and we cannot have two perpendicular planes containing the given line, for that would make the line itself perpendicular to the hyperplane, which is contrary to hypothesis (same reference, and Cor.).

THEOREM 3. *Through a line not lying in a plane absolutely perpendicular to a given plane, passes one and only one hyperplane perpendicular to the given plane.*

PROOF. The hyperplane perpendicular to the given plane along the projection of the given line upon the plane, contains the given line (Art. 51, Th. 2); and we cannot have two perpendicular hyperplanes containing the given line, for that would put the line itself into a plane absolutely perpendicular to the given plane, which is contrary to hypothesis (Art. 50, Th. 4).

53. Planes with linear elements all perpendicular to a hyperplane.

THEOREM. *Given two planes not in one hyperplane, if any two of their linear elements (Art. 27) have a common perpendicular line, they all have a common perpendicular hyperplane, to which the two given planes are also perpendicular.*

PROOF. Let α and β be the two given planes, and let a be one of the linear elements in α and b one of the linear elements in β. If a and b have a common perpendicular line, the hyperplane perpendicular to either of these lines at the point where it meets the perpendicular line, is perpendicular to the plane of the two (Art. 52, Th. 1), and therefore perpendicular to the other (Art. 51, Th. 1). This hyperplane is also perpendicular to the planes α and β, as well as to every plane containing a or b (Art. 52, Th. 1). Now any other linear element in β is the intersection of β with a plane through a, and any other linear element in α is the intersection of α with a plane through b.

The hyperplane is therefore perpendicular to all of these elements (Art. 51, Th. 1, Cor.).

If two elements in one of the two given planes are given as having a common perpendicular line, then the perpendicular hyperplane is perpendicular to the plane in which they lie and to every plane containing either one of them. But any element of the other plane is the intersection of two planes through the two given elements, and is therefore, as before, perpendicular to the hyperplane. Thus the hyperplane is perpendicular to elements in both planes, and so perpendicular to all the elements and to the two given planes.*

V. HYPERPLANE ANGLES

54. Definition.   Interior.   Plane angles.   A *hyperplane angle* consists of two half-hyperplanes having a common face but not themselves parts of the same hyperplane, together with the common face.

The common face is the *face of the hyperplane angle*, and the two half-hyperplanes are the *cells*.

The *interior of a hyperplane angle* consists of the interiors of all segments whose points are points of the hyperplane angle, except those segments whose interiors also lie in the hyperplane angle; that is, the interior of a hyperplane angle consists of the interiors of those segments which have a point in each cell.   The hyperplane angle divides the rest of hyperspace into two regions, interior and exterior

---

* The linear elements of two planes not in a hyperplane will all pass through a point common to the two planes, or will all be perpendicular to a hyperplane perpendicular to the two planes, except in the Hyperbolic Non-Euclidean Geometry, where there are lines in a plane which do not intersect and do not have a common perpendicular, namely, the parallel lines of this geometry.   It follows from the theorem that in this geometry the linear elements of two planes are all parallel if two of them are parallel.   They will then be axes of a set of *boundary-hypersurfaces*, and their geometry will correspond to the Euclidean three-dimensional geometry of boundary-hypersurfaces (see the author's *Non-Euclidean Geometry*, p. 52).

to the hyperplane angle. Each cell of a hyperplane angle lies on one side of the hyperplane of the other cell; and the portion of hyperspace which lies on that side of the hyperplane of each cell on which lies the other cell, lies *between* the two cells and constitutes the interior of the hyperplane angle.

Two half-lines drawn from a point O in the face of a hyperplane angle, one in each cell, and each perpendicular to the face, are the sides of an angle which is called the *plane angle at O of the hyperplane angle.*

THEOREM 1. *The plane absolutely perpendicular at a point O to the face of a hyperplane angle, intersects the hyperplane angle in the plane angle at O.*

THEOREM 2. *A hyperplane perpendicular to the face of a hyperplane angle intersects the hyperplane angle in a dihedral angle which at any point of its edge has the same plane angle as the hyperplane angle.*

PROOF. The intersection consists of two half-planes with a common edge lying in the face of the hyperplane angle. The plane absolutely perpendicular to the face at any point O of this edge, lies in the perpendicular hyperplane, and in this hyperplane is perpendicular to the edge of the dihedral angle formed by the two half-planes (see Art. 50, Th. 2). This plane intersects the dihedral angle in the same angle in which it intersects the hyperplane angle — an angle which is, therefore, the plane angle at O of both.

THEOREM 3. *Two hyperplane angles are congruent if a plane angle of one is equal to a plane angle of the other.*

PROOF. We have given two hyperplane angles with the plane angle at a point O of one equal to the plane angle at a point O' of the other. If we make these angles coincide, the faces of the two hyperplane angles will coincide, each face being absolutely perpendicular to the plane of the common plane angle at the vertex of this angle. Now one side of the common plane angle lies in one cell of each of the hyperplane angles, and the other side lies in the other cell of each. The two cells of one hyperplane angle, therefore, coincide with the two cells of the other, and the two hyperplane angles coincide throughout and are congruent (Art. 20, Th. 2 (1) and Th. 3).

If we make a cell of one of these hyperplane angles coincide with a cell of the other, with the points O and O' coinciding and with the other cells on the same side of the hyperplane of the common cell, the hyperplane angles will coincide throughout. For the planes of the given plane angles will be absolutely perpendicular to the plane of the common face at the same point and will coincide, and the plane angles themselves will coincide, having one side in common and the other sides in the same half-plane with respect to the line of the common side.

When two hyperplane angles coincide, every point in the face of one coincides with a point in the face of the other, and the plane angles at any such common point coincide and are equal.

THEOREM 4. *The plane angle of a hyperplane angle is the same at all points of the face.*

PROOF. The absolutely perpendicular planes at any two points of the face are in a perpendicular hyperplane (Art. 45, Th.), in which the corresponding angles are two plane angles of the same dihedral angle. Therefore the two plane angles are equal.*

* The theorem that the plane angle of a dihedral angle is the same at all points of the edge is usually made to depend on the axiom of parallels. It can be proved, however, without the use of this axiom:

Let A and B be two points of the edge, and let O be the point midway between them. We can turn the dihedral angle so that the half-line OA will fall upon the original position of the half-line OB and the half-line which bisects the plane angle at O upon its own original position. This will make the plane angle at O coincide

Hereafter we shall speak of the *plane angle* of a hyper-plane angle without thinking of it as located at any particular point of the face.

COROLLARY. *Two hyperplane angles which are congruent in any position will always coincide as soon as they have a common cell and the other cells lie on the same side of the hyperplane of this common cell.*

55. The hyperplane angle as a magnitude. *Supplementary hyperplane angles* are those which can be placed so as to have one cell in common while their other cells are opposite half-hyperplanes. Each of them is then the *supplement* of the other. A *right hyperplane angle* is one which is congruent to its supplement. The hyperplanes of the cells of a right hyperplane angle are said to be *perpendicular*.

If two hyperplane angles have a common face and the cells of one lie in the interior of the other, or if they have one cell in common while one cell of one lies in the interior of the other, then the interior of one hyperplane angle is a part of the interior of the other. We shall find it convenient to speak of one hyperplane angle as a *part of the other* and as *less in magnitude*.

Let two hyperplane angles be placed so as to have one cell in common while their other cells and their interiors lie on opposite sides of the hyperplane of this common cell. Then, if either hyperplane angle is less than the supplement of the other, these two cells and the common face will form a hyperplane angle which we can call the *sum of the given hyperplane angles*.

as a whole with its original position and the dihedral angle as a whole will occupy its original position. Then the plane angle at A will take the former position of the plane angle at B; and the two plane angles must be equal.

This theorem should have been proved in the author's *Non-Euclidean Geometry* at some point before Art. 11, p. 26, as has been pointed out by Professor J. L. Coolidge.

THEOREM 1. *Two supplementary hyperplane angles have supplementary plane angles; a right hyperplane angle has a right plane angle; the smaller of two unequal hyperplane angles has the smaller plane angle; and the plane angle of the sum of two hyperplane angles is the sum of their plane angles. The converse theorems are also true.*

THEOREM 2. *If we divide the plane angle of a hyperplane angle into any number of equal parts, the lines of division will determine additional cells by means of which the given hyperplane angle is divided into the same number of equal parts; in particular, given a hyperplane angle α, any other hyperplane angle may be divided into a sufficient number of equal parts so that one of these parts shall be less than α.*

Thus we can build up a complete theory of the measurement of hyperplane angles, taking any particular one as the unit of measure.

The student will notice the analogy of the hyperplane angle to the dihedral angle of the ordinary geometry. The theory of measurement is identical in the two cases, and so does not involve any new conceptions.

We may consider the class of half-hyperplanes with a common face as having a geometry, a one-dimensional geometry, in which these half-hyperplanes are the elements (compare "Point Geometry," Art. 64, and "Edge Geometry," Art. 78, and see Introduction, p. 15). Disregarding the common face, we may say in this geometry that the hyperplane angle consists of two half-hyperplanes. The hyperplane angle corresponds to the segment, and the magnitude of the hyperplane angle to the length of the segment.

56. Hyperplane angles measured by their plane angles.

THEOREM. *Two hyperplane angles are in the same ratio as their plane angles, and the hyperplane angle may be measured by its plane angle.*

PROOF. If we divide the plane angle of a hyperplane angle into some number of equal parts, the half-lines of division, taken with the face of the hyperplane angle, will determine half-hyperplanes which will divide the hyperplane angle (its interior) into the same number of equal parts. We can therefore prove in the usual way that hyperplane angles are proportional to their plane angles, first when the plane angles are commensurable and then (by the method of limits or some equivalent method) when the plane angles are incommensurable.

Now a right hyperplane angle has a right plane angle (Art. 55, Th. 1). Therefore, the measure of the hyperplane angle in terms of a right hyperplane angle is always the same as the measure of its plane angle in terms of a right angle.

57. The bisecting half-hyperplane.

THEOREM 1. *The half-hyperplane bisecting a hyperplane angle is the locus of points in the interior of the hyperplane angle equidistant from the hyperplanes of the cells.*

PROOF. Through any point lying in the interior of a hyperplane angle we can pass a plane absolutely perpendicular to the face of the hyperplane angle (Art. 43, Th. 2). This plane will intersect the cells of the hyperplane angle in the sides of a plane angle, and the bisecting half-hyperplane in the half-line which bisects the plane angle. Now this plane is perpendicular to the hyperplanes of the cells of the hyperplane angle (Art. 50, Def.), and the distances of the given point from these hyperplanes are the distances of the point from the sides of the plane angle (Art. 51, Th. 1). If, then, the point is in the half-hyperplane bisecting the hyperplane angle, it is in the half-line bisecting the plane angle, and these distances are equal; or, if these distances are equal, the point is in the half-line bisecting the plane angle, and therefore in the half-hyperplane bisecting the hyperplane angle. That is, the bisecting half-hyperplane is the locus of points in the interior of the hyperplane angle equidistant from the hyperplanes of its cells.

THEOREM 2.* *The distance of a point in one cell of a hyperplane angle from the bisecting half-hyperplane, is greater than one-half the distance of the point from the hyperplane of the other cell.*

This is proved, like the preceding theorem, by passing a plane through the given point absolutely perpendicular to the face of the hyperplane angle.

58. Perpendicular hyperplanes. Lines lying in one and perpendicular to the other.

THEOREM 1. *If two hyperplanes are perpendicular, any line in one perpendicular to their intersection is perpendicular to the other, and any line through a point of one perpendicular to the other lies entirely in the first.*

PROOF. In the first case, we have a line along which lies one side of a plane angle of each of the four right hyperplane angles whose cells lie in the two hyperplanes, and, since these plane angles are right angles, the line is perpendicular to that line of the second hyperplane along which lie their other sides. That is, the given line is perpendicular to a line in the second hyperplane as well as to the plane in which the two hyperplanes intersect, and therefore it is perpendicular to the second hyperplane (Art. 38, Th. 4).

The proof of the second part of the theorem is like the corresponding proofs given in Art. 51.

THEOREM 2. *If a line is perpendicular to a hyperplane, any hyperplane which contains the line is perpendicular to the hyperplane.*

* Used in the proof of the first theorem of Art. 96.

THEOREM 3. *If three intersecting hyperplanes with only a line common to all three are perpendicular to a given hyperplane, the line of intersection is perpendicular to the given hyperplane.*

59. Planes lying in one and perpendicular to the other of two perpendicular hyperplanes.

THEOREM 1. *If two hyperplanes are perpendicular, any plane in one, perpendicular to their intersection, is perpendicular to the other, and any plane through a line of one, perpendicular to the other, lies entirely in the first unless the line itself is perpendicular to the second.*

PROOF. In the first case, a line can be drawn in the given plane perpendicular to the plane of intersection, and therefore perpendicular to the second hyperplane. The given plane must then be perpendicular to the second hyperplane (Art. 52, Th. 1).

On the other hand, if the plane is given as perpendicular to the second hyperplane, and contains a line *b* which lies in the first hyperplane and is not perpendicular to the second, we can pass a plane through *b* in the first hyperplane perpendicular to the intersection, and therefore perpendicular to the second hyperplane, by the first part of this theorem. But through a line not perpendicular to a hyperplane there passes only one plane perpendicular to the hyperplane (Art. 52, Th. 2). Therefore the given plane must coincide with the plane just drawn, and lies entirely in the first hyperplane.

THEOREM 2. *If a plane is perpendicular to a hyperplane, any hyperplane which contains the plane is perpendicular to the hyperplane.*

For in the plane are lines perpendicular to the given hyperplane, and any hyperplane which contains the plane will contain these lines, and must itself be perpendicular to the hyperplane (Art. 58, Th. 2).

Theorem 3. *If two intersecting hyperplanes are perpendicular to a given hyperplane, their intersection is also perpendicular to the given hyperplane.*

60. Projection of a plane upon a hyperplane. Angle of a half-plane and a hyperplane.

Theorem 1. *The projection of a plane upon a hyperplane is a plane or a part of a plane; it does not lie entirely in one line unless the given plane is perpendicular to the hyperplane.*

Proof. The given plane and any point of its projection determine a hyperplane which is perpendicular to the given hyperplane (Art. 58, Th. 2). The lines which project the points of the plane upon the given hyperplane are the same as the lines which project the points of the plane upon the plane of intersection of the two hyperplanes (Art. 58, Th. 1, and Art. 38, Th. 3). The projection upon the given hyperplane is therefore the same as the projection upon the plane of intersection. Now the given plane is not perpendicular to the plane of intersection if it is not perpendicular to the given hyperplane (Art. 59, Th. 1). Therefore the projection is not a line, but is the plane of intersection itself, or a part of this plane.*

Corollary. *When a half-plane with its edge in a given hyperplane does not lie in the hyperplane and is not perpendicular to it, its projection upon the hyperplane is a half-plane, or a portion of a half-plane, having the same edge.*

Theorem 2. *When a half-plane with its edge in a given hyperplane does not lie in the hyperplane and is not perpendicular to it, the dihedral angle which it makes with the half-plane having the same edge and containing its projection is less than the dihedral angle which it makes with any other half-plane of the hyperplane having the same edge.*

* It is a single convex part, any point lying between the projections of two points being also the projection of a point of the given plane. See foot-note, p. 79.

PROOF. Let α be the given half-plane, β the half-plane
with the same edge containing the projection of α upon the
hyperplane, and γ any other half-plane lying in the hyperplane and having its edge in common with α and β. A
hyperplane perpendicular to this common edge will intersect the three half-planes in three half-lines, a, b, and c,
and these half-lines, taken two at a time, are the sides of
plane angles of the dihedral angles whose faces are any
two of the three half-planes.

Now the last-named hyperplane and the hyperplane
of α and β contain the half-lines a and b, and are both perpendicular to the given hyperplane (the former by Art. 58,
Th. 2). Hence they intersect in a plane which contains a
and b and is perpendicular to the given hyperplane (Art.
59, Th. 3), and therefore contains the projection of a upon
the given hyperplane (Art. 51, Th. 1). In other words,
the half-line b is the half-line which contains the projection of a upon the given hyperplane; and a makes an angle
with b which is less than the angle which it makes with c
(Art. 41, Th. 2). Therefore the dihedral angle which α makes
with β is less than the dihedral angle which it makes with γ.

When a half-plane with its edge in a given hyperplane
does not lie in the hyperplane and is not perpendicular to
it, the plane angle of the dihedral angle which it makes
with the half-plane having the same edge and containing
its projection is called the *angle of the half-plane and hyperplane*. When a half-plane with its edge in a given hyperplane is perpendicular to the hyperplane, it is said to make
a *right angle with the hyperplane*.

The student may prove the following theorem:

When a plane intersects a hyperplane but does not lie in it and is
not perpendicular to it, that plane of the hyperplane which passes
through the intersection and is perpendicular to the projection, is
perpendicular to the given plane.

CHAPTER III

ANGLES OF TWO PLANES AND ANGLES OF HIGHER ORDER

I. THE COMMON PERPENDICULAR OF TWO LINES

61. Existence of minimum distance between two lines. The theorems having to do with the common perpendicular of two lines not in the same plane are usually made to depend on the axiom of parallels. We shall give a form of statement and proof for these theorems that will show their independence of this axiom, so far as they are independent of it. We shall give the proofs in full, because they will be a guide to us in proving a similar set of theorems for planes in hyperspace.*

THEOREM. *Given two lines a and b not in the same plane, there is a point of a whose distance from b is less than or equal to the distance from b of any other point of a.*

PROOF. Let *M* be some point of *a*. The perpendicular from *M* to the line *b* lies with *b* itself in a plane which intersects *a* at the point *M*, so that the half-lines of *a* from *M*, forming an angle with this plane, move away from it indefinitely. That is, we can take a definite portion of *a*, a segment and its interior, and say that any point of *a* outside of this portion will be distant from the plane, and there-

---

* In this method of treatment one or two modifications are necessary for the Elliptic Geometry. Thus in the proof in this article the statement that the line *a* moves off indefinitely is not true in the "third hypothesis" (see the author's *Non-Euclidean Geometry*, p. 22). But in this case we can take the entire line for *AB*, putting *A* and *B* together at some point and regarding them as the two ends of the line. Another slight modification will be pointed out in connection with Th. 2 of the next article.

fore distant from b, by more than the distance of M from b.*

Let AB denote such a portion of a, and let P be any point of AB. The distance of P from the line b has for all positions of P a lower limit $l \geqq 0$. By this we mean that for every positive number ϵ there are positions of P where the distance, though never less than l, will be less than $l + \epsilon$.

This is a theorem of irrational numbers, proved as follows: If we separate all numbers into two classes, putting into the first class all negative numbers and every positive number which is never greater than the distance of P from b, and into the second class every positive number which is greater than the distance of some point P from b, the numbers of the first class will all be less than those of the second class, and we determine in this way a number which occupies the point of separation of the two classes. This is the number l. l is, then, never greater than the distance of P from b; but $l + \epsilon$ is a number of the second class, and there is some position of P for which its distance from b is less than $l + \epsilon$.

On any portion of AB we prove in the same way that the distance of a point P from b has a lower limit, and the lower limit for any portion of AB taken is greater than or equal to the lower limit for any portion within which it is contained, and so greater than or equal to l.

Now we separate the points of AB into two classes, putting A into the first class, and putting any other point C into the first class if for the points of AC the lower limit of the distance from b is greater than l, but into the second class if this lower limit is equal to l. The points of the first class all come before those of the second class; and by this separation we determine a point C', the point of sepa-

---

* See reference in previous foot-note.

ration, which may be A itself, or B, or some point between A and B.

The distance of C' from b is exactly l.

For suppose this distance to be $l + \delta$, where δ is some positive number. Take C_1 on a towards A and C_2 towards B, each at a distance of $\frac{1}{2}\delta$ from C'. If C' coincides with A, or is at a distance from A less than $\frac{1}{2}\delta$, we take C_1 at A; or if C' coincides with B, or is at a distance from B less than $\frac{1}{2}\delta$, we take C_2 at B. In AC_1, when C_1 does not coincide with A, the lower limit of the distance from b is a number greater than l. In AC_2 this lower limit is l.

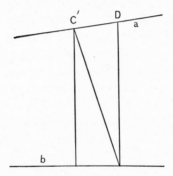

Therefore in C_1C_2 the lower limit is l, and hence there is in C_1C_2 a point D whose distance from b is less than $l + \frac{1}{2}\delta$, $\frac{1}{2}\delta$ being a "positive number," a value of ϵ. Now

$$C'D^* \leqq \tfrac{1}{2}\delta.$$

Therefore the distance of C' from the foot of the perpendicular drawn to b through D is less than $l + \delta$ (one side of a triangle less than the sum of the other two). That is, the distance of C' from one point of b, and there-

---

* In an equation or inequality "$C'D$" is used, as in our text-books, for the length of the segment $C'D$ (see Introduction, p. 21), that is, for the distance between the points C' and D.

fore certainly from b, is less than $l + \delta$, whereas we have assumed this distance to be equal to $l + \delta$.

This proves that the distance of C' from b is exactly l, and is less than or equal to the distance from b of any other point of a.

The distance l is not zero, since a and b do not intersect.

62. Existence of a common perpendicular. An infinite number if more than one.

THEOREM 1. *Given two lines a and b not in the same plane, the line along which we measure the minimum distance from b of a point of a is perpendicular to both.*

PROOF. Let M be a point of a whose distance from b is less than or equal to the distance from b of any other point of a, and let N be the projection of M upon b, so that the line MN is perpendicular to b at N. If MN is not perpendicular to a, then the projection of N upon a will be a point whose distance from one point of b, and therefore certainly from b, is less than the distance of M from b. But this is contrary to hypothesis; hence the line MN must be a common perpendicular to the lines a and b.

THEOREM 2. *If two lines not in the same plane have more than one common perpendicular, they have an infinite number of common perpendiculars; along all of these perpendiculars the distance between them is the same, and any two of the perpendiculars cut off the same distance on them.*

---

* In the Elliptic Geometry we should say, "If two lines not in the same plane have more than one common perpendicular within a restricted region," and in the proof we must assume that the points M, N, M', and N' are all within such a region.

This theorem will prove that it is only in the Elliptic Geometry (of the three principal geometries, see Introduction, p. 19, foot-note) that two lines not in the same plane can have more than one common perpendicular. For it is only in this geometry that two lines not in the same plane can be everywhere equidistant (see first paragraph of proof in Art. 61 and the reference in the foot-note on p. 105).

PROOF. Let a and b be two lines not in the same plane, and let MN and $M'N'$ be two common perpendiculars, perpendicular to a at M and M', and perpendicular to b at N and N'.

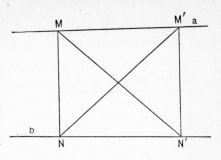

The distance $M'N'$ is then equal to the distance MN. For suppose we had

$$M'N' < MN.$$

Then in the right triangles which have NN' in common, we should have

$$M'N < MN',$$

and in the right triangles which have MM' in common,

$$MN' < M'N.$$

Our hypothesis leads to a contradiction.   We must have

$$M'N' = MN,$$

$$M'N = MN',$$

and in the right triangles which have MN in common

$$MM' = NN'.$$

Now on a and b lay off equal distances from M and N to points P and Q respectively, both towards M' and N' or both away from M' and N', and draw PQ, MQ, etc.

The right triangles MNP and MNQ are equal, having the two legs of one equal respectively to the two legs of the other.   Therefore

$$MQ = PN.$$

In the same way we prove

$$M'Q = PN'.$$

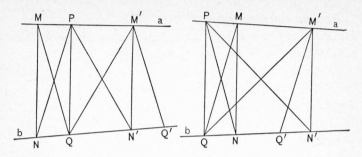

On b we take Q' in the same direction from N' that Q is from N, so that

$$N'Q' = NQ,$$

and therefore so that

$$QQ' = NN'.$$

Then we have equal right triangles MNQ and $M'N'Q'$,

$$M'Q' = MQ = PN,$$

the triangles PNN' and $M'Q'Q$ mutually equilateral, and

$$\angle M'Q'Q = \angle PNN'.$$

Finally, now, the triangles PNQ and $M'Q'N'$ have two sides and the included angle of one equal respectively to two sides and the included angle of the other, and

$$\angle M'N'Q' = \angle PQN.$$

But the angle $M'N'Q'$ is a right angle. Therefore PQN is a right angle, and PQ is perpendicular to b.

In the same way we prove that PQ is perpendicular to a.

PQ is also equal to MN and to $M'N'$: the lines a and b are equidistant along all of these perpendiculars.

The last theorem is true and the proof holds good for two lines in the same plane.

63. The common perpendicular line of a line and plane, and the common perpendicular plane of two planes which have a common perpendicular hyperplane.

THEOREM I. *Given a line a and a plane β not in the same hyperplane, there is a point of a whose distance from β is less than or equal to the distance from β of any other point of a, and the line along which we measure this minimum distance is perpendicular to both.*

PROOF. Let *b* be the line along which lies the projection of *a* upon *β*. Any line perpendicular to *a* and *b* will be perpendicular to *β*, and any line perpendicular to *a* and *β* will be perpendicular to *b*, and will be the projecting line of a point of *a*. Now *a* and *b* lie in a hyperplane but not in a plane (Art. 46, Th. 1), and the distance of any point of *a* from its projection upon *β* is less than its distance from any other point of *β*. Therefore, any point of *a* whose distance from *b* is less than or equal to the distance from *b* of any other point of *a*, will be a point whose distance from *β* is less than or equal to the distance from *β* of any other point of *a*; and the line along which we measure this minimum distance will be perpendicular to *a* and *β*, being perpendicular to *a* and *b*.

THEOREM 2. *If a line and plane not in one hyperplane have more than one common perpendicular line they have an infinite number of these perpendiculars, one through every point of the line; along all of these perpendiculars the distance between them is the same, and any two of the perpendiculars intersect the line and plane at the same distance from each other.*

THEOREM 3. *If two planes not in one hyperplane have a common perpendicular hyperplane (Art. 53), they have a common perpendicular line and a common perpendicular plane.*

PROOF. The common perpendicular hyperplane intersects the two planes in lines which do not lie in one plane
(Art. 27, Th. 3), and which have one common perpendicular
line. This line is perpendicular to the two given planes
(Art. 51, Th. 2), and the plane containing this line and the
linear elements which it intersects is perpendicular to the
two given planes.*

THEOREM 4. *If two planes not in one hyperplane have
a common perpendicular hyperplane and more than one
common perpendicular plane, they have an infinite number
of common perpendicular planes, one through each linear
element; and any two of these planes are equidistant along the
intersections of the given planes with the given perpendicular
hyperplane or with all the perpendicular hyperplanes if
there can be more than one.*†

II. POINT GEOMETRY

**64. A geometry whose elements are the half-lines
drawn from a given point.** We shall make a particular
study of the angles formed at a point *O* by the lines, planes,
and hyperplanes which pass through *O*; and our presentation of the subject will be simpler if we omit all mention of

---

* In the Hyperbolic Non-Euclidean Geometry we have planes which do not
intersect and do not have a common perpendicular hyperplane, namely, planes
with parallel elements. These planes, however, do have a common perpendicular
plane. We can prove this by considering the geometry of an orthogonal boundary-
hypersurface. See foot-note, p. 95.

† It is only in the Elliptic Geometry that a line and plane not in one hyperplane
can have more than one common perpendicular line, and it is only in this geometry
that two planes not in one hyperplane having a common perpendicular hyperplane
can have more than one common perpendicular plane (see foot-note, p. 108). Two
planes in the Elliptic Geometry always have a point in common, a point common to
all their linear elements (Art. 27, Th. 3, remark). The above theorem should be
slightly "restricted," applied to some restricted region containing a part of the perpendicular hyperplane; because two planes having a point in common always have
two common perpendicular planes at such a point. But this case will be fully treated
in Arts. 66–69.

this point, leaving it to be understood that the lines, planes, and hyperplanes which pass through O are the only ones considered. In this way we can avoid frequent repetition of the phrase "pass through O." Thus we can speak of two planes as intersecting only when they intersect in a line, always understanding that they intersect at O; and since all lines, planes, and hyperplanes have O in common, we can always say that two planes in a hyperplane intersect, and that any plane and hyperplane or any two hyperplanes intersect: it will not be necessary in each particular case to assume such intersection or to mention the fact that it exists.*

We shall call the geometry of the various kinds of angles which we may have at a point *Point Geometry.*†

As O completely separates the two opposite half-lines drawn from it along any line, it is better to consider the half-line as one of the elements of Point Geometry, rather than the entire line. To every half-line there is, then, one opposite; and a plane or hyperplane containing one of two opposite half-lines always contains the other. Two planes in a hyperplane, or any plane and hyperplane, intersect in two opposite half-lines. Each hyperplane has two perpendicular half-lines, one opposite the other.

Point Geometry in space of four dimensions is a three-dimensional geometry. That is, we get all the elements of the Point Geometry if we take four elements not in one hyperplane, all elements coplanar with any two of them, and all elements coplanar with any two obtained by this process. We can interpret the two-dimensional and three-dimensional geometries given in chap. I as point geometries, if we give a proper meaning to their undefined

---

* Compare the remark on the limitation of hyperspace to four dimensions, Art. 26, and foot-note, p. 59.

† Klein, *Nicht-euklidische Geometrie*, Göttingen, 1893, vol. I, p. 8, uses the expression "Metrik im Punkte."

I

terms and confine ourselves when necessary to a restricted (angular) region.

III. THE ANGLES OF TWO PLANES *

65. Theorems in regard to perpendicular planes stated in the language of Point Geometry. In this section we use the language of Point Geometry, all planes and hyperplanes being assumed to pass through a given point O, and all half-lines to be drawn from O.

For perpendicular planes we have proved certain theorems which can here be stated as follows (Arts. 43, 44, 47, and 49):

THEOREM 1. *Each plane has one and only one absolutely perpendicular plane.*

THEOREM 2. *If two planes intersect, their absolutely perpendicular planes intersect.*

THEOREM 3. *A plane perpendicular to one of two absolutely perpendicular planes is perpendicular to the other.*

This theorem is included in the following.

THEOREM 4. *Given two pairs of absolutely perpendicular planes, if either plane of one pair is perpendicular to one plane of the other pair, or if either plane of one pair intersects both planes of the other pair, then each plane of either pair intersects both planes of the other pair and is perpendicular to both planes of the other pair.*

THEOREM 5. *If two planes have a common perpendicular plane, the plane absolutely perpendicular to the latter is also a common perpendicular plane to the two given planes.*

---

* This subject is treated by C. J. Keyser, "Concerning the Angles and the Angular Determination of Planes in 4-Space," *Bulletin of the American Mathematical Society*, vol. 8, 1902, pp. 324–329, and by I. Stringham, "On the Geometry of Planes in a Parabolic Space of Four Dimensions," *Transactions of the American Mathematical Society*, vol. 2, 1901, pp. 183–214. Stringham gets his results entirely by quaternians.

THEOREM 6. *Two planes which intersect have one and only one pair of common perpendicular planes.*

In the case of the last theorem, the two given planes intersect in a pair of opposite half-lines and lie in a hyperplane, and their absolutely perpendicular planes intersect in a pair of opposite half-lines and lie in a hyperplane. One common perpendicular plane is the plane containing these four half-lines, and the other is the plane of intersection of the two hyperplanes (see proof of theorem of Art. 49). The two given planes contain the faces of four dihedral angles, and their absolutely perpendicular planes contain the faces of four dihedral angles. The plane angles of all of these dihedral angles lie in the plane of intersection of the two hyperplanes, since this plane lies in both hyperplanes and is perpendicular to the edges of the dihedral angles. The two hyperplanes contain the cells of four hyperplane angles whose common face is their plane of intersection; and each of the plane angles of these hyperplane angles has for one side a half-line of the intersection of the two given planes, and for the other side a half-line of the intersection of their absolutely perpendicular planes.

When the given planes are perpendicular, so that each of the common perpendicular planes can be determined by half-lines or as the intersection of two hyperplanes, then in each we have angles which are at the same time the plane angles of a set of dihedral angles and the plane angles of a set of hyperplane angles.

66. Existence of a minimum angle between two planes. The theorems and proofs of this article and the next two follow the analogy of the theorems and proofs of Arts. 61 and 62. The two theories are, indeed, the same, as we shall see later (Art. 123).

THEOREM.   *Given two planes α and β, there is a half-line of α whose angle with β is less than or equal to the angle made with β by any other half-line of α.* *

PROOF.   We will write *angle ab* to denote a certain angle of 360° † in α (around the point O), putting two half-lines a and b together in some position in α and regarding them as the two sides of the angle.

Let m be any half-line of α, either a or b or a half-line in some position between a and b.   The angle which m makes with β has for all positions of m a lower limit $\phi \geqq 0$. That is, for every positive angle ϵ there are positions of m where this angle, though never less than ϕ, will be less than $\phi + \epsilon$.   This is a theorem of irrational numbers proved as on p. 106.

Within any angle of α, that is, any portion of the angle ab, we prove in the same way that the angle which m makes with β has a lower limit; and the lower limit for any portion of the angle ab is greater than or equal to the lower limit for any portion within which it is contained, and so greater than or equal to ϕ.

Now we separate the half-lines of the angle ab into two classes, putting a into the first class, and putting any other half-line c into the first class if for all positions of m in the angle ac the lower limit of the angle which it makes with β is greater than ϕ, but into the second class if this lower limit is equal to ϕ.   The half-lines of the first class come before those of the second class; and by this separation we determine a half-line c' occupying the place of separation of the two classes, c' being a itself, or b, or some half-line between a and b.

The angle which c' makes with β is exactly ϕ.

For suppose this angle to be $\phi + \delta$, where δ is some

---

* α and β pass through O, and a half-line is always a half-line drawn from O.
† Using the term angle as it is used in trigonometry.

positive angle. In α take half-lines c_1 towards a and c_2 towards b, each making an angle of $\frac{1}{2}\delta$ with c'. If c' coincides with a, or makes with a an angle less than $\frac{1}{2}\delta$, we take c_1 along a; or if c' coincides with b, or makes with b an angle less than $\frac{1}{2}\delta$, we take c_2 along b. In the angle ac_1, when c_1 does not coincide with a, the lower limit of the angle which the half-line m makes with β is greater than ϕ. In the angle ac_2 this lower limit is ϕ. Therefore in the angle c_1c_2 the lower limit is ϕ, and hence there is

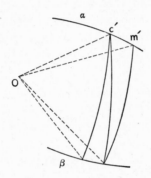

a half-line m' in the angle c_1c_2 which makes an angle with β less than $\phi + \frac{1}{2}\delta$, $\frac{1}{2}\delta$ being a " positive angle," a value of ϵ. Now

$$\angle c'm' \leqq \tfrac{1}{2}\delta,$$

and the half-line c', forming a trihedral angle with m' and the projection of m' upon β, makes with the projection an angle less than the sum of the other two face angles of the trihedral angle, that is, less than $\phi + \delta$. Thus c' makes with one half-line of β, and therefore certainly with β, an angle less than $\phi + \delta$, whereas we have assumed this angle to be equal to $\phi + \delta$.

This proves that the angle which c' makes with β is exactly ϕ, and is less than or equal to the angle made with β by any other half-line of α.

When α and β intersect, $\phi = 0$; in all other cases ϕ is some definite positive angle, an acute angle unless α and β are absolutely perpendicular.

67. Existence of common perpendicular planes.

THEOREM. *When two planes α and β do not intersect, the plane of the minimum angle which a half-line of α makes with β is perpendicular to α and β.*

PROOF.* Let m be a half-line of α which makes with β an angle ϕ, less than or equal to the angle made with β by any other half-line of α, and let n be the projection of m upon β, so that the plane mn is perpendicular to β along n. If this plane is not perpendicular to α, the projection of n upon α will be a half-line of α which makes with one half-line of β, and therefore certainly with β, an angle less than ϕ. But this is contrary to hypothesis; and the plane mn must therefore be a common perpendicular plane to α and β.

The plane mn, the common perpendicular plane of the preceding theorem, intersects α and β in two pairs of opposite half-lines, and in this plane we have two pairs of vertical angles, one pair of acute angles each equal to ϕ, and one pair of obtuse angles (unless α and β are absolutely perpendicular).

The plane absolutely perpendicular to the plane mn is also perpendicular to α and to β (Art. 65, Th. 5). Let ϕ' be one of the acute (or right) angles lying in the intersection of this plane with α and β. We may let m' and n' be the half-lines forming the angle ϕ', m' in α and n' in β. n and n' (when ϕ' is not a right angle) are the projections of m and m' upon β, and that portion of α which lies within the right angle mm' will be projected upon that portion of

---

* Given by C. J. Keyser, see reference on p. 114.

. β which lies within the right angle nn' (see foot-note, p. 79).*

68. Planes with an infinite number of common perpendicular planes. In the following proof we shall use a figure drawn to represent points at a given distance from O. Half-lines (drawn from O) are represented in this figure by points, and planes by lines. Any three points of the figure not appearing on one line represent half-lines which are the edges of a trihedral angle; or we can think of the points as vertices of spherical triangles, the different triangles of the figure lying on equal spheres but not on the same sphere.

This figure is not all visible in any one hyperplane. Only four points taken at random at the given distance from O could be seen at any one time; or along with a complete view of one spherical triangle would appear only those points of the figure which lie on the sphere of this triangle. The entire figure does, however, lie in a hypersphere (chap. V), and it is not difficult to imagine a figure lying in a portion of a hypersphere as a slightly curved space.

THEOREM. *If two planes α and β cut out equal angles on a pair of common perpendicular planes, they have an infinite number of common perpendicular planes, the plane projecting any half-line of either upon the other being perpendicular to both. On all of these common perpendicular planes they cut out equal angles; and if α and β are not absolutely perpendicular, any two of these planes cut out on β angles equal to the angles which they cut out on α.*

Conversely, if α and β, not being absolutely perpendicular, have more then two common perpendicular planes, the acute angles which they cut out on any pair of these common perpendicular planes are equal.

* Combining this theorem with the theorem of Art. 49, with Th. 3 of Art. 63, and with the first foot-note on p. 112, we can say that any two planes have a common perpendicular plane.

Proof. Two planes α and β have a pair of common perpendicular planes on which they cut out the acute angles ϕ and ϕ'. Let the half-lines m and n be the sides of one of the angles ϕ, and let m' and n' be the sides of one of the angles ϕ', m and m' in α, and n and n' in β. In the

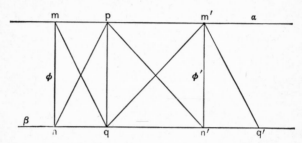

right angles mm' and nn' lay off equal acute angles mp and nq. The right trihedral angles $O-mnp$ and $O-mnq$ have the face angles including the right dihedral angle of one equal respectively to the face angles including the right dihedral angle of the other. Therefore

$$\angle mq = \angle pn.$$

In the same way we prove

$$\angle m'q = \angle pn'.$$

Now supposing ϕ' to be equal to ϕ, we take the half-line q' in the same direction (around O) from n' that q is from n, so that

$$\angle n'q' = \angle nq,$$

and therefore so that

$$\angle qq' = \angle nn'.$$

Then we have right trihedral angles $O-mnq$ and $O-m'n'q'$, in which the face angles including the right dihedral angle of one are equal respectively to the face angles including the right dihedral angle of the other. Therefore

$$\angle m'q' = \angle mq = \angle pn.$$

Now the trihedral angles $O\text{-}pnn'$ and $O\text{-}m'q'q$ have the three face angles of one equal respectively to the three face angles of the other, and so in these trihedral angles the dihedral angles along the half-lines q' and n are equal. Finally, the trihedral angles $O\text{-}pnq$ and $O\text{-}m'q'n'$ have these same dihedral angles, and the adjacent face angles of one equal respectively to the adjacent face angles of the other, $\angle pn = \angle m'q'$, and $\angle qn = \angle n'q'$. Therefore the dihedral angles along q and n' in these trihedral angles are equal, and as the latter is a right dihedral angle the former is also a right dihedral angle, and the plane pq is perpendicular to β.

In the same way we prove that the plane pq is perpendicular to α.

The angle pq is equal to the angle $m'n'$ and to the angle mn, that is, it is equal to ϕ.

Conversely, the angles mn and $m'n'$ being the acute angles ϕ and ϕ', let p and q be half-lines within the angles mm' and nn', q the projection of p upon β and p the projection of q upon α, so that the plane pq is perpendicular both to α and to β. Then the angle pq is equal to the angle mn, that is to ϕ, and the angles ϕ and ϕ' are equal.

Suppose, for example, that we had

$$\angle pq < \angle mn.$$

Then in the right trihedral angles which have the face angle nq in common we should have

$$\angle pn < \angle mq,$$

but in the right trihedral angles which have the face angle mp in common,

$$\angle mq < \angle pn.$$

Our hypothesis leads to a contradiction. We must have

$$\angle pq = \angle mn.$$

In the same way we prove

$$\angle pq = \angle m'n',$$

and therefore

$$\angle m'n' = \angle mn,$$

or

$$\phi' = \phi.$$

Now in the right trihedral angles which have the face angle mn in common, since also

$$\angle pn = \angle mq,$$

we have

$$\angle mp = \angle nq.$$

69. The angles between two planes. Isocline planes. The acute (or right) angles ϕ and ϕ' which two planes cut out on their common perpendicular planes are called the angles between the two planes. When one of these angles is zero the two planes intersect and lie in a hyperplane. The other angle is then the measure of the acute (or right) dihedral angles whose faces lie in the two planes. When one angle is zero and one a right angle the planes are simply perpendicular. When one angle is a right angle the planes are sometimes said to be perpendicular even if the other angle is not zero, but we have used the word perpendicular alone as applied to planes only when the other angle is zero (see foot-note, p. 85). When both angles are right angles the planes are absolutely perpendicular.

THEOREM 1. *The angles which a plane makes with one of two absolutely perpendicular planes are the complements of the angles which it makes with the other; and any two planes make the same angles as their absolutely perpendicular planes.*

PROOF. Let α and β be two planes and α' and β' their absolutely perpendicular planes. In a plane perpendicular to these four the complete intersection consists of two pairs of perpendicular lines; that is, of eight half-lines which can be taken in the order $\alpha\,\beta\,\alpha'\,\beta'\alpha\,\beta\,\alpha'\beta'$ around the point O, and which are alternately perpendicular.

When the angles of two planes are equal the planes have an infinite number of common perpendicular planes, but they cut out the same angle on them all. The two planes

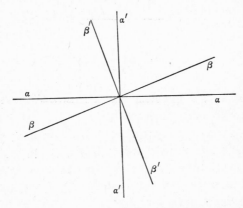

are then said to be *isocline.** Absolutely perpendicular planes are always isocline, and a plane isocline to one of two absolutely perpendicular planes is isocline to the other. Any two lines taken one in each of two absolutely perpendicular planes determine a common perpendicular plane (Art. 65, Th. 4), but in the case of two isocline planes which are not absolutely perpendicular only one of the common perpendicular planes passes through any line of either. Any two of these common perpendicular planes cut out equal angles on the two given planes and are themselves isocline.

THEOREM 2.† *If two half-lines in a plane α make equal angles with a plane β, the half-line bisecting the angle between*

---

* See p. 125, and foot-note.

† Used by Veronese in finding the perpendicular planes, *Grundzüge*, § 150.

*them and the half-line bisecting the angle between their pro-
jections upon β will lie in one of the planes perpendicular to
α and β.*

PROOF. Let p and p' be the half-lines in α, and q and q'
their projections upon β, so that the angles pq and $p'q'$
are equal. Then if m is the half-line bisecting the angle

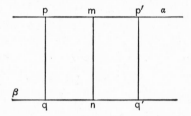

pp' and n the half-line bisecting the angle qq', the plane
mn will be one of the common perpendicular planes of α
and β.

To prove this we consider in succession the following
pairs of trihedral angles:

$$O\text{–}pqq' \text{ and } O\text{–}p'q'q,$$
$$O\text{–}p'pq \quad '' \quad O\text{–}pp'q',$$
$$O\text{–}pqn \quad '' \quad O\text{–}p'q'n,$$
$$O\text{–}pmn \quad '' \quad O\text{–}p'mn,$$
$$O\text{–}mpq \quad '' \quad O\text{–}mp'q',$$
$$O\text{–}mnq \quad '' \quad O\text{–}mnq'.$$

In each case two face angles and the included dihedral
angle of one trihedral angle are equal respectively to two
face angles and the included dihedral angle of the other,
or the three face angles of one trihedral angle are equal
respectively to the three face angles of the other.

COROLLARY. *If more than two pairs of opposite half-
lines in one of two planes make any given angle with the other
plane, the two planes are isocline.*

The student may work out the details in proof of the following theorems:

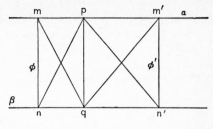

Given that the angles mn and $m'n'$ are the angles ϕ and ϕ' made by two planes α and β, let p be a half-line within the right angle mm', and q its projection upon β. Then if the angle pq is greater than ϕ it will be less than ϕ'. That is, we have in succession the inequalities

$$\angle pq > \angle mn,$$
$$\angle pn > \angle mq,$$
$$\angle mp > \angle nq;$$

and then, further,

$$\angle pm' < \angle qn',$$
$$\angle pn' < \angle m'q,$$
$$\angle pq < \angle m'n'.$$

This requires that ϕ' shall be greater than ϕ; and the magnitude of the angle pq is always between ϕ and ϕ'.

Now instead of taking q as the projection of p upon β, let us take p and q as in Art. 68, so that $\angle mp = \angle nq$. Then we shall have equal dihedral angles at p and q, namely,

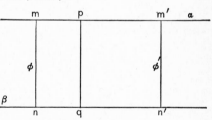

$$\text{dihedral angle } mpq = \text{dihedral angle } nqp;$$

and the plane of the half-lines bisecting the angles mn and $m'n'$ will intersect the plane pq at right angles and will contain the half-line bisecting the angle pq.

The angle pq, because of the equal dihedral angles at p and q, has been called an *isoclinal angle* of the planes α and β, and the angles ϕ and ϕ' are its minimum and maximum values.*

* See p. 199 of article by Stringham referred to at the beginning of this section. Stringham says that "Two planes may be said to be mutually isoclinal when their isoclinal angle is constant," and he speaks of two such planes as "isoclines" (p. 210). We have used the term isocline as an adjective. Stringham's isoclinal angle is not of special importance in this development of the subject.

IV. POLYHEDROIDAL ANGLES

70. Polyhedroidal angles. Interior of a polyhedroidal angle. Vertical polyhedroidal angles. A *polyhedroidal angle* consists of the half-lines drawn through the points of a polyhedron (Art. 29) from a given point not in the hyperplane of the polyhedron, together with this given point. The half-lines are called *elements*, the polyhedron is the *directing-polyhedron*, and the pont is the *vertex*. The elements which pass through the vertices of the polyhedron are called *edges*, the elements which pass through the points of any edge of the polyhedron lie in the interior of a *face angle*, and the elements which pass through the points of any face of the polyhedron lie within a *polyhedral angle* of the polyhedroidal angle. The interiors of the polyhedral angles are the *cells*. Adjacent polyhedral angles are joined by their face angles, these lying in the planes of intersection of their hyperplanes. A polyhedroidal angle is *convex* when each of these hyperplanes contains no element of the polyhedroidal angle except those which belong to the polyhedral angle of this hyperplane and to its interior. The polyhedroidal angle is convex when the directing-polyhedron is convex. We shall consider only convex polyhedroidal angles.

The *interior of a polyhedroidal angle* consists of the half-lines drawn from the vertex through the points of the interior of the directing-polyhedron. The interior of a convex polyhedroidal angle lies within any one of its hyperplane angles; and a point lying within all of the hyperplane angles lies in the interior of the polyhedroidal angle. The polyhedroidal angle separates the rest of hyperspace into two portions, interior and exterior to it. The polyhedroidal angle whose elements are half-lines opposite to the elements of a given polyhedroidal angle is

vertical to the latter.   In two vertical polyhedroidal angles
the face angles, dihedral angles, and polyhedral angles of one
are all vertical to the corresponding parts of the other, and
the face angles and dihedral angles of one are equal to the
corresponding face angles and dihedral angles of the other.

A polyhedroidal angle taken together with its vertical
polyhedroidal angle may be regarded as a particular case
of a hyperconical hypersurface (Art. 33).

A hyperpyramid, or the hypersolid which we call the interior of
a hyperpyramid, may be described as cut from the interior of a polyhedroidal angle by a hyperplane that cuts all of its elements and does
not pass through its vertex.

71. Tetrahedroidal angles. The rectangular system.

The simplest polyhedroidal angle is the *tetrahedroidal angle*,
having a tetrahedron for directing-polyhedron.   Any four
hyperplanes with a point but not a line common to them
all are the hyperplanes of a tetrahedroidal angle, and any
four half-lines drawn from a point and not in one hyperplane are the edges of a tetrahedroidal angle.   The four
hyperplanes, or the lines of the four half-lines, determine
a set of sixteen tetrahedroidal angles filling completely
the hyperspace about the point, and associated in eight
pairs of vertical tetrahedroidal angles.   In a tetrahedroidal
angle there are six planes, three pairs* of opposites, the two
planes of a pair meeting only at the vertex.   Otherwise
the six planes all intersect, three in each edge.   We may
also speak of each half-line as opposite to the trihedral
angle formed by the other three half-lines.

A point is in the interior of a tetrahedron if it is within
any three of its dihedral angles whose edges lie in one plane,
or if it is within two dihedral angles whose edges contain
a pair of opposite edges of the tetrahedron.   In the same

* We do not mean here that they are absolutely perpendicular.

way, a point is in the interior of a tetrahedroidal angle if it is within any three of its hyperplane angles whose faces lie in one hyperplane, or if it is within two hyperplane angles whose faces are the planes of two opposite face angles.

At each vertex of a pentahedroid is a tetrahedroidal angle.

A particular case is the rectangular system : four half-lines mutually perpendicular, six face angles which are right angles lying in three pairs of absolutely perpendicular planes, the trihedral angles rectangular trihedral angles, the dihedral angles right dihedral angles, and the four hyperplanes mutually perpendicular (see Art. 48).

72. Tetrahedroidal angles with corresponding face angles equal. We can make two tetrahedrons correspond, the four vertices of one to the four vertices of the other, in any order, corresponding edges, faces, etc., being those determined by corresponding vertices. Then we have the following theorem in regard to tetrahedrons with corresponding edges equal :

THEOREM 1. *If each of the six edges of a tetrahedron is equal to the corresponding edge of a second tetrahedron, when the four vertices of one are made to correspond in some order to the four vertices of the other, then the faces and dihedral angles of one will be equal to the corresponding faces and dihedral angles of the other.*

For any two corresponding faces are triangles which are mutually equilateral and therefore equal, the angles of one equal to the corresponding angles of the other ; then any two corresponding trihedral angles have the face angles of one equal to the corresponding face angles of the other, and therefore corresponding dihedral angles are equal.*

---

* The axiom of parallels is usually employed in the proof of this theorem, but the proof can be modified so as to make it independent of this axiom (compare proof of Th. 2). Indeed, any theorem in regard to angles at a point must be independent of the axiom of parallels (see the author's *Non-Euclidean Geometry*, p. 26).

In the same way we can make two tetrahedroidal angles
correspond, the four edges of one to the four edges of the
other, in any order, corresponding parts being those determined by corresponding edges. For these we have the
following theorem analogous to the theorem just given:

THEOREM 2. *If each of the face angles of a tetrahedroidal
angle is equal to the corresponding face angle of a second
tetrahedroidal angle, when the four edges of one are made to
correspond in some order to the four edges of the other, then
corresponding dihedral angles and corresponding hyperplane
angles will all be equal.*

PROOF.* Lay off convenient distances on the edges of
the two tetrahedroidal angles, the distances in one equal
to the corresponding distances in the other, forming two
pentahedroids.   Let them be called $OABCD$ and
$O'A'B'C'D'$. The five tetrahedrons of one correspond to
the five tetrahedrons of the other, and in all of these tetrahedrons corresponding edges, corresponding face angles,
and corresponding dihedral angles are equal. Thus, in
particular, the corresponding dihedral angles of the two
tetrahedroidal angles are all equal.

In the face OAB we take a convenient point H, say a
point on the line perpendicular to the edge AB at its middle
point, and through H pass a plane absolutely perpendicular
to the plane OAB. This absolutely perpendicular plane
will cut the half-hyperplanes OAB–C and OAB–D in half-
lines which are the sides of the plane angle at H of the hyperplane angle C–OAB–D (Art. 54, Th. 1). In the half-
hyperplane OAB–C the half-line drawn from H perpendicular to the plane OAB will meet the tetrahedron
$OABC$ at a point P which is not a point of the plane
OAB (Art. 21, Th. 1). If P is not a point of the half-plane

---

* It will help the student to note the analogy of this proof to the proof of the
corresponding theorem about trihedral angles as given in many of our text-books.

K

AB–C it will lie in the face OAC or in the face OBC or in the edge OC, and the half-plane AB–P will intersect the edge OC (Art. 8, Th. 2). We can then modify our construction, taking the point C at this intersection, so that the half-plane AB–P will be the same as the half-plane AB–C, and the perpendicular from H will in any case meet the half-plane AB–C at the point P. Now let K be the middle point of AB. Then the angle at K in the triangle HKP is the plane angle of the dihedral angle O–AB–C.

In the same way we can modify the position of D, if necessary, so that the half-line drawn from H in the half-hyperplane OAB–D perpendicular to the plane OAB will meet the half-plane AB–D at a point Q; and in the triangle HKQ the angle at K will be the plane angle of the dihedral angle O–AB–D.

It is the angle PHQ, formed by these two perpendiculars, which is the plane angle at H of the hyperplane angle C–OAB–D.

We repeat the construction in the second pentahedroid, using the same letters with accents, making the distance of H' from $A'B'$ equal to the distance of H from AB, and changing the positions of C' and D', if necessary, so that their distances from O' are equal, respectively, to the final distances of C and D from O. We have, then, to prove that the angle $P'H'Q'$ is equal to the angle PHQ.

In the tetrahedrons $OABC$ and $O'A'B'C'$ the dihedral angle AB is equal to the dihedral angle $A'B'$. Therefore their plane angles are equal, that is,

$$\angle\,HKP \;=\; \angle\,H'K'P';$$

and, as $HK = H'K'$, the right triangles HKP and $H'K'P'$ are equal. Thus we have

$$KP \;=\; K'P'$$

and
$$HP \;=\; H'P'.$$

Similarly, triangles HKQ and $H'K'Q'$ are equal,

$$KQ = K'Q',$$

and $$HQ = H'Q'.$$

Now in the tetrahedron $ABCD$ the angle PKQ is the plane angle of the dihedral angle AB. Thus

$$\angle\,PKQ = \angle\,P'K'Q',$$

the triangles PKQ and $P'K'Q'$ are equal, and

$$PQ = P'Q'.$$

Then, finally, the triangles PHQ and $P'H'Q'$ are mutually equilateral, and

$$\angle\,PHQ = \angle\,P'H'Q'.$$

In this way we prove that any hyperplane angle of one tetrahedroidal angle is equal to the corresponding hyperplane angle of the other.

We shall see in the next section that the two theorems of this article are identical, and that the proof of Th. 1, interpreted as a proof in Point Geometry, holds for Th. 2 (Art. 76).

73. The bisectors of the hyperplane angles of a tetrahedroidal angle.

THEOREM. *The half-hyperplanes bisecting the six hyperplane angles of a tetrahedroidal angle contain a half-line common to them all, the locus of points within the tetrahedroidal angle equidistant from its four hyperplanes.*

PROOF. Let O be the vertex and a, b, c, and d the four edges of a tetrahedroidal angle. The half-hyperplane bisecting the hyperplane angle c–ab–d is the locus of points within this hyperplane angle equidistant from the hyperplanes of its cells, namely, the hyperplanes abc and abd

(Art. 57, Th. 1).   The half-hyperplane bisecting the hyper-plane angle *b–ac–d* is the locus of points within this hyper-plane angle equidistant from the hyperplanes *abc* and *acd*. These bisecting half-hyperplanes intersect in a half-plane *α* whose edge is the line which contains *a*.   *α* lies entirely within both of the hyperplane angles, and is the locus of points within both hyperplane angles equidistant from the three hyperplanes *abc*, *abd*, and *acd*.

Now points within the hyperplane angle *c–ab–d* are on the same side of the hyperplane *abd* as the half-line *c*; and points within the hyperplane angle *b–ac–d* are on the same side of the hyperplane *acd* as the half-line *b*.   The half-plane *α*, lying within both of these hyperplane angles, is therefore within the hyperplane angle *b–ad–c* (Art. 54), and so entirely in the half-hyperplane bisecting this hyper-plane angle.

There are four such half-planes, *α*, *β*, *γ*, and *δ*, having for edges the lines containing *a*, *b*, *c*, and *d*, respectively, each lying within the three hyperplane angles whose faces contain its edge, and each common to the half-hyperplanes bisecting the three hyperplane angles.

The half-hyperplane bisecting the hyperplane angle *c–ab–d* contains both *α* and *β*.   Therefore these half-planes, whose edges pass through *O*, intersect in a half-line *g* drawn from *O* (Art. 22, Th.), and the points of *g* are equi-distant from all four of the hyperplanes.   The points of *g* lie within five of the hyperplane angles of the tetrahedroidal angle.   In particular, they lie within each of the two oppo-site hyperplane angles *b–ac–d* and *a–bd–c*.   Therefore *g* lies within all six of the hyperplane angles (Art. 71), is common to the four planes *α*, *β*, *γ*, and *δ*, and contains all the points within the tetrahedroidal angle which are equi-distant from the four hyperplanes.

V. PLANO–POLYHEDRAL ANGLES

74. Plano-polyhedral angles, analogous to polyhedral angles and to polygons. Plano-trihedral angles. We come now to another class of angles which are analogous to polyhedral angles, more so, indeed, than the polyhedroidal angles of the preceding section.

Polyhedral angles are themselves analogous to polygons. Thus we may define a *polyhedral angle* as consisting of a finite number of half-lines, drawn from a point O, and taken in a definite cyclical order, together with the point O and the interiors of the angles whose edges are consecutive half-lines of this order (see Art. 14).

In the same way we may have a finite number of half-planes having a common edge, and define a *plano-polyhedral angle* as consisting of these half-planes taken in a definite cyclical order, together with their common edge and the interiors of the dihedral angles whose faces are consecutive half-planes of this order. The half-planes are the *faces*, their common edge is the *vertex-edge*, and the interiors of the dihedral angles are the *cells*. If α, β, γ, . . . are the faces in order, the cells are the interiors of the dihedral angles $\alpha\beta$, $\beta\gamma$, . . ., and the plano-polyhedral angle may be described as the plano-polyhedral angle $\alpha\beta\gamma$ . . . .

In the analogy of polyhedral angles and plano-polyhedral angles, as in the analogy of dihedral angles and hyperplane angles, it is a face in the hyperspace figure which corresponds to an edge in the figure of the ordinary geometry, and a cell which corresponds to a face. In the ordinary geometry the polyhedral angle lies, of course, entirely in a hyperplane; and so here the plano-polyhedral angle is assumed to lie in one space of four dimensions.

Half-planes which lie within the cells and have the vertex-edge for edge, and those which are the faces of the plano-polyhedral angle, are all called *elements* and are in cyclical order (Art. 6).

A plano-polyhedral angle is *simple* when no half-plane occurs twice as an element; we shall always assume that it is simple. A simple plano-polyhedral angle is *convex* when the hyperplane of each cell contains no element except those of the cell itself and the two faces of the cell. Each face of a convex plano-polyhedral angle is a half-plane lying in the common face of two half-hyperplanes which contain two adjacent cells. These two half-hyperplanes are the cells of a hyperplane angle, one of the *hyperplane angles of the plano-polyhedral angle*.

In a polyhedroid each edge lies in the vertex-edge of a plano-polyhedral angle whose cells contain the adjacent cells of the polyhedroid, and the edges of a polyhedroidal angle lie in the vertex-edges of plano-polyhedral angles which belong to the polyhedroidal angle.

The plano-polyhedral angle whose elements are half-planes opposite to the elements of a given plano-polyhedral angle is *vertical* to the latter. In two vertical plano-polyhedral angles the dihedral angles and hyperplane angles of one are all vertical to the corresponding parts of the other.

A plano-polyhedral angle with three faces is called a *plano-trihedral angle*. Any three half-planes having a common edge but not lying in one hyperplane are the faces of a plano-trihedral angle. Any three hyperplanes which intersect but have only a line common to all three are the hyperplanes of a plano-trihedral angle. The planes of three such half-planes, or three such hyperplanes, determine eight plano-trihedral angles, completely filling the hyperspace about their line of intersection, and associated in four pairs of vertical plano-trihedral angles.

The plano-polyhedral angles of a pentahedroid are all plano-trihedral angles.

75. Polyhedral sections of a plano-polyhedral angle. Right sections. A hyperplane intersecting the edge of a plano-polyhedral angle, but not containing the edge, intersects the faces in half-lines which are the edges of a polyhedral angle; and the plano-polyhedral angle may be considered as determined by a polyhedral angle and a line through its vertex not in its hyperplane. When either the plano-polyhedral angle or the polyhedral angle is convex, the other is convex.

A plano-polyhedral angle might be regarded as a polyhedroidal angle with a directing polyhedral angle instead of a directing-polyhedron: that is, the half-lines drawn through the points of a polyhedral angle from a given point not in its hyperplane form a certain portion of a plano-polyhedral angle.

THEOREM. *A hyperplane perpendicular at a point O to the vertex-edge of a plano-polyhedral angle intersects the latter in a polyhedral angle whose face angles are the plane angles at O of the dihedral angles of the plano-polyhedral angle, and whose dihedral angles have at O the same plane angles as the hyperplane angles of the plano-polyhedral angle.*

PROOF. The hyperplane, being perpendicular to the vertex-edge at O, intersects the hyperplanes of the dihedral angles in planes perpendicular to their common edge at this point. Therefore the face angles of the polyhedral angle are the plane angles of the dihedral angles of the plano-polyhedral angle. The given hyperplane is also perpendicular to the planes of the faces of the plano-polyhedral angle (Art. 52, Th. 1). These planes are the faces of the hyperplane angles of the plano-polyhedral angle; therefore the dihedral angles of the polyhedral angle have at O the same plane angles as the hyperplane angles of the plano-polyhedral angle (Art. 54, Th. 2).

The polyhedral angle in which the plano-polyhedral angle is cut by a hyperplane perpendicular to the edge is a *right section* of the plano-polyhedral angle.

76. Theorems proved by means of a right section. The plano-polyhedral angle in Point Geometry.

Certain theorems in regard to plano-polyhedral angles follow, as analogous to theorems true of polyhedral angles:

THEOREM 1. *The sum of two dihedral angles of a plano-trihedral angle is greater than the third.*

THEOREM 2.* *The sum of the dihedral angles of a convex plano-polyhedral angle is less than the sum of four right dihedral angles.*

THEOREM 3.† *If two plano-trihedral angles have the three dihedral angles of one equal respectively to the three dihedral angles of the other, their homologous hyperplane angles are equal; and if two plano-trihedral angles have two dihedral angles and the included hyperplane angle of one equal respectively to two dihedral angles and the included hyperplane angle of the other, the remaining parts of one are equal to the corresponding parts of the other.*

The plano-polyhedral angle plays the part of polyhedral angle in the three-dimensional Point Geometry at any point of the edge, and the polyhedroidal angle plays the part of polyhedron in the Point Geometry at its vertex. Thus Th. 1 of Art. 72 and its proof themselves become a statement and proof of the second theorem of the same article.

The student may prove the following theorems independently of the axiom of parallels:

The area of a triangle is greater than the area of its projection on any plane containing one of its sides, not the plane of the triangle itself (see the author's *Non-Euclidean Geometry*, p. 7, Cor.).

---

* The proof of this theorem can be made independent of the axiom of parallels.
† See foot-note, p. 128.

The area of any face of a tetrahedron is less than the sum of the areas of the other three faces.

Any trihedral angle in a tetrahedroidal angle is less than the sum of the other three.

77. The directing-polygon, and half-plane elements.

THEOREM. *A convex polyhedral angle can be cut by a plane in a convex polygon.*

PROOF.* In a convex polyhedral angle each pair of consecutive edges lies in the face of a half-space which contains all the other edges (compare Art. 14, Th. 2). Let the vertex be O and the edges the half-lines $a, b, c, d, \ldots$, and on these edges take points $A, B, C, D, \ldots$. All of these points except A and B lie on one side of the plane ABO; and the half-planes AB–C, AB–D, $\ldots$, together with the half-plane AB–O, are in a definite order around the line AB, all but the half-plane AB–O on the same side of the plane ABO. Therefore one of these half-planes, say AB–C, comes next after AB–O around the line AB, and lies between AB–O and each of the others, so that it cuts the interiors of the segments $OD, \ldots$.

That is, the plane ABC cuts all of the edges of the polyhedral angle in points, and the polyhedral angle itself in a polygon, a convex polygon since the polyhedral angle is convex.

It follows that a convex plano-polyhedral angle may be considered as determined by a convex polygon and a line not in a hyperplane with the plane of the polygon. The elements of the plano-polyhedral angle (Art. 74) are then half-planes having the given line for common edge and containing each a point of the polygon. The polygon is

---

* This is a theorem of geometry of three dimensions, for a convex polyhedral angle is defined as lying in a hyperplane, and in the proof we speak of the hyperplane of the polyhedral angle as "space," and of any half-hyperplane lying within this hyperplane as a "half-space."

called the *directing-polygon*, and each side of the polygon lies in the interior of a cell of the plano-polyhedral angle.

Two vertical plano-polyhedral angles taken together may be regarded as a particular case of a plano-conical hypersurface (see Art. 35).

A double pyramid, or the hypersolid which we call the interior of a double pyramid, may be described as cut from the interior of a plano-polyhedral angle by two hyperplanes which contain the directing-polygon and each a point of the vertex-edge.

78. Edge Geometry. The elements half-planes with a common edge.

We can build up a geometry by taking for elements the half-planes which have a given line for edge. We will call this geometry an *Edge Geometry*. The half-planes which lie in the same plane on opposite sides of this common edge will be called *opposite elements*, and to every element there is one which is opposite. Any two non-opposite elements determine a hyperplane which contains the given line. The geometry will be the geometry of these half-planes and hyperplanes. We may think of a hyperplane as consisting of half-planes; and in the development of this geometry we shall omit all mention of the given line, and think of two figures as intersecting only when they have one or more half-plane elements in common (compare Point Geometry, Art. 64).

By confining ourselves when necessary to a properly restricted region (angular region about the vertex-edge), to a region, for example, consisting of all the elements which make an angle of less than 90° with any given element, and by giving a suitable interpretation to the terms used, we have the geometry developed in Arts. 1–16. Thus for point we say half-plane, for line hyperplane, and for segment dihedral angle. The half-planes in any hyperplane have the relations of order referred to in Art. 5, all of the half-planes in a hyperplane being, however, in cyclical order (Art. 6). We get all of the half-planes of this geometry if we take three not in a hyperplane, all that lie in a hyperplane with any two of them, and all that lie in a hyperplane with any two obtained by this process. This geometry is, therefore, two-dimensional.

We have the following theorem equivalent to Th. 2 of Art. 4, and so essentialy equivalent to the two axioms of Art. 3: If α' and β' are two distinct non-opposite half-planes of the hyperplane $\alpha\beta$, then the hyperplane $\alpha'\beta'$ is the same hyperplane (Art. 20).

We can also prove a theorem corresponding to the Axiom of Pasch. Suppose that α, β, and γ are three half-plane elements not in one hyperplane, and that a hyperplane λ, not containing any one of these three, contains a half-plane in the interior of the dihedral angle $\beta\gamma$, and does not contain a half-plane in the interior of the dihedral angle $\alpha\beta$. The half-planes β and γ are then on opposite sides of the hyperplane λ, and the half-planes α and β are on the same side. Therefore the half-planes α and γ are on opposite sides of this hyperplane, and the hyperplane must contain a half-plane lying in the interior of the dihedral angle $\alpha\gamma$ (Art. 28).

A convex plano-polyhedral angle necessarily lies within a restricted region, and therefore the geometry of convex polygons holds true in this way of convex plano-polyhedral angles. Such an angle divides all the elements which do not belong to it into two classes, those in the *interior* and those *outside*. The interior consists of the interiors of all the dihedral angles whose faces are elements of the plano-polyhedral angle except those whose interiors also lie in it; and any half-hyperplane whose face contains a half-plane lying in the interior of a convex plano-polyhedral angle, will itself contain one and only one element of the latter.

Other theorems of triangles and convex polygons can be interpreted in the same way.

79. The interior of a convex plano-polyhedral angle. Dropping the language of our Edge Geometry, we may say that a convex plano-polyhedral angle divides the rest of hyperspace into two parts, *interior* and *exterior*. The interior contains the interiors of all segments whose points are points of the plano-polyhedral angle except those whose interiors also lie in it. The interior belongs to the interior of each of its hyperplane angles; and any point which is in the interior of each of the hyperplane angles of a convex plano-polyhedral angle is in the interior of the latter. In the case of a plano-trihedral angle, if a point is in the interior of two of the hyperplane angles it is in the interior of the plano-trihedral angle.

THEOREM. *The three half-hyperplanes which bisect the hyperplane angles of a plano-trihedral angle intersect in a half-plane, the locus of points in the interior of the plano-trihedral angle equidistant from the hyperplanes of its cells.*

CHAPTER IV

SYMMETRY, ORDER, AND MOTION

I. ROTATION AND TRANSLATION

80. Rotation in a plane and rotation in a hyperplane. In a plane a figure can rotate around a point, or we may think of the entire plane as rotating on itself around one of its points, one direction of rotation being to the right and the other to the left.

In a hyperplane, or in the space of our experience, a plane perpendicular to a given line at a point O, rotating on itself around O, always remains perpendicular to the line. We say that the plane rotates around the line as *axis*, or *axis-line*. On the other hand, a plane can rotate around one of its own lines as axis-line through a certain dihedral angle; and if a plane perpendicular to the axis rotates with a plane which contains the axis, the former rotates through an angle which is the plane angle of the dihedral angle through which the latter rotates. Thus we can compare the rotations of two planes perpendicular to an axis, since the plane angles of a dihedral angle are the same at any two points of its edge (see foot-note, p. 97).

THEOREM. *When all the planes perpendicular to a line in a hyperplane rotate around the line in the same direction and through the same angle or at the same rate, figures in the hyperplane remain invariable, any two points being always at the same distance from each other.*

PROOF. Let A and B be two points, O and O' their projections upon the axis, and A' and B' their positions after a rotation through an angle ϕ.   We are to prove that $A'B'$ is equal to AB.

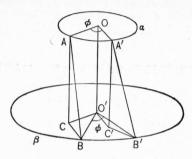

The half-plane $OO'-B$ rotates in the same direction and through the same dihedral angle ϕ as the half-plane $OO'-A$. That is,

dihedral angle $A-OO'-A'$ = dihedral angle $B-OO'-B'$, and therefore

dihedral angle $A-OO'-B$ = dihedral angle $A'-OO'-B'$.

Let α and β be the planes in which A and B rotate, planes perpendicular to the axis OO', and let C and C' be the projections of A and A' upon β.   Then the angles $CO'B$ and $C'O'B'$ are plane angles of the last mentioned dihedral angles, and are equal.   Thus we prove that the triangles $CO'B$ and $C'O'B'$ are equal, and then that the right triangles ACB and $A'C'B'$ are equal.   Therefore

$$AB = A'B'.$$

That is, any figure in a hyperplane can rotate around a line, and we can think of the entire hyperplane as rotating on itself around one of its lines.

81. Rotation in hyperspace.*   The axis-plane.   Double rotation.   In space of four dimensions one of two absolutely

* This subject is treated by F. N. Cole, "On Rotations in Space of Four Dimensions," *American Journal of Mathematics*, vol. 12, 1890, pp. 191–210.

perpendicular planes rotating on itself around the point where the two planes meet always remains absolutely perpendicular to the other. We can say, then, that the rotating plane rotates around the other plane, and we can call the other plane an *axis-plane*. Two planes absolutely perpendicular to a given plane at points O and O' lie in a hyperplane in which they are perpendicular to the line OO' (Art. 45, Th.). Thus we can compare the rotations of two planes absolutely perpendicular to the axis-plane by considering them as rotations in a hyperplane around an axis-line.

THEOREM 1. *When all the planes absolutely perpendicular to a given plane rotate around the given plane as axis-plane in the same direction and through the same angle or at the same rate, all figures remain invariable, any two points being always at the same distance from each other.*

PROOF. Any two points, with the absolutely perpendicular planes through them, lie in a hyperplane in which the rotation takes place around a line perpendicular to these planes. Therefore, by the theorem of the preceding article, the distance between the two points remains unchanged.

Thus any figure in hyperspace can rotate around a plane.

THEOREM 2. *Rotations around two absolutely perpendicular planes are commutative; after two such rotations all points of hyperspace take the same positions, whichever rotation comes first.*

PROOF. Let α and β be the two planes. A point in one of these planes remains in it, and is subject only to the rotation around the other, whichever rotation comes first. Let P be any point outside of α and β. Let us suppose that the rotation around β turns P to P', and that the rotation around α turns P to P'' and P' to Q; then the rotation around β will turn P'' to Q, so that the final position of P

will be at Q, whether the rotation around α comes first, or the rotation around β. P and P'' are in a plane β_1 absolutely perpendicular to α at a point B, and P' and Q are

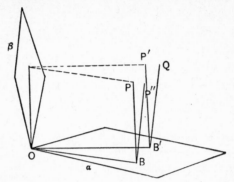

in a plane β'_1 absolutely perpendicular to α at the point B' to which B moves in the rotation around β.

In the rotation around β the hyperplane containing P and α rotates on itself around its intersection with β, and the half-lines BP and $B'P'$, lying in this hyperplane, and perpendicular to α, are coplanar. Also the hyperplane containing P'' and α rotates on itself and the half-line BP'' is coplanar with the half-line at B' into which it is turned.

In the rotation around α the former hyperplane is turned into the latter. But there is another hyperplane, the hyperplane containing β_1 and β'_1, which rotates on itself around the line BB', and in this hyperplane the half-plane $BB'-P$ is turned to the position of the half-plane $BB'-P''$, and the half-line $B'P'$, which lies in the former, to the position of $B'Q$, which must, therefore, lie in the latter.

Thus the half-line $B'Q$, and the half-line at B' into which BP'' is turned by the rotation around β, lying in the half-plane $BB'-P''$, and perpendicular to the edge BB', must coincide.

We can break up the rotation around α and the rotation around β into any number of equal parts and take these smaller rotations alternately, and by a limiting process we can derive a resultant motion of which the two rotations are the components.

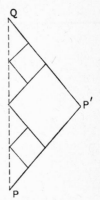

We shall call a combination of rotations around two absolutely perpendicular planes a *double rotation*.

82. Translation along a line. Another simple form of motion is *translation along a line*. In this motion all the points of the line move the same distance or at the same rate, and in the same direction along the line. In the translation of a plane or of a plane figure along a line the plane as a whole remains constantly coinciding with itself, and each point of the plane or of the plane figure which is not a point of the line remains constantly on the same side of the line and at the same distance from it, moving in such a way that its projection upon the line is translated along the line as a point of the line itself. The line is called the *line of translation*. The position of a point is fixed at each instant, and any two points remain at a constant distance from each other.

The translation of any figure along a line is a motion such that each plane containing the line of translation, or the intersection of the figure by any such plane, is itself translated along the line through the given distance or at the given rate. Any two points, together with their projections upon the line of translation, if not all in one plane, are the vertices of a tetrahedron which remains congruent to itself in the translation. Therefore, any two points remain

L

at a constant distance from each other, and any figure remains invariable in the translation.*

In a hyperplane a translation along a line combined with a rotation around the same line gives a *screw motion*. After a screw motion the points of the hyperplane all take the same positions, whether the translation and rotation are simultaneous or taken in succession.

A screw motion in a hyperplane can be regarded as a screw motion in hyperspace. In general, a screw motion in hyperspace consists of a translation along a line combined with a rotation around a plane containing the line. Hyperplane figures in the hyperplane which is perpendicular to the plane along the line (Art. 50) move in this hyperplane in a screw motion along the same line.

II. SYMMETRY †

83. Symmetrical positions. Symmetry in a plane. Two points are *symmetrically situated with respect to the point* which lies midway between them. The point midway is called their *centre of symmetry*. Two points are *symmetrically situated with respect to a line, plane, or hyperplane* which is perpendicular to the line of the two points at their centre of symmetry. Such a line, plane, or hyperplane is called the *line, plane, or hyperplane of symmetry*.

---

* For the points not on the line of translation the character of the motion depends on the theory of parallels:

In the Elliptic Geometry translation along a line is a rotation around the pole, polar line, or polar plane of this line, so that translation is not different from rotation.

In the Euclidean Geometry the translation takes place along a system of parallel lines.

In the Hyperbolic Geometry points which are not on the line of translation move along a system of equidistant-curves. In the Hyperbolic Geometry we can also have translation along a system of boundary-curves, the curves cutting orthogonally a system of parallel lines, planes, or hyperplanes. In this case there is no line of translation nor centre or axis of rotation (see the author's *Non-Euclidean Geometry* chap. II, II).

† See Veronese on order and symmetry, *Grundzüge*, §§ 146, 147, and references.

Two *figures* are *symmetrically situated with respect to a point, line, plane,* or *hyperplane,* when the points of the two figures can be made to correspond in such a way that all pairs of corresponding points are so situated.

THEOREM 1.	*Two figures in a plane symmetrically situated with respect to a point can be made to coincide point for point by a rotation of one of them through* 180° *around the centre of symmetry.*

THEOREM 2.	*Two figures in a plane symmetrically situated with respect to a line will not lose this relation of symmetry, if they are rotated in the plane around any point of the line through the same angle in opposite directions.*

We can in this way bring any point of one figure into coincidence with the corresponding point of the other, in the line of symmetry, and then by a second rotation around this new point we can bring a second pair of corresponding points into coincidence.

THEOREM 3.	*When a plane figure is rotated in a hyperplane which contains the plane through* 180° *around some line of the plane, it comes again into the same plane, to a position which is symmetrical to its first position with respect to the line; and so two figures in a plane symmetrically situated with respect to a line of the plane can be made to coincide by a rotation of one of them, in a hyperplane which contains the plane, through* 180° *around the line of symmetry.*

84. Symmetry in a hyperplane.

THEOREM 1.	*In a hyperplane (or in ordinary space) any two figures symmetrically situated with respect to a line can be made to coincide point for point by a rotation of one of them through* 180° *around the line of symmetry.*

THEOREM 2.	*Two figures in a hyperplane symmetrically situated with respect to a point O can be put into positions of*

*symmetry with respect to any plane containing O by a rotation
of one of them through* 180° *around the line perpendicular to
this plane at O.*

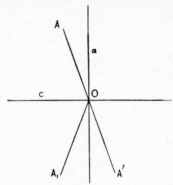

PROOF. Let α be the plane containing O, and c the line
perpendicular to α at this point. Let A and A' be two
corresponding points. If we rotate the figure to which A
belongs through 180° around c, we shall bring A again into
a plane with its first position and with A' and c, to a position where we will call it A_1; and then this point and A'
will be symmetrically situated with respect to the plane α.

THEOREM 3. *Two figures in a hyperplane symmetrically
situated with respect to a plane will not lose this relation of
symmetry, if they are rotated in the hyperplane around any
line of the plane through the same angle in opposite directions.*

THEOREM 4. *When a hyperplane figure is rotated in hyperspace through* 180° *around some plane of its hyperplane
(Art. 81), it comes again into the same hyperplane, to a position which is symmetrical to its first position with respect to
the plane; and so two figures in a hyperplane symmetrically
situated with respect to a plane of the hyperplane can be made
to coincide by a rotation of one of them through* 180° *around
the plane of symmetry.*

Thus figures which we call symmetrical could be made to coincide if the space in which we live were a hyperplane in space of four dimensions. This fact is mentioned and illustrated in nearly all popular descriptions of the fourth dimension. See, for example, *Fourth Dimension Simply Explained* (referred to on p. 9), pp. 28, 48, 158, 214, etc.

85. Symmetry in hyperspace with respect to a plane and with respect to a point. In space of four dimensions we have symmetry with respect to a point, a line, a plane, and a hyperplane (Art. 83).

THEOREM 1. *Any two figures symmetrically situated with respect to a plane can be made to coincide point for point by a rotation of one of them through 180° around this plane as axis-plane.*

THEOREM 2. *Two figures symmetrically situated with respect to a point can be made to coincide by a rotation of one of them through 180° around each of two absolutely perpendicular planes through the point.*

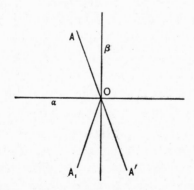

PROOF. Let O be the centre of symmetry, and let α and β be two absolutely perpendicular planes through O. Let A and A' be two corresponding points. If we rotate the figure to which A belongs through 180° around the plane α

we shall bring A to a position where we will call it A_1. The three points A, A', and A_1 are in a plane perpendicular to α and β, all three at the same distance from α and at the same distance from β. In this plane A' and A_1 are symmetrically situated with respect to β, and a second rotation, around β, will make the two figures coincide entirely.

We can take for α and β any two planes which are absolutely perpendicular at O. Either figure can be rotated around one of these two planes, and then the same figure or the other figure can be rotated around the other plane.

86. Symmetry in hyperspace with respect to a line.

THEOREM. *Two figures symmetrically situated with respect to a line c can be put into positions of symmetry with respect to any hyperplane containing c by a rotation of one of them through* 180° *around the plane perpendicular to this hyperplane along c.*

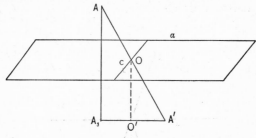

PROOF. Let θ be the hyperplane containing c, and α the plane perpendicular to θ along this line. We are to prove that a rotation of one figure through 180° around α brings any point A of it into a position where this point and the corresponding point A' of the other figure are symmetrically situated with respect to θ.

The two points A and A' are symmetrically situated with respect to the point O where the line AA' meets c.

If we rotate the figure to which A belongs through 180°
around α we shall bring A to a position where we will call
it A_1, and we shall have A' and A_1 symmetrically situated
with respect to the plane β which is absolutely perpendicular to α at O (see proof of Th. 2 of Art. 85).

If A lies in β, A_1 will coincide with A', and these two
points will be coinciding points in β.

If A does not lie in β, the line $A'A_1$ is bisected by β at a
point O' and is perpendicular to β. The hyperplane θ,
perpendicular to α along c, contains the plane β which is
absolutely perpendicular to α at O (Art. 50), and meets
the line $A'A_1$ at its middle point O' where this line meets β.
We shall prove that the line $A'A_1$ is perpendicular also to
another plane of θ at O', namely, the plane determined by
c and the point O'. Thus we shall prove that the line $A'A_1$
is perpendicular not only to β but also to the hyperplane
θ (Art. 38, Th. 4).

A_1 lies in the line drawn through A perpendicular to α,
and therefore in a hyperplane with A, A', and α. Moreover, the line c, lying in the plane α, is perpendicular to OO'
lying in the absolutely perpendicular plane β, and to AA'
by hypothesis. Assuming that A does not lie in β, we have
the line c perpendicular to the plane $AA'A_1$, and then the
plane determined by c and O' perpendicular to the same
plane $AA'A_1$; for two planes in a hyperplane are perpendicular when one contains a line perpendicular to the other.
Now $A'A_1$ is perpendicular to OO', the intersection of these
two planes, since OO' lies also in β. Therefore $A'A_1$ is
perpendicular to the plane determined by c and O'; for a
line in one of two perpendicular planes perpendicular to
their intersection is perpendicular to the other.

This proves that A' and A_1 are symmetrically situated
with respect to θ; that is, that a rotation through 180°
around α puts any point A of one of the two figures into

a position where this point and the corresponding point of
the other figure are symmetrically situated with respect
to θ, the hyperplane perpendicular to α along c.

In a single hyperplane we can see A, A', A_1, the plane α, the line
of symmetry c, and the line OO' in β; but we cannot see the rest of
β, and of the hyperplane θ we can see only the plane determined by
c and O'.

87. Symmetry in hyperspace with respect to a hyperplane.

THEOREM I.   *Two figures symmetrically situated with
respect to a hyperplane will not lose this relation of symmetry,
if they are rotated around any plane of the hyperplane through
the same angle in opposite directions.*

PROOF.   Let A and A' be two corresponding points, and
let α be some plane in the hyperplane of symmetry.   The
line AA' is perpendicular to the hyperplane of symmetry,
and the plane β through A absolutely perpendicular to α
is also perpendicular to this hyperplane (Art 50, Def.).
Therefore AA' lies in the plane β (Art. 51, Th. I). β intersects the hyperplane of symmetry in a line c which
passes through O where β meets α, and in the plane β the
points A and A' are symmetrically situated with respect to
the line c.

Now when the two figures rotate around α, the points
A and A' rotate in β around the point O, and if the rotation takes place through the same angle in opposite directions these points remain symmetrically situated with
respect to the line c (Art. 83, Th. 2).   In the new position
of the figures the line AA', lying in β, is perpendicular to c,
and is bisected by c.   This line is therefore perpendicular
to the hyperplane of symmetry (Art. 51, Th. I), and the
points A and A' are still symmetrically situated with respect to this hyperplane.

THEOREM 2. *If two figures are symmetrically situated with respect to a hyperplane we can bring any four non-co-planar points of one into coincidence with the corresponding points of the other, in the hyperplane of symmetry, without disturbing this relation of symmetry.*

PROOF. Taking any plane in the hyperplane of symmetry we can bring a point A into the hyperplane of symmetry, and so into coincidence with its corresponding point A'; then taking a plane through A in the hyperplane of symmetry we can bring a second point B into this hyperplane; a plane through A and B enables us to bring a third point C into this hyperplane; and, finally, the plane ABC enables us to bring the fourth point into this hyperplane.

THEOREM 3. *If two figures are symmetrically situated with respect to a point, line, plane, or hyperplane, any segment of one is of the same length as the corresponding segment of the other, and any two corresponding angles, dihedral angles, or hyperplane angles are equal.*

III. ORDER

88. The two directions along a line. Two points which are distinguished in some way from each other enable us to distinguish the two directions along the line determined by them (Art. 5). When we speak of the *line AB* we shall often have in mind the direction on this line that B is from A. We can speak of the line BA as a different line. Sometimes when we wish to call attention to a direction along the line, or when there may be some question as to our meaning, we shall say *order AB* instead of line AB.

89. Right and left in a plane. The two fundamental principles of order. In a plane * the two half-planes which are on opposite sides of a line (Art. 12) can be distinguished

* Or at least *in a restricted portion of a plane,* and so with all of this section.

as right and left with respect to a particular direction along the line. This notion we shall associate with the notion of a right and left direction of rotation in the plane, by considering the rotation of half-lines. Two opposite half-lines drawn in a plane from a given point would have to turn in opposite directions around this point in order to pass to the same side of the line on which they lie; and two half-lines drawn from a point along different lines would have to turn in opposite directions in order to turn towards each other through the interior of the angle of which they are the sides.* We have then two principles on which we can base the theory of order in a plane:

I. *A and B being any two points of a plane, a point which is on one side of the line AB is on the opposite side of the line BA.*

II. *O, A, and B being any three non-collinear points of a plane, B is on one side of the line OA and A is on the opposite side of the line OB.*

We shall speak of II as holding true of the half-lines *OA* and *OB*, and we can express it by saying that two half-lines drawn from a point along different lines lie in their plane on opposite sides of each other.

Which shall be the right side of a line and which the left is an arbitrary matter that cannot be determined; but, having assumed the two sides of one line, we shall be able by means of I and II to determine the two sides of every line in the plane. We prove this in what follows.

90. The right and left sides of lines through a point.

THEOREM 1. *Given a line BC and a half-line OA drawn along some other line from a point O of the interior of the*

---

* The half-lines drawn from a point in a plane are in cyclical order (Art. 6).

*segment BC, if II holds true of the half-lines OA and OB and
of the half-lines OA and OC, then I will hold true of the line
BC.*

For, *B* and *C* are on opposite sides of the line *OA* (Art. 12,
Th. 2), and by II it follows that *A* must be on opposite
sides of the lines *OB* and *OC*, or, what is the same thing,
of the lines *CB* and *BC*.

COROLLARY. *If I holds true of BC and II holds true of
OA and OB, then II will hold true of OA and OC.*

THEOREM 2. *Given three half-lines, OA, OB, and OC,
drawn in a plane from a point O along three different lines;
if I holds true of the line OA, and II holds true of the half-
lines OA and OB and of the half-lines OA and OC, then II
will hold true of the half-lines OB and OC.*

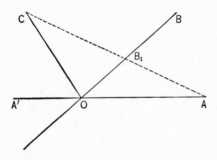

PROOF. Let *OA'* be the half-line opposite to *OA*. *A* and
A' are on opposite sides of any other line through *O* (Art.
12, Th. 2), and if I holds true of the line *OA*, we can substitute *OA'* for *OA* in any application of II. Hence, if *A* and
C lie on the same side of the line *OB*, we can take *A'* in place
of *A*; that is, we can assume that *A* and *C* lie on opposite
sides of the line *OB*, so that there is a point B_1 of this line
lying in the interior of the segment *AC*, a point of the half-
line *OB* or of the opposite half-line. Then

B_1 and C lie on the same side of the line OA,

and B_1 " A "   "   " OC;

or, since OA and OC lie on opposite sides of each other,

B_1 lies on opposite sides of the lines OA and OC.

Now B_1 and B lie on the same side of every line through O except the line B_1B itself, or they lie on opposite sides of every line through O except this line, and in any statement like the last we can substitute B for B_1.   That is,

B lies on opposite sides of the lines OA and OC.

But by the conditions of the theorem

OA and OB lie on opposite sides of each other,

and by hypothesis

C and A lie on opposite sides of OB.

Therefore we must have, finally,

OB and OC lie on opposite sides of each other.

Given a half-line OA, we have only to assume that I holds true of the line in which this half-line lies and that II holds true of all the half-lines drawn from O in other lines of the plane taken with OA.   By the first theorem I will hold true of all the lines through O, and by the second theorem II will hold true of any two non-opposite half-lines drawn from O.

91. Right and left with respect to the sides of a triangle. The notation, order ABC. Given three non-collinear points of a plane, A, B, and C, we shall write *order ABC* to denote that side of a line, right or left, on which A is of the line BC.

Then if I holds true of the line BC, order ACB is the opposite of order *ABC*, and if II holds true of the half-lines *BC* and *BA*, order *CBA* is the opposite of order *ABC*. In other words, the opposite side of a line is indicated according to I by interchanging the last two letters, and according to II by writing the set of three letters backwards.

THEOREM. *Given three non-collinear points, A, B, and C, if I holds true of the lines BC, CA, and AB, and if II holds true of the half-lines BC and BA and of the half-lines CB and CA, then II will hold true of the half-lines AB and AC.*

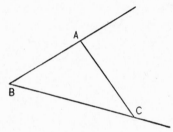

PROOF. We have given that order *CBA* is the opposite of order *ABC*, and that order *BCA* is the opposite of order *ACB*; also that *ABC* and *ACB*, *BCA* and *BAC*, and *CAB* and *CBA* are pairs of opposite orders. We are to prove that order *CAB* is the opposite of order *BAC*.

This will appear at once if we arrange these expressions in a table. We find, in fact, that one side of a line, right or left, is denoted by any one of the three expressions

order *ABC*, order *BCA*, order *CAB*,

and the other side by any one of the three expressions

order *ACB*, order *BAC*, order *CBA*.

When I holds true of all three of these lines and II of all three pairs of half-lines, we can say that a cyclical permutation of the three letters does not change the meaning of the expressions order ABC and order ACB.

Given the right and left sides of a line BC, we can assume that I holds true of this line.   Then by II we can determine the right and left sides of all lines intersecting BC.   I will hold true of all these lines, and II will hold true of any half-lines drawn from a common point along two of these lines.

Now if a line AD does not intersect BC, we can draw a transversal, say the line AB, and determine the right and left sides of this new line by applying II to the half-line AB and the two opposite half-lines drawn from A along this line.   If we draw any other transversal DC, II, being true of AD and AC and of CA and CD (Art. 90, Th. 2), will hold true of DA and DC, as also of the opposite half-line, AD produced, and DC.   Thus the right and left sides of the line AD are determined by means of the line BC and any transversal.

We shall say, therefore, that I and II constitute a definition of right and left for all lines of the plane, given the right and left sides of one particular line.

Order ABC may be used to denote a direction of rotation in the plane around the point B.   If we traverse the triangle ABC, passing along AB from A to B, and so on, we shall turn at each vertex (through an exterior angle) in the same direction, the direction indicated by order ABC.

92. Order in a plane unchanged by any motion in the plane.   Figures symmetrical in a plane.

THEOREM 1.   *Given two triangles ABC and $A'B'C'$ in the same plane, order $A'B'C'$ is the same as order ABC if each of the three segments AA', BB', and CC' is less than $\frac{1}{2}h$, where h is the shortest altitude of either of these triangles.*

PROOF. A and A' are on the same side of BC, since AA'
is less than the distance of A from the line BC. Therefore
order $A'BC$ is the same as order ABC.

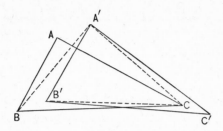

Let m and n be the perpendicular lines which bisect the
four angles formed by the lines AC and BC. Then A is
at a distance greater than $\frac{1}{2}h$ from each of these bisecting
lines, the perpendicular
from A to a bisecting
line being one-half of an
oblique line from A to
the line BC. It follows
that A and A' lie to-
gether in one of the four
right angles formed by

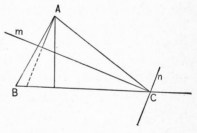

the two bisecting lines. Likewise B and B' lie together
in one of these four right angles, in one of the two, indeed,
which are adjacent to the right angle containing A and
A'. Now the line $A'C$ consists of the point C and two
opposite half-lines lying in two vertical right angles,
neither of which is the angle containing B and B'. Therefore, no point of the interior of the segment BB' can be a
point of the line $A'C$, and order $A'B'C$ is the same
as order $A'BC$.

Starting now with order $A'B'C'$, we prove that this is
the same as order $A'B'C$, and therefore that order $A'B'C'$
is the same as order ABC.

When the two triangles are equal we can consider them as representing two positions of a triangle moving in the plane. We shall say, then, that the order of a triangle cannot be changed by any motion of the triangle in its plane,* regarding this statement, however, as in part a definition of the phrase *motion in a plane*. In particular, order is not changed by a rotation or translation of the triangle in its plane.

THEOREM 2. *Two figures in a plane symmetrically situated with respect to a line cannot be made to coincide point for point by any motion in the plane unless they are groups of collinear points.*

PROOF. We can make any two points of one coincide respectively with the corresponding points of the other in the line of symmetry, without disturbing the relation of symmetry (Art. 83, Th. 2), but in this position any corresponding points not·collinear with these two will be on opposite sides of the line. Therefore any two corresponding triangles are in opposite orders,† and the order of one cannot be changed to the order of the other by any motion in the plane.

If two figures in a plane symmetrically situated with respect to a line have each a line of symmetry with respect to which they are self-symmetrical (for example, two isosceles triangles), one can be made to coincide with the other as a whole by a motion in the plane, but not point for point. Any point of one not a point of its line of symmetry will coincide with that point of the other which corresponds to its symmetrical point.

* Or at least in a restricted portion of the plane.
† When we say that two sets of points are in the same order or in opposite orders we assume that each point of one set is associated with one and only one point of the other set, and then, taking the points of one set in any order we please, we compare this order with the corresponding order of the points of the other set.

93. Order in a hyperplane. The two fundamental principles. The notation, order *ABCD*. In a hyperplane the two half-hyperplanes which are on opposite sides of a plane (Art. 23) can be distinguished with respect to the order of a triangle in the plane; and by associating the two sides of a plane with the two directions of rotation in the hyperplane of a half-plane around its edge, we can derive, as before, two principles which together will serve to define the two sides of any plane when we have given the two sides of a particular plane:

I. *A, B, and C being any three non-collinear points of a hyperplane, a point which is on one side of the plane of order ABC is on the opposite side of the plane of order ACB.*

II. *A, B, C, and D being any four non-coplanar points of a hyperplane, B is on one side of the plane of order ACD and A is on the opposite side of the plane of order BCD.*

We shall speak of II as holding true of the half-planes *CD–A* and *CD–B*, and we can express it by saying that two half-planes with a common edge,* lying in different planes, lie in their hyperplanes on opposite sides of each other.

Theorems exactly analogous to those stated in Art. 90 of the half-lines drawn in a plane from a point *O* hold true of the half-planes with a common edge lying in a hyperplane.

As to Art. 91, suppose that three planes intersect by twos in three different lines, *a, b,* and *c,* and let *A* be a point of *a* which is not a point of *b* or *c, B* a point of *b* which is not a point of *a* or *c,* and *C* a point of *c* which is not a point of *a* or *b* and not collinear with *A* and *B.* It will make no difference whether the three lines, and so the three planes, have a point common to them all or not. We can treat the half-planes *aB, bC, . . . bA, . . .* just as in Art. 91 we have treated the half-lines *AB, BC, . . . BA, ...*

---

* The edge taken in the same " order" in both.

M

Given the two sides of a particular plane in a hyperplane, and assuming that I holds true of this plane, we can by II determine the two sides of any plane in the hyperplane intersecting this plane, and then of any other plane in the hyperplane by using a plane which intersects this plane and the given plane. That is, we determine the two sides of every plane in the hyperplane by following exactly the methods of Art. 91.

Given four non-coplanar points, A, B, C, and D, we shall write *order ABCD* to denote that side of a plane on which A is of the plane of order BCD.

In accordance with the definitions and theorems given for order in a plane, we can say that a cyclical permutation of the last three letters does not change the meaning of the expression order $ABCD$, and that a non-cyclical permutation of these letters changes the expression to one denoting the opposite order, if I, as stated for hyperplanes, holds true.

On the other hand, if II holds true, for example, of the half-planes CD–A and CD–B, then order $BACD$ is the opposite of order $ABCD$. That is, the order is changed to the opposite, according to II, by an interchange of the first two letters.

By combining these operations we find that there are twelve different arrangements * of the four letters for which the expressions of the form order $ABCD$ denote one side of a plane, and twelve for which these expressions denote the opposite side.

We cannot speak of the right and left sides of a line except as we associate the line with some plane in which it lies; but direction along a line is a property of the line itself and is independent of any plane or space that contains it.

Likewise, we cannot speak of one and the other side of a plane except as we associate the plane with some hyperplane in which it

---

* Corresponding to the group of twelve even permutations of four things.

lies; but "order in the plane," or direction of rotation, is independent of any hyperplane.

94. Order in a hyperplane unchanged by any motion in the hyperplane. Figures symmetrical in a hyperplane.

THEOREM 1. *Given two tetrahedrons, $ABCD$ and $A'B'C'D'$, in the same hyperplane, order $A'B'C'D'$ is the same as order $ABCD$ if each of the four segments AA', BB', CC', and DD' is less than $\frac{1}{2}h$, where h is the shortest altitude of either of these tetrahedrons.*

PROOF. A and A' are on the same side of the plane BCD, since AA' is less than the distance of A from this plane. Therefore order $A'BCD$ is the same as order $ABCD$.

Let α and β be the perpendicular planes which bisect the four dihedral angles formed by the planes ACD and BCD. Then we prove, exactly as in Art. 92, that A and A' lie together in one of the four right dihedral angles formed by these two bisecting planes, and that B and B' lie together in an adjacent right dihedral angle. It follows that no point of the interior of the segment BB' can be a point of the plane $A'CD$, and that order $A'B'CD$ is the same as order $A'BCD$.

Starting now with order $A'B'C'D'$, we prove first that this is the same as order $A'B'C'D$, and then the same as order $A'B'CD$.

Thus we have, finally, order $A'B'C'D'$ the same as order $ABCD$.

We shall say that the order of four non-coplanar points of a hyperplane figure cannot be changed by any motion of the figure in its hyperplane, thus defining in part the phrase *motion in a hyperplane.*

THEOREM 2. *Two figures in a hyperplane symmetrically situated with respect to a plane cannot be made to coincide by any motion in the hyperplane unless they are plane figures.*

Figures which we call symmetrical in the ordinary geometry, figures "with the parts of one equal to the corresponding parts of the other but arranged in the opposite order," can be placed in positions of symmetry with respect to a plane. They will be so placed as soon as we have placed three non-collinear points of one upon the corresponding points of the other. But it is better to define symmetrical figures in a hyperplane as figures which are not plane figures, but can be placed in positions of symmetry with respect to a plane by a motion of one or both in their hyperplane.

95. Order in hyperspace. The two fundamental principles. The notation, order *ABCDE*.

In hyperspace we shall distinguish the two sides of a hyperplane (Art. 28) with respect to the order of four non-coplanar points of it. We proceed as before and write down two principles which together will serve to define the two sides of any hyperplane when we have given the two sides of a particular hyperplane:

I. *A, B, C, and D being any four non-coplanar points, a point which is on one side of the hyperplane of order ABCD is on the opposite side of the hyperplane of order ABDC.*

II. *A, B, C, D, and E being any five points not in one hyperplane, B is on one side of the hyperplane of order ACDE, and A is on the opposite side of the hyperplane of order BCDE.*

We can express II by saying that two half-hyperplanes with a common face,* lying in different hyperplanes, lie on opposite sides of each other.

Theorems analogous to those of Art. 90 follow at once for half-hyperplanes having a common face.

As to Art. 91, suppose that three hyperplanes intersect by twos in three different planes, α, β, and γ, and let A be

---

* The face taken in the same order in both.

a point of α which is not a point of β or γ, B a point of β which is not a point of α or γ, and C a point of γ which is not a point of α or β and not collinear with A and B. We can then carry through the methods of Art. 91 just as we do in the case of a hyperplane (Art. 93).

Given five points, A, B, C, D, and E, not points of one hyperplane, we shall write *order ABCDE* to denote that side of a hyperplane on which A is of the hyperplane of order $BCDE$.

Order $ABDEC$ denotes the same side of a hyperplane; order $ABCED$ and order $BACDE$ denote the opposite side of a hyperplane. Thus we can obtain sixty different permutations * of the five letters for which the expressions of the above form denote one side of a hyperplane, and sixty for which these expressions denote the opposite side.

96. Order in hyperspace unchanged by any motion. Symmetrical figures.

THEOREM 1. *Given two pentahedroids, $ABCDE$ and $A'B'C'D'E'$, order $A'B'C'D'E'$ is the same as order $ABCDE$ if each of the five segments AA', BB', CC', DD', and EE' is less than $\frac{1}{4} h$, where h is the shortest altitude of either of these pentahedroids; that is, the shortest distance between a vertex and the hyperplane of the opposite cell.*

PROOF. A and A' are on the same side of the hyperplane $BCDE$, since AA' is less than the distance of A from this hyperplane (Art. 40, Th. 1, Cor.). Therefore order $A'BCDE$ is the same as order $ABCDE$.

Now by considering the perpendicular hyperplanes which bisect the four hyperplane angles formed by the hyperplanes $ACDE$ and $BCDE$, we prove, exactly as in Art. 92, that order $A'B'CDE$ is the same as order $A'BCDE$ (using in this case Th. 2 of Art. 57).

---

* Corresponding to the group of sixty even permutations of five things.

Moreover, we find in this proof that B is at a distance greater than $\frac{1}{2} h$ from the hyperplane $A'CDE$. In the same way we prove that C is at a distance greater than $\frac{1}{2} h$ from the hyperplane $A'BDE$. Then, since the segments BB' and CC' are each less than $\frac{1}{4} h$, we can bisect the four hyperplane angles formed by these two hyperplanes and prove that no point of the segment CC' is a point of the hyperplane $A'B'DE$. Therefore order $A'B'C'DE$ is the same as order $A'B'CDE$.

Starting now with order $A'B'C'D'E'$, we prove first that this is the same as order $A'B'C'D'E$, and then that it is the same as order $A'B'C'DE$.

Thus we have, finally, order $A'B'C'D'E'$ the same as order $ABCDE$.

We shall say that in any figure the order of five points not in a hyperplane cannot be changed by any motion of the figure in hyperspace, thus defining in part the phrase *motion in hyperspace.*

THEOREM 2. *Two figures symmetrically situated with respect to a hyperplane cannot be made to coincide point for point by any motion in hyperspace unless they are hyperplane figures.*

In studying geometry of four dimensions we shall use the word *symmetrical* only with reference to figures which are not themselves hyperplane figures and which can be placed in positions of symmetry with respect to a hyperplane by some motion in hyperspace. All the segments, angles, dihedral angles, and hyperplane angles of one figure are equal to the corresponding parts of the other (Art. 87, Th. 3), but the points of the two figures are arranged in opposite orders.

We have in two vertical plano-polyhedral angles an example of symmetrical figures, the two plano-polyhedral angles being symmetrically situated with respect to a line (Art. 86, Th.).

Two vertical polyhedroidal angles, on the other hand, are equal and can be made to coincide, being symmetrically situated with respect to a point (Art. 85, Th. 2).

IV. MOTION IN GENERAL

97. Motion of a plane on itself. In the ordinary geometry we speak of the motion of a plane figure in its plane, and of figures in space. With a plane figure we can associate the entire plane. Even in the case of motion in a plane we can think of the entire plane as moved on itself. In the motion of a plane on itself the order of any three non-collinear points cannot be changed (Art. 92, Th. 1, remark).

THEOREM 1. *Given any two positions of a plane, a motion which takes three non-collinear points of it from their first to their second positions will take every point of it from its first to its second position.*

PROOF. In the first place, each point of the line containing two of the given points remains collinear with them and at the same distances from them. Moreover, since the plane as a whole after such a motion coincides with its second given position, any point not a point of this line remains at the same distance from it and with the same projection upon it : it must come to its second position or to a position symmetrical to its second position with respect to this line. But the latter is impossible, as its distance from the third given point would then be changed.

COROLLARY. *If after a motion of a plane on itself one point of the plane occupies the position that it occupied before, then every point will occupy the position that it occupied before, or every point will occupy a position that could have been*

*reached by a rotation of the plane on itself through a certain
angle around the given point.*

THEOREM 2. *In a motion of a plane on itself, if two
positions of any point differ, let A be the first and B the
second position of such a point, and let C be the second position of the point whose first position was B. If the line of
symmetry of B and C coincides with the line of symmetry of
A and B, that is, if C coincides with A, then the second
position could have been reached by a rotation of the plane on
itself through 180° around the centre of symmetry of the two
points. If the lines of symmetry do not coincide but do
intersect in a point P, the second position could have been
reached by a rotation of the plane around P. If the lines of
symmetry do not coincide but do have a common perpendicular line, the second position could have been reached by
a translation along this perpendicular* (see the author's
Non-Euclidean Geometry, chap. II, I, 8, proof, p. 42).*

98. Motion of a hyperplane on itself. We can now
speak of the motion of a figure in hyperspace. With a
hyperplane figure we can associate the entire hyperplane,
whether the motion of the figure be anywhere in hyperspace or within the hyperplane itself. Indeed, in the ordinary geometry we can associate with a figure any additional
points, and so speak of all space as moved about on itself,
even though we know of no hyperspace within which it
lies. In a motion of a hyperplane on itself the order of any
four non-coplanar points cannot be changed (Art. 94, Th. 1,
remark).

THEOREM 1. *Given two positions of a hyperplane, a
motion which takes four non-coplanar points of it from their*

---

* In the Hyperbolic Geometry the lines of symmetry may be parallel. The
second position is then one which could have been reached by a translation along a
system of boundary-curves (see the author's *Non-Euclidean Geometry*, chap. II, II).

first to their second positions will take every point of it from its first to its second position.

PROOF. In the first place, each point of the plane containing three of the given points will come to its second position (Art. 97, Th. 1). Moreover, since the hyperplane as a whole coincides with its second given position, any point not a point of this plane remains at the same distance from it and with the same projection upon it: it must come to its second position or to a position symmetrical to its second position with respect to this plane. But the latter is impossible, as its distance from the fourth given point would then be changed.

COROLLARY 1. *Given two positions, one obtained from the other by a motion of a hyperplane on itself, then any motion of the hyperplane on itself which takes three non-collinear points of it from their first to their second positions will take every point from its first to its second position. In particular, a motion of a plane on itself (Art. 97, Th. 2) will determine a motion on itself of any hyperplane containing the plane.*

COROLLARY 2. *If after a motion of a hyperplane on itself each of two points of the hyperplane occupies the position that it occupied before, then every point will occupy the position that it occupied before, or every point will occupy a position that could have been reached by a rotation of the hyperplane on itself through a certain angle around the line containing the two given points.*

THEOREM 2. *If after a motion of a hyperplane on itself one point of it occupies the position that it occupied before, then every point will occupy the position that it occupied before, or every point will occupy a position that could have been reached by a rotation of the hyperplane on itself through a certain angle around a line containing the given point.*

The proof follows that of Th. 2 of Art. 97.   The points
A, B, and C lie on a sphere, on a circle whose axis is the
axis of the rotation.

**99. Every motion in a hyperplane equivalent to a motion
of a plane on itself or to a screw motion.**

THEOREM.   *If after a motion of a hyperplane on itself
there is no point which occupies the position that it occupied
before, then every point will occupy a position that could
have been reached by the motion on itself of some plane of the
hyperplane or by a screw motion.*

PROOF.   Let A be the first position and B the second
position of some point, let C be the second position of the
point whose first position was B, and let D be the second
position of the point whose first position was C.   We will
assume that A, B, C, and D are not collinear, and if they
are coplanar that the triangles ABC and BCD are in
opposite orders in their plane.   Then

$$AB = BC = CD,$$
and
$$\triangle ABC = \triangle BCD.$$

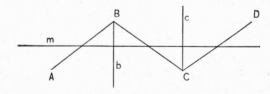

Let b and c be the half-lines bisecting the angles ABC
and BCD.   The lines containing these half-lines have a
common perpendicular m, even if coplanar, ABC and BCD
being in opposite orders (see the author's *Non-Euclidean
Geometry*, chap. I, I, 10).   The figure $DCBA$ taken with
c and b is congruent to the figure $ABCD$ taken with b and c,
and if we place the former upon the latter, each of these

half-lines will take the position which the other occupied before. If the lines containing these half-lines have only one common perpendicular m, this perpendicular will also fall upon itself, and its distances from B and C are equal. If these lines have more than one common perpendicular, one of these perpendiculars will be a line through B intersecting the half-line c, and another will be a line through C intersecting the half-line b. Then the perpendicular mid-way between them, being equidistant from B and C, can be taken for the line m (see Art. 62, Th. 2).

When A, B, C, and D are coplanar, a screw motion along m with a rotation of 180° and a translation that puts A upon B will put the entire hyperplane into its second position.

Supposing that A, B, C, and D are not coplanar, let A', B', C', and D' be their projections upon m. Then, in the first place, the tetrahedrons $CBB'C'$ and $BCC'B'$ are congruent. Furthermore, A and C of the isosceles triangle ABC are symmetrically situated with respect to the line containing b, and m is symmetrical to itself with respect to this same line. Therefore A' and C' are symmetrically situated with respect to this line, and the tetrahedrons $ABB'A'$ and $CBB'C'$ are congruent (Art. 84, Th. 1). It follows that the tetrahedrons $ABB'A'$ and $BCC'B'$ are congruent. In the same way we prove that these are congruent to the tetrahedron $CDD'C'$. Then a screw motion along m putting A upon B will put $ABB'A'$ upon $BCC'B'$ and $BCC'B'$ upon $CDD'C'$; that is, it will put B and C into their second positions and move the entire hyperplane from its first to its second position.

The student may prove the following theorems:

Two successive rotations of a hyperplane on itself around two different axis-lines are together equivalent to a single rotation around an axis-line, if the two given lines intersect. When the two axis-lines are perpendicular to a plane the two rotations together will be equivalent to some kind of motion which the plane can have on itself (Art. 97, Th. 2).

Conversely, if two successive rotations of a hyperplane on itself are together equivalent to a single rotation, the axes of the three rotations will be the three lines of intersection of three planes intersecting two by two: they will meet in a point if two of them meet in a point; or they will be perpendicular to a plane if two of them are perpendicular to a plane.*

100. Motion in hyperspace.

In the motion of a figure in hyperspace we can associate with it any additional points, and so speak of all hyperspace as moved about on itself. In this article we shall speak of a figure rather than of all hyperspace, but we shall assume that all points that we need to consider are included in the figure. In any motion in hyperspace the order of five points not points of one hyperplane cannot be changed (Art. 96, Th. 1, remark).

THEOREM 1. *Given two positions of a figure, one of which can be obtained from the other by a motion in hyperspace, then any motion in hyperspace which takes four non-coplanar points from their first to their second positions will take every point of the figure from its first to its second position.*

For each point of the hyperplane of the four given points comes to its second position in this motion (Art. 98, Th. 1) and any point which is not a point of this hyperplane remains at the same distance from it, on the same side of it, and with the same projection upon it, so that it must also come to its second position.

COROLLARY 1. *In particular, a motion of a hyperplane on itself will determine a motion in hyperspace of any figure containing the hyperplane or containing four non-coplanar points of it.*

---

* The only other possibility is in the Hyperbolic Geometry, where the three axes may be parallel.

COROLLARY 2. *If after a motion of a figure in hyperspace each of three non-collinear points occupies the position that it occupied before, then every point of the figure will occupy the position that it occupied before, or every point will occupy a position that could have been reached by a rotation of the figure through a certain angle around the plane of the three points.*

THEOREM 2. *If after a motion of a figure in hyperspace each of two points occupies the position that it occupied before, then every point of the figure will occupy the position that it occupied before, or every point will occupy a position that could have been reached by a rotation of the figure around a certain plane containing the two given points.*

PROOF. Each point of the line containing the two given points occupies the position that it occupied before, and any hyperplane perpendicular to this line taken as a whole occupies the position that it occupied before (Art. 38, Th. 1). Now such a hyperplane could be put into this second position by a motion on itself, since each point of the given line except its intersection with the hyperplane always remains on the same side of the hyperplane with respect to any given order of points in the hyperplane (Art. 96, Th. 1). But in the hyperplane one point occupies the position that it occupied before, namely, its intersection with the given line. Therefore, the second position of the hyperplane could have been reached by a rotation around an axis-line through this point (Art. 98, Th. 2), and the second position of the figure could have been reached by a rotation around the plane determined by this axis-line and the line containing the two given points.

This theorem might also be proved by interpreting Th. 2 of Art. 97 as a theorem of Edge Geometry (Art. 78).*

---

* Edge Geometry is Elliptic; and in the Elliptic Geometry a translation along a line is a rotation around the pole of the line. In other words, the lines of symmetry of AB and BC always meet in a point.

101. Motion in which one plane remains fixed or moves only on itself.

THEOREM 1. *If after a motion of a figure in hyperspace one point occupies the position that it occupied before, then every point will occupy the position that it occupied before, or every point will occupy a position that could have been reached by a single or double rotation* (Art. 81).

This can be proved by interpreting the theorem of Art. 99 as a theorem of the three-dimensional Point Geometry at the given point. *A, B, C,* and *D* are to be interpreted as half-lines, *b* and *c* as the bisecting half-planes of the dihedral angles *ABC* and *BCD*, and *m* as a common perpendicular plane of the plane containing *b* and the plane containing *c*. The screw motion on *m* is then to be interpreted as a double rotation around *m* and the plane absolutely perpendicular to *m* at this point.

THEOREM 2. *In a motion of a figure in hyperspace, if two positions of any points differ, let four of these points be taken in such a way that A, B, C, and D are their first positions, and B, C, D, and E their second positions* (see Art. 99). *There is then through C a plane* γ, *a plane of symmetry for A and E and for B and D. Let* δ *be the corresponding plane through D, lying in the second position of the plane whose first position is that of* γ. *Then if* γ *and* δ *intersect, or have a common perpendicular hyperplane, the second position of the figure is one which could have been reached from the first by a motion in which one plane remains fixed or moves only on itself.**

* In the Hyperbolic Geometry we can have planes γ and δ which do not intersect and do not have a common perpendicular hyperplane. These planes do, however, have a common perpendicular plane η (see first foot-note, p. 112). The theorem is therefore true without restriction, whatever our theory of parallels, and can be stated very simply as follows:

In a motion of a figure in hyperspace, if two positions of any points differ, the second position of the figure is one which could have been reached from the first by a motion in which one plane remains fixed or moves only on itself.

PROOF. The proof need be given here only for the case where the four points are non-coplanar and their positions are in different hyperplanes or in opposite orders in the same hyperplane. Then

$$AB = BC = CD = DE,$$
$$\angle ABC = \angle BCD = \angle CDE,$$

and tetrahedrons $ABCD$ and $BCDE$ are congruent. Moreover, the tetrahedron $DCBA$ is congruent to the tetrahedron $ABCD$, and $EDCB$ to $BCDE$ (Art. 93). The hyperplane angle E–DCB–A is the same as the hyperplane angle A–BCD–E, and the figure $EDCBA$ is congruent to the figure $ABCDE$. When these figures do not lie in one hyperplane they have the same order (Art. 95), and when they do lie in one hyperplane, $ABCD$ and $BCDE$ being in opposite orders, any order of points of one figure in this hyperplane is changed to the order of the corresponding points of the other by a rotation of the hyperplane through 180° around one of its planes (Art. 84, Th. 4, and Art. 94). The centre of symmetry of A and E and the centre of symmetry of B and D do not change their positions when we reverse the figure, placing $EDCBA$ upon $ABCDE$. Moreover, these two centres of symmetry cannot be collinear with C. If they were, the entire figure $ABCDE$ would lie in one hyperplane, and, taken in two ways as above, would have symmetrical positions with respect to a line, so that corresponding points would be in the same order in the hyperplane (Art. 84, Th. 1). There is then a plane γ determined by these two points and C, a plane of symmetry of A and E and of B and D, and the figure is reversed by a rotation in hyperspace through 180° around γ. At A, B, D, and E are also planes corresponding to γ, say α, β, δ, and ϵ; δ, for example, being in the second position of the plane whose first position is that of γ. The figure consisting of A, B, C, and γ is congruent to the figure consisting of B, C, D, and δ. It is also congruent to the figure consisting of E, D, C, and γ. Therefore the last two figures are congruent to each other.

If all these points and planes lie in a hyperplane, then the middle points of AB, BC, CD, and DE lie in a plane η perpendicular to all the planes α, β, γ, δ, and ϵ. For the line determined by the middle points of AB and DE and the line determined by the middle points of BC and CD are both perpendicular to γ, and therefore lie in a plane perpendicular to γ (see foot-note, p. 77); and, since this plane is determined by any three of the middle points, it is perpendicular to δ and to β, and then also to α and to ϵ. The points A, B, C, D, and E are at the same distance from η, A, C, and E lying on one side of η and B and D on the other side; and the projections of AB, BC, CD, and DE upon η are equal. Let A', B', C', D', and E' be the projections upon η of A, B, C, D, and E. If we rotate the hyperplane through 180° around the plane η and at the same time move this plane on itself so as to move A' to B' and B' to C', then we shall have moved A to B and B to C. Four non-coplanar points of the hyperplane will be in their second positions: that is, four non-coplanar points of the given figure will be in their second positions, and the given figure itself will be entirely in its second position (Art. 100, Th. 1).

The planes γ and δ, not lying in one hyperplane, may intersect in a point O, a point common to δ and β, and therefore also to all five of the planes, α, β, γ, δ, and ϵ. O corresponds to itself in the symmetry of the planes β and δ with respect to γ, and in the two congruent figures $BCD\delta$ and $EDC\gamma$. O is therefore at the same distance from B, C, and D, and so also from A and E. The projections of O upon the hyperplanes of the tetrahedrons $ABCD$ and

$EDCB$ will be corresponding points in the congruence of these two tetrahedrons. O will lie within the hyperplane angle A–BCD–E or within the vertically opposite hyperplane angle. That is, O will lie on opposite sides of the hyperplanes of orders $ABCD$ and $EBCD$, and so on the same side of the hyperplanes of orders $ABCD$ and $BCDE$ (Art. 93). O will then coincide with itself in the two positions of the figure, and the second position is one which could have been reached by a single or double rotation around O (Th. 1).

If γ and δ, not lying in one hyperplane, do not intersect but do have a common perpendicular hyperplane, they have a common perpendicular plane η (Art. 63, Th. 3); and if there is only one common perpendicular plane, this plane will coincide with itself when we place $EDC\gamma$ upon $BCD\delta$. This plane cuts γ and δ in linear elements, and is at the same distance from C and D. If γ and δ have more than one common perpendicular plane,* one of these planes passes through C and another through D, and there is a plane mid-way between these two (Art. 63, Th. 4) which can be taken for η, coinciding with itself in these two positions of the figure, and therefore at the same distance from C and D. The plane η, being perpendicular to γ and passing through a line of δ, will intersect β in a corresponding line and be perpendicular to β also, since β and δ are symmetrically situated with respect to γ. In other words, the plane η is a common perpendicular plane to all five of the planes $\alpha, \beta, \gamma, \delta$, and ϵ, and is at the same distance from all five of the points A, B, C, D, and E. Let A', B', C', D', and E' be the projections of these points upon η. Then

$$A'B' = B'C' = C'D' = D'E';$$

---

* Two planes not in a hyperplane can have more than one common perpendicular plane only in the Elliptic Geometry, and in the Elliptic Geometry two planes always intersect at least in a point (see second foot-note, p. 112). Therefore it is not really necessary to consider this case.

N

$B'C'$ and $C'D'$, for example, are symmetrically situated with respect to the plane γ, or, we may say, to the intersection of γ and η. The hyperplane angles B–η–C and C–η–D are equal, and so therefore are all four of the hyperplane angles A–η–B, etc. These four hyperplane angles are in the same order around the plane η, and, if we rotate the figure around η through the hyperplane angle A–η–B the half-hyperplanes η–A, η–B, etc., will be turned to the positions of the half-hyperplanes η–B, η–C, etc. If at the same time we move η on itself so that A' shall move to B' and B' to C', A will move to B and B to C: four non-coplanar points of the figure will move to their second positions, and the entire figure will move to its second position (Art. 100, Th. 1).

102. Composition of rotations.

THEOREM 1. *Two successive rotations around two different axis-planes are together equivalent to a single rotation around an axis-plane, if the two axis-planes intersect in a line* (Art. 100, Th. 2).

THEOREM 2. *If two successive rotations are together equivalent to a single rotation around an axis-plane, the axis-planes of the two rotations are in a hyperplane, and when they have a point in common they intersect in a line.*

PROOF. The points of the axis-plane of the third rotation are left by the second rotation in their original positions. Let A be the position of one of these points. If the first rotation moves this point to another position B, the second rotation will move it back from B to A. Then the hyperplane of symmetry of A and B will contain the axis-planes of both of these rotations.*

---

* The three axis-planes will all intersect in one line, or will all be perpendicular to one plane, or (in the Hyperbolic Geometry) they will be parallel.

The first theorem of Art. 101 and the two theorems of this article, so far as rotations around a fixed point are concerned, were proved by N. F. Cole, see reference on p. 142.

V. RECTANGULAR SYSTEMS

103. Ways in which a rectangular system is congruent to itself. Four mutually perpendicular lines through a point O* form a rectangular system (Art. 48), a system of rectangular axes in hyperspace.   Distinguishing positive and negative directions along lines through O, we let a, b, c, and d be the positive half-lines of such a system.   Any three of these half-lines form a rectangular trihedral angle in a hyperplane perpendicular to the fourth; and, without disturbing the fourth, we can permute the three cyclically by a rotation in the hyperplane around the half-line which makes equal angles with them.   By combining relations of this type we find twelve different ways in which the four half-lines can be thus permuted.   The system is con- gruent to itself in all of the twelve arrangements of the same order.†

On the other hand, we can obtain any arrangement of three of these half-lines by a rotation in hyperspace.   If, for example, we take an axis-plane through the first and bisecting the angle formed by the second and third, a rotation through 180° around this plane will permute the second and third half-lines without disturbing the first, but the direction of the fourth half-line will be reversed by this process, and the system of four half-lines will not completely occupy its original position: in fact, it will

---

* We can regard this section as a section in Point Geometry; and in the next section we shall use exclusively the language of Point Geometry.

† Arrangements of the four half-lines in the three-dimensional Point Geometry at O. This geometry is "restricted," but is sufficiently extended to include four mutually perpendicular half-lines.

If we take with O four points A, B, C, and D on the four given half-lines, the various arrangements of the half-lines will correspond to the various arrangements of the five points in which O comes first.

Thus if we say   order *abcd* = order *OABCD*,
then we have   "   *abdc* =   "   *OABDC*,
                                        etc.

occupy a symmetrical position with respect to the hyper-plane of the first three half-lines.

The rectangular system determines three pairs of absolutely perpendicular planes. We can write them as the planes bc and ad, ca and bd, and ab and cd. If we let bc denote that order of rotation which, turning b through an angle of 90°, would make it coincide with c, — and so for the other planes, — then we can express the different possible arrangements of four mutually perpendicular half-lines as arrangements of order in these pairs of absolutely perpendicular planes. In the case of any one pair there are four congruent arrangements, and four other congruent arrangements symmetrical to the first four. Thus, in the pair of planes determined, one by b and c and the other by a and d, we have the four arrangements congruent to one another,

bc and ad, ad and bc, cb and da, and da and cb;

and symmetrical to these the four other congruent arrangements,

bc and da, da and bc, cb and ad, and ad and cb.

The three pairs bc and ad, ca and bd, and ab and cd, are congruent to one another, each pair taken in any one of four different ways.

VI. ISOCLINE PLANES *

104. Rectangular systems used in studying the angles of two planes. In this section, as in the third section of chap. III (Arts. 65–69), we shall use the language of Point Geometry, all lines, planes, and hyperplanes being assumed to pass through a given point O.

---

* A study of the hypersphere and its relation to the Point Geometry at its centre (Art. 123) will help the student to understand this section.

Many of the theorems of this section are proved by Stringham in the paper referred to on p. 114.

Let a, b, c, and d be four mutually perpendicular half-lines of a rectangular system. Suppose in the planes ba and cd we lay off from b and c the angles ϕ and ϕ'. The half-lines which terminate these angles determine a plane α which makes with the plane of bc the angles ϕ and ϕ', ba and cd being the pair of common perpendicular planes perpendicular to α and to bc.

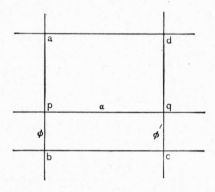

Given any two planes α and β, with their common perpendicular planes γ and γ', we can take for bc the plane β and for ba and cd the planes γ and γ'. ad will be the plane β' absolutely perpendicular to β, and the angles ϕ and ϕ' will be laid off as above in the planes ba and cd.

When we say that the plane α makes with bc the angles ϕ and ϕ', we imply a sense of rotation in α corresponding to the order bc. If p and q are the terminal half-lines of these angles, then α is the plane pq, with a sense of rotation which turns p through 90° to the position of q. ϕ and ϕ' can then be any angles whatever, positive or negative. With a particular plane α (of order pq) each of the angles ϕ and ϕ' can be changed by any multiples of 2π, or both at the same time by odd multiples of π. ϕ and $\phi' + \pi$ are angles made with bc by the plane qp.

The angles which α makes with the plane ad are the complements of ϕ and ϕ'.

When $\phi' = \phi$, α is isocline to the planes bc and ad; and by giving different values to ϕ we have an infinite number of planes isocline to bc and ad and isocline to one another. These planes are all perpendicular to ba and to cd, and constitute what is called a *series of isocline planes*.

105. The common perpendicular planes of an isocline series. Conjugate series. When the plane α is isocline to bc, these two planes have an infinite number of common perpendicular planes on which they cut out the same angle ϕ, and any two of the common perpendicular planes cut out the same angle on α as on bc (Art. 69).

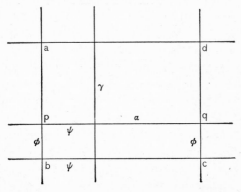

If, for example, in the planes bc and α we lay off an angle ψ from b and p, the terminal half-lines of these angles will themselves form the angle ϕ and will determine a plane γ perpendicular to the plane bc and to α.

This plane γ, being perpendicular to bc, is perpendicular to its absolutely perpendicular plane ad, and therefore is one of the common perpendicular planes of α and ad. The terminal half-lines of the angles ψ, forming in γ an angle ϕ, determine in γ a sense of rotation corresponding to ba; and the half-line of γ, making an angle of $+ 90°$ with that terminal half-line which lies in bc, will be a half-line of ad, making with a the angle ψ in the same way that this angle was formed in the planes bc and α.

The plane γ may, then, be regarded as determined by the angles equal to ψ laid off on the planes bc and ad. But this construction is independent of the angle ϕ and the position of α. The plane γ is therefore perpendicular to all the planes of the isocline series obtained by giving different values to ϕ and laying off these angles in ba and cd from b and c.

By giving different values to ψ we have an infinite number of planes γ perpendicular to all the planes α of the isocline series. Starting with ba, we construct these planes in the same way that the α-series was constructed, and so they themselves form an isocline series with the planes of the α-series for their common perpendicular planes, each plane α perpendicular to all of them.

Thus we have, associated with a rectangular system, two series of isocline planes, each plane of either series perpendicular to all the planes of the other series. We shall call them *conjugate series of isocline planes*.

The planes α are not the only planes * which are isocline to bc. We can rotate the rectangular system around bc as an axis-plane, the half-lines a and d rotating in ad through any angle to new positions, and in this new rectangular system we can construct a new series of planes isocline to bc and ad, with a new series of common perpendicular planes, perpendicular to all of these but not perpendicular to any plane of the first series except to bc and ad themselves.

106. The two senses in which planes can be isocline. Conjugate series isocline in opposite senses. There are

---

* Not the only planes through O.

two senses in which a plane can be isocline to a given plane corresponding to the two possible arrangements of a rectangular system. With a given rectangular system, using the construction of Art. 104, we can say that the plane α is isocline to bc in one sense when we make $\phi' = \phi$, and in the opposite sense when we make $\phi' = -\phi$.

Starting with a plane β and a pair of absolutely perpendicular planes γ and γ' perpendicular to β, let b and c be half-lines common to β and to γ and γ' respectively. If we lay off two angles in the same direction from b in the plane γ and in the same direction from c in γ', or if we lay off two angles in opposite directions from b in γ and in opposite directions from c in γ', we shall have two planes isocline to β in the same sense. But if we take the same direction in one of the two perpendicular planes and opposite directions in the other, we shall get two planes isocline to β in opposite senses.

When two planes are isocline to a given plane in opposite senses we can speak of one as *positively isocline* and the other as *negatively isocline*.

If α is the plane pq of Art. 104 and is isocline to bc, we can determine the sense in which it is isocline by considering the order of the four half-lines b, c, p, and q. Now in this determination we can take in each plane, instead of the two given half-lines, any two non-opposite half-lines, determining their order by a positive rotation of less than 180°. That is, if p' and q' are two half-lines in the plane pq such that a positive rotation of less than 180° turns p' to the position of q', we shall have order $bcp'q' =$ order $bcpq$; for p and q can be turned to the positions of p' and q' without becoming opposite, and so without changing this order (Art. 94, Th. 1). In the same way we can take for b and c any two non-opposite half-lines in the plane bc such that a positive rotation of less than 180° will turn the first to the position of the second.

Conversely, we can determine the order of four non-coplanar half-lines drawn from O with reference to the order of two isocline planes or of any two planes which have only the point O in common.

THEOREM 1. *If α is isocline to β, β will be isocline to α in the same sense.*

THEOREM 2. *Two conjugate series of isocline planes are isocline in opposite senses.*

For these correspond to two arrangements of the forms *bcad* and *bacd*, which are of opposite orders.

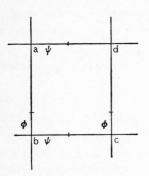
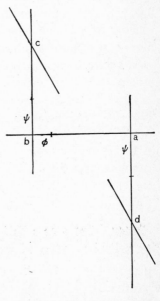

In fact, if we rotate the rectangular system around the plane which passes through b and bisects the angle ac, we shall interchange a and c and the planes ba and bc. d will have its direction reversed so that the plane ad will coincide with the original position of dc, not with the original position of cd. One of the angles ψ (of Art. 105) is now laid off in the direction of one of the angles ϕ in the original position of the figure, while the present position of the other angle ψ and the original position of the other angle ϕ are opposite.

Two absolutely perpendicular planes are isocline in both senses, but in only one sense when we distinguish in each a particular direction of rotation. Thus in the rectangular system ad and da are isocline to bc in opposite senses.

107. Planes through any line isocline to a given plane. Planes to which given intersecting planes are isocline.

THEOREM I. *Through any half-line not in a given plane nor perpendicular to it* two planes can be passed isocline, one positively and the other negatively, to the given plane.*

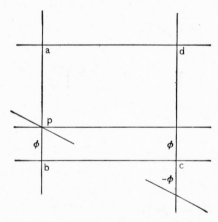

PROOF. Let p be a half-line not in a given plane β nor perpendicular to β. If we pass a plane through p perpendicular to β, we can determine a rectangular system with four mutually perpendicular half-lines, a, b, c, and d, so taken that β is the plane bc and p a half-line in the interior of the angle ba. Then we can take ϕ equal to the angle bp in this plane, and lay off ϕ and $-\phi$ from c in the

---

* It is always to be remembered that in this section, as in the third section of chap. III, all half-lines are supposed to be drawn from the point O and all planes to pass through O.

plane cd. The terminal lines of these angles determine with p two planes isocline to β in the two senses.

THEOREM 2. *Two intersecting planes determine a pair of planes (absolutely perpendicular to each other) to which they are isocline in one way in the two senses respectively, and another pair to which they are isocline in the other way in the two senses respectively.*

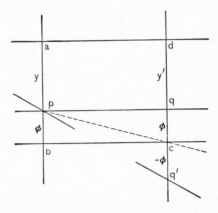

PROOF. Let p be one of the opposite half-lines in which the given planes intersect, and let γ and γ' be their common perpendicular planes, γ passing through the half-line p, and γ' the plane of the plane angles of the dihedral angles which they form (Art. 49). Let q and q' be the half-lines which form one of these plane angles, and let c be the half-line bisecting the angle qq'.

In γ and γ' we establish directions of positive rotation. Then in γ' the half-lines q and q' form with c angles which may be called ϕ and $-\phi$. If now in γ we take a half-line b so that the angle bp shall be equal to ϕ, we shall have the plane bc to which the two given planes are isocline in the two senses, as also to its absolutely perpendicular plane.

If, on the other hand, we take b so that the angle bp shall

be equal to $-\phi$, we shall have another plane bc to which
the two given planes are isocline in the two senses, as also
to its absolutely perpendicular plane.

**108. The common perpendicular planes when two
planes are isocline to a third.**

THEOREM I. *If two planes are isocline in the same sense
to a plane α, the common perpendicular planes which they
have with α through any half-line of α form a constant dihedral
angle, the same for all positions of the line in α.*

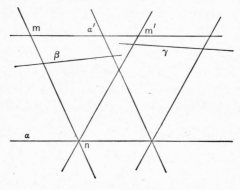

PROOF.   Let β and γ be two planes isocline to α in the
same sense, and let n be any half-line of α.   The common
perpendicular planes of α and β form a series of the opposite
sense, and the common perpendicular planes of α and γ
form a series of the opposite sense.   Through the line containing n passes one plane from each series, two planes
forming two pairs of vertical dihedral angles along this
line and intersecting the absolutely perpendicular plane α'
in two pairs of opposite half-lines which are the sides of
the plane angles of these dihedral angles.   Let mm' be
one of these angles, m and m' so taken that β shall intersect the interior of the right angle mn and γ the interior
of the right angle $m'n$.   Now to a second position of n,

forming a certain angle with its first position, will correspond second positions of m and m' forming the same angle with their first positions, the angles being laid off in the same direction (around O) in the plane α'.   Therefore the angle mm' will be the same in its second position as in its first, and the corresponding dihedral angles along n formed in the two positions of the perpendicular planes will be equal.

COROLLARY.   *If two planes isocline in the same sense to a plane α have with α a single pair of common perpendicular planes, perpendicular to all three, then all the common perpendicular planes of either and α are perpendicular to all three, and the two planes with α belong to a single series of isocline planes.*

THEOREM 2.   *If two planes are isocline in opposite senses to a plane α, the two planes with α have one and only one pair of common perpendicular planes, perpendicular to all three.*

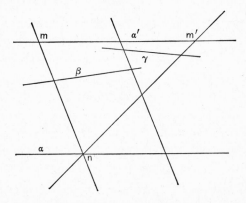

PROOF.   Let β and γ be two planes isocline to α in opposite senses, and let n be any half-line of α.   The common perpendicular planes of α and β and the common perpendicular planes of α and γ form two series of opposite senses. One plane of each series contains the half-line n, and these two contain half-lines, m and m' respectively, in the absolutely perpendicular plane α', so taken that β shall intersect the interior of the right angle mn and γ the interior of the right angle $m'n$. Then the half-line which bisects the angle mm' will lie in a plane common to the two series; for this half-line forms equal angles in opposite directions with m and m', and the planes of the two series which contain this half-line contain the half-lines of α which form the same angle in the same direction from n, and which therefore coincide (Art. 106). We have then a plane, and so a pair of planes, perpendicular to β and γ and to α; that is, a pair of planes common to the two series of perpendicular planes.

These are the only planes that can be perpendicular to β and γ and to α. Any such plane will be perpendicular to all the planes of the $\alpha\beta$-series and to all the planes of the $\alpha\gamma$-series. Through any half-line of it not a half-line of α or α' pass two distinct planes, one belonging to each of these series; that is, there are planes of one series that intersect planes of the other series, and two intersecting planes can have only one pair of common perpendicular planes (Art. 49).

COROLLARY. *Two planes which are isocline to a plane α in opposite senses and make the same angle with α always intersect.*

For they intersect each of the two perpendicular planes which they have in common with α, and the common angle which they form with α is laid off in the same direction from α in one of these perpendicular planes, though in opposite directions in the other.

109. Two planes isocline to a third in the same sense isocline to each other.

THEOREM.   *Two planes isocline to a third in the same sense are isocline to each other in this sense also.*

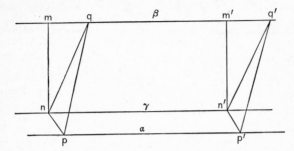

PROOF.   Let β and γ be two planes isocline in the same sense to a plane α. β and γ have at least one pair of common perpendicular planes mn and $m'n'$, where m, n, m', and n' are half-lines taken in the intersections of β and γ with these perpendicular planes in such a way that the angles mm' and nn' are two positive right angles in these two planes. n and n' lie in planes np and $n'p'$ perpendicular to γ and α, p and p' being taken in α in such a way that the angles pn and $p'n'$ shall be two equal angles of the isocline planes γ and α.   Then p and p' lie in planes pq and $p'q'$ perpendicular to α and β, q and q' being taken in β in such a way that the angles pq and $p'q'$ shall be two equal angles of the isocline planes α and β.

Since mm' and nn' are right angles, pp' and qq' are also right angles, qq' a positive right angle like mm' (see Art. 104).   Then we have

$$\angle \, mq = \angle \, m'q'.$$

Again, the dihedral angle along p formed by the half-planes containing n and q, is equal to the dihedral angle along p' formed by the half-planes containing n' and q', since β and γ are isocline to α in the same sense (Art. 108, Th. 1).   Therefore, the trihedral angles npq and $n'p'q'$

have two face angles and the included dihedral angle of one equal respectively to two face angles and the included dihedral angle of the other, so that the third face angles are equal; namely,

$$\angle nq = \angle n'q'.$$

Then in the right trihedral angles mnq and $m'n'q'$ there are two face angles, one adjacent and one opposite to the right dihedral angle, which have the same values in one trihedral angle as in the other. The third face angles in these two trihedral angles are therefore equal; namely,

$$\angle mn = \angle m'n'.$$

This proves that β and γ are isocline.

Now β and γ must be isocline to each other in the same sense as to α. Otherwise α and γ, being isocline to β in opposite senses, would have with β one pair of common perpendicular planes perpendicular to all three (Art. 108, Th. 2). But as β and γ are isocline to α in the same sense, there can be no planes perpendicular to all three unless the three belong to the same isocline series.

110. Poles and polar series.

THEOREM 1. *Given two conjugate series of isocline planes* (Art. 105), *there is a pair of absolutely perpendicular planes to which the planes of the two series are isocline in opposite senses, all at an angle of* $45°$.

PROOF. Let β be any plane of the first series and γ a plane of the conjugate series. These planes intersect at right angles and are therefore both isocline, in opposite senses, to a pair of planes α and α', each forming an angle of $45°$ with α and the same angle with α' (Art. 107, Th. 2). All the planes, then, of the first series are isocline to α and α' in the same sense as β, and all the planes of the conjugate series in the same sense as γ (Art. 109, Th.). Now every plane of the conjugate series has one pair of opposite half-lines in common with β, and every plane of the first series has one pair of opposite half-lines in common with γ, and these half-lines all make an angle of $45°$ with α and the same angle with α'. Therefore, all the planes of both series are isocline to α and α' at an angle of $45°$.

THEOREM 2. *All the planes isocline to a given plane at an angle of $45°$ lie in two conjugate series.*

PROOF. Two planes which are isocline to a plane α in opposite senses, and make with α an angle of $45°$, intersect and are perpendicular to each other (Art. 108, Th. 2, Cor. and Art. 107). Thus all the planes β, isocline in one sense, are perpendicular to any one of the planes γ, isocline in the opposite sense; and through each half-line of γ passes one and only one of these planes (Art. 107, Th. 1). But any two that are not absolutely perpendicular determine a series of planes all perpendicular to γ, one through each pair of opposite half-lines of γ, and all making an angle of $45°$ with α. Therefore these are the planes β, and the planes β all belong to one series. In the same way we prove that the planes γ, isocline in the opposite sense, all belong to one series.

The two isocline planes forming an angle of $45°$ with all the planes of a given series may be called the *poles of the series*, and the series may be called one of their *polar series*. Two absolutely perpendicular planes always have two polar series, conjugate to each other.

COROLLARY. *When two series of the same sense have a pair of planes in common, these planes are the poles of the series determined by the poles of the two given series.*

THEOREM 3. *In a complete system of all planes * isocline to a given plane in a given sense, any two series have a pair of planes in common.*

* At O.

o

For the poles of the two given series determine a pair of conjugate series whose poles, being 45° from each of them, are planes common to the two given series.

111. Planes intersecting two isocline planes.

THEOREM I. *If a plane intersects two isocline planes, each of the four dihedral angles formed about one line of intersection is equal to the corresponding dihedral angle of the four formed about the other line of intersection* (see Art. 104).

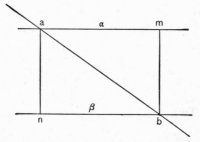

PROOF. Let α and β be two isocline planes, and let a and b be half-lines lying in the intersections of these planes with a third plane. Through each of the half-lines a and b passes a plane perpendicular to α and β. Let n and m be half-lines in the intersections of these planes with β and α respectively, so taken that the angles na and bm shall be two of the equal angles formed by the isocline planes. Then the angles am and nb will also be equal, and the two trihedral angles abn and bam will have the three face angles of one equal respectively to the three face angles of the other. It follows that the dihedral angle along a of the trihedral angle bam is equal to the dihedral angle along b of the trihedral angle abn. But the latter dihedral angle is vertical to the dihedral angle which corresponds to the former. These corresponding dihedral angles are therefore equal, and each of the four dihedral angles along a is equal to the corresponding dihedral angle along b.

THEOREM 2. *Given two isocline planes α and β, not absolutely perpendicular, with non-opposite half-lines a and a' in α and b and b' in β so taken that*

$$\angle \, aa' = \angle \, bb' \, ;$$

then the planes ab and a'b' will be isocline in the opposite sense.

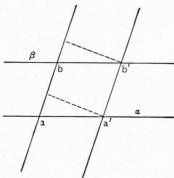

PROOF. If these planes are isocline, they are isocline in the sense opposite to that of α and β, for the orders $aba'b'$ and $aa'bb'$ are opposite (Art. 106).

Now the half-lines a' and b' make equal angles with the plane ab, for their projections upon this plane form with the four given half-lines two equal trihedral angles. Moreover, there is a plane λ to which α and β are isocline in the given sense and ab is isocline in the opposite sense (Art. 107, Th. 2). These planes and the four given half-lines all form the same angle with λ. Then the plane β, and the plane through a' isocline in the opposite sense to ab and to λ, form this same angle with λ and must intersect (Art. 108, Th. 2, Cor.) in two opposite half-lines which form with the plane ab the angle that a' forms with ab. In other words, the plane $a'b'$ is this isocline plane through a', isocline to ab in the sense opposite to that of α and β.

The four half-lines a, b, a', and b' are the edges of a polyhedral angle in hyperspace, not in a hyperplane, having properties somewhat analogous to those of the parallelogram of the Euclidean Plane Geometry.

112. Isocline rotation. In a simple rotation around α, or in a double rotation around α and its absolutely perpendicular plane α' (Art. 81), the complete system of all planes isocline to α in a given sense is transformed into itself, the planes generally into one another.

When the two rotations around α and α' are equal, all the planes isocline in the sense corresponding to the rotation rotate on themselves, the series conjugate to any series of these planes moving as a series on itself. Every half-line (drawn from O) rotates in a plane isocline to α, and any one of these planes and its absolutely perpendicular plane can be regarded as the axis-planes of the rotation, no particular pair of planes playing in this way a special part.

We shall call this rotation *isocline rotation*, and the common angle of the two rotations the *angle of the isocline rotation*.

THEOREM 1. *In an isocline rotation every plane that does not rotate on itself remains isocline to itself in the sense opposite to the rotation.*

PROOF. Let γ be any plane rotated to a position γ'. Two half-lines a and b of γ rotate to positions a' and b', rotating in two isocline planes, and we have

$$\angle \, aa' = \angle \, bb'.$$

Therefore γ and γ' are isocline in the sense opposite to the rotation (Art. 111, Th. 2).

THEOREM 2. *A simple rotation of angle θ around a plane α moves any plane of a polar series to a position where it makes an angle of $\frac{1}{2}\,\theta$ with its original position.*

PROOF. In an isocline rotation of angle θ, any plane conjugate to a series of the system with respect to which the rotation takes place is rotated on the planes of this series through an angle θ. Now the isocline rotation can be decomposed into two equal simple rotations around the two poles, say α and α', of the series. Either of these simple rotations, therefore, moves the given plane to a position where it makes an angle of $\frac{1}{2}\theta$ with its original position. But the effect of a simple rotation around α is the same on both of its polar series. After such a rotation any plane of either series in its final position makes an angle of $\frac{1}{2}\theta$ with its original position.

The planes isocline to a given plane, in a given sense, and at a given angle, constitute a *conical hypersurface of double revolution.* The hypersurface contains also all the planes isocline to the given plane in the opposite sense and at the same angle, but the planes of either set contain all the half-lines which make this angle with the given plane, and therefore completely fill the hypersurface (see Art. 118). In particular, two conjugate series lie together in such a hypersurface, which therefore may be said to consist of the planes of either of these series (see Art. 124).

The student will find it useful to think of the planes isocline in a given sense to a given plane as the elements of a two-dimensional geometry which is exactly like the geometry of the sphere, absolutely perpendicular planes corresponding to opposite points on the sphere, and series of planes to great circles. For distance between two elements we should take double the angle between the two planes, and to measure the angle between two series we can measure the dihedral angle between conjugate planes intersecting in one of the common planes of the series (Art. 108, Th. 1). These conjugate planes are not themselves a part of the two-dimensional geometry, but the measure of the angle so determined will be the same as the distance intercepted on the polar series of its vertex-plane. An isocline rotation with respect to the planes of this system is to be regarded as no motion at all in this geometry, but a simple rotation or a double rotation which is not an isocline rotation corresponds to a rotation of the sphere, in the latter case through an angle equal to the difference of the two component rotations.*

* Stringham calls a series of planes an *ordinal system*, and the set of planes isocline to a given plane at a given angle forms with him a *cardinal system*. He uses these terms, however, with reference to a particular pair of absolutely perpendicular planes. They correspond to meridian and parallel circle taken on the sphere with reference to a particular axis. See p. 212 of the paper referred to on p. 114.

CHAPTER V

HYPERPYRAMIDS, HYPERCONES, AND THE HYPER-SPHERE

I. PENTAHEDROIDS AND HYPERPYRAMIDS *

113. Pentahedroids: the point equidistant from the five vertices, the point equidistant from the five cells, and the centre of gravity.

THEOREM 1. *In a pentahedroid, if two of the tetrahedrons can be inscribed in spheres, the lines drawn through the centres of these spheres perpendicular to their hyperplanes lie in a plane; when they meet in a point this point is equidistant from the five vertices of the pentahedroid, the five tetrahedrons can all be inscribed in spheres, and the five lines drawn through the centres of these spheres perpendicular to their hyperplanes all pass through the same point.†*

PROOF. The common face of the two tetrahedrons is the interior of a triangle inscribed in a circle common to the two spheres. The absolutely perpendicular plane at the centre of this circle contains the centres of the spheres and is perpendicular to the hyperplanes of the two tetrahedrons. It therefore contains the lines perpendicular to the hyperplanes at these points (Art. 51, Th. 1).

Now the line drawn through the centre of a sphere perpendicular to its hyperplane is the locus of points equidis-

---

* This section and the next are continuations of the last section of chap. I, and the latter should be read again at this point.

† There are other possibilities in the Hyperbolic Geometry, which the student may investigate if he is familiar with this geometry.

tant from the four vertices of any tetrahedron inscribed
in the sphere (Art. 40, Th. 2). If, then, the two perpendiculars meet, the point where they meet must be at the
same distance from the five vertices of the pentahedroid;
and a line through this point perpendicular to the hyperplane of any one of the five tetrahedrons contains a point
of this hyperplane equidistant from the vertices of the
tetrahedron.

THEOREM 2. *The half-hyperplanes bisecting the ten
hyperplane angles of a pentahedroid all pass through a point
within the pentahedroid, a point equidistant from the hyperplanes of its five cells.*

PROOF. At a vertex A we have a tetrahedroidal angle
with six hyperplane angles, and the bisecting half-hyperplanes of these hyperplane angles have in common a half-
line a, the locus of points within the tetrahedroidal angle
equidistant from its four hyperplanes (Art. 73, Th.).
Drawn from another vertex B we have another half-line
b, the locus of points within the tetrahedroidal angle at
this vertex equidistant from the four hyperplanes of this
tetrahedroidal angle. Now the plano-polyhedral angle
AB contains three hyperplane angles which belong to the
tetrahedroidal angle at A and also to the tetrahedroidal
angle at B, and the bisecting half-hyperplanes of these
three hyperplane angles intersect in a half-plane α which
must contain both a and b (Art. 79, Th.). The plane of α
intersects the pentahedroid in a triangle, and, as the half-
lines a and b pass within the angles at A and B of this
triangle, they must intersect in a point O within the pentahedroid (see Art. 8, Th. 1). We have, then, a point O
equidistant from the five hyperplanes of the pentahedroid,
lying within the pentahedroid, and lying in each of the ten
half-hyperplanes bisecting the ten hyperplane angles of the
pentahedroid.

THEOREM 3. *The half-lines drawn from the vertices of a pentahedroid through the centres of gravity of the opposite cells meet in a point.*

PROOF. Given the pentahedroid $ABCDE$, we will write *half-plane AB* to denote the half-plane whose edge is the line AB and which itself contains the centre of gravity of the triangle CDE, and we will write *triangle AB* to denote the triangle whose vertices are A and B and this same centre of gravity. In this way we can speak of the half-plane and triangle determined by any two vertices of the pentahedroid and the centre of gravity of the opposite face. All points in the interior of the triangle AB are in the interior of the pentahedroid.

The four half-planes AB, AC, AD, and AE contain respectively the half-lines drawn from the vertices B, C, D, and E through the centres of gravity of the opposite faces in the tetrahedron $BCDE$. They contain, therefore, the centre of gravity of this tetrahedron, as well as the vertex A. In the same way the four half-planes AB, BC, BD, and BE contain the vertex B and the centre of gravity of the tetrahedron $ACDE$. Thus we have in the half-plane AB two half-lines drawn from the vertices A and B through points in the opposite sides of the triangle AB. These two half-lines, therefore, intersect in a point P in the interior of the triangle AB, and so in the interior of the pentahedroid (Art. 8, Th. 1). But A and B are any two vertices. Hence the half-lines drawn from the vertices of the pentahedroid through the centres of gravity of the opposite cells must all intersect one another in the interior of the pentahedroid.

These intersections all coincide. If, for example, the half-lines from A, B, and C intersected in three different points, these half-lines, and so the vertices A, B, and C, would lie in the plane of these three points. But this is impossible, the intersections being in the interior of the pentahedroid.*

The point where these half-lines intersect is called the *centre of gravity of the pentahedroid*.

114. Pentahedroids with corresponding edges equal. Regular pentahedroids.

We can make two pentahedroids correspond, the five vertices of one to the five vertices of the other, in any order, just as we have made two tetrahedrons correspond in Art. 72.

THEOREM. *If each of the edges of a pentahedroid is equal to the corresponding edge of a second pentahedroid, when the five vertices of one are made to correspond in some order to the five vertices of the other, the pentahedroids will be congruent or symmetrical.*

PROOF. All the faces and all the face angles, dihedral angles, and hyperplane angles of one are equal to the corresponding parts of the other, as proved in the two theorems of Art. 72; and any two corresponding tetrahedrons can be made to coincide, even though they happen to be in a hyperplane in opposite orders (Art. 84, Th. 4). Then by putting two such tetrahedrons together we can prove that the pentahedroids will coincide entirely if their orders are the same, and that they will be symmetrically situated

---

* The corresponding theorem for tetrahedrons is proved in the same way.

The theorem which determines the centre of gravity of a triangle is usually made to depend on the axiom of parallels. The theorem is true, however, in the Hyperbolic and Elliptic Geometries, and therefore is independent of the axiom of parallels. It can be proved very simply in these two geometries and in the Euclidean Geometry by means of trigonometrical formulæ (see Chauvenet's *Trigonometry*, 9th ed., Philadelphia, 1881, Part II, Art. 188, p. 253). Or, having proved the theorem for Euclidean Geometry by means of parallels, we can prove it for any spherical triangle by projection from the centre of the sphere upon the plane of the plane triangle which has the same vertices, and then in the Non-Euclidean Geometries for any plane triangle which can be inscribed in a circle, and so in a sphere, by reversing this projection.

The term *centre of gravity* is used here without any reference to the physical properties of the point. Another name is *centroid*.

with respect to the common hyperplane of these tetrahedrons if their orders are opposite.

When the pentahedroids are symmetrical, corresponding tetrahedroidal angles and corresponding plano-polyhedral angles are symmetrical.

If we take a regular tetrahedron and draw a line through its centre perpendicular to its hyperplane, every point of this line will be equidistant from the four vertices of the tetrahedron, and we can take a point at a distance from the four vertices equal to one of the edges of the tetrahedron. We have then a pentahedroid in which the ten edges are all equal. All the parts of any one kind, face angles, dihedral angles, faces, etc., are equal; for the pentahedroid is congruent to itself in sixty different ways (Art. 95), and can be made to coincide with itself, any part coinciding with any other part of the same kind. Such a pentahedroid is called a *regular pentahedroid* (see Art. 166).

115. The terms right and regular as used of hyperpyramids and double pyramids. When the base of a hyperpyramid is the interior of a regular polyhedron, the interior of the segment consisting of the vertex and the centre of the base is called the *axis of the hyperpyramid;* and when the line containing the axis is perpendicular to the hyperplane of the base the hyperpyramid is *regular*.

THEOREM 1. *In a regular hyperpyramid the lateral pyramids are equal regular pyramids. The axis of any one of these lateral pyramids is the hypothenuse of a right triangle whose legs are the axis of the hyperpyramid and a radius of the sphere inscribed in the base.*

The *slant height of a regular hyperpyramid* is the altitude of any one of the lateral pyramids.

When the base of a double pyramid (see Art. 32) is the interior of a regular polygon, the interior of the triangle determined by the vertex-edge and the centre of the base is called the *axis-element of the double pyramid;* and when the plane of this triangle is absolutely perpendicular to the plane of the base we have a *right double pyramid.* A right double pyramid is *isosceles* when the extremities of the vertex-edge are at the same distance from the plane of the base. Such a double pyramid is also called *regular.*

THEOREM 2. *In a right double pyramid (the base being regular) the lateral faces are congruent, the lateral cells are congruent, and the two end-pyramids are regular. In a regular double pyramid the end-pyramids are congruent.*

II. HYPERCONES AND DOUBLE CONES

116. Spherical hypercones and right hypercones. A *spherical hypercone* is one whose base is the interior of a sphere. The *axis of a spherical hypercone* is the interior of a segment consisting of the vertex and the centre of the base. A *right spherical hypercone*, or simply a *right hypercone*, is one whose axis lies in a line perpendicular to the hyperplane of the base.

A section of a spherical hypercone by a hyperplane containing the vertex and any point of the base is a circular cone.

THEOREM 1. *When a right triangle takes all possible positions with one leg fixed, the vertices and the points of the other two sides of the triangle make up a right spherical hypercone. The fixed side is the axis, the hypothenuse is an element, and the other leg is a radius of the base.*

THEOREM 2. *If in the hyperplane of a cone of revolution we pass a plane through its axis and rotate around this plane that portion of the cone which lies on one side of it, we shall have all of a right spherical hypercone except that portion which makes up the section of the cone by the plane.*

The *slant height of a right spherical hypercone* is the distance from the vertex to any point of the sphere whose interior is the base; it is the length of the hypothenuse of the right triangle of Th. 1.

117. Circular double cones and right double cones. A *circular double cone* is one whose base is the interior of a circle. The *axis-element of a circular double cone* is the interior of the triangle determined by the vertex-edge and the centre of the base. A *right circular double cone*, or simply a *right double cone*, is one whose axis-element lies in a plane absolutely perpendicular to the plane of the base, and the double cone is also *isosceles* when the extremities of the vertex-edge are at the same distance from the plane of the base.

THEOREM 1. *In a right double cone the elements are congruent, and the two end-cones are cones of revolution. In an isosceles right double cone the end-cones are congruent.*

THEOREM 2. *A right double cone may be generated by the rotation of a tetrahedron which has an edge and face in a perpendicular line and plane, the rotation taking place around the latter.*

Let *ABCD* be the tetrahedron with the line *CD* perpendicular to the plane *ABC*. In the rotation around this plane the face *ABD* will generate the set of elements of the double cone, the face *ABC* will be the axis-element, the faces *ACD* and *BCD* will generate the interiors of the end-cones, and the edge *CD* will generate all of the base except the centre.

118. Hypersurfaces consisting of planes through a point with only this point common to any two of them. The conical hypersurface of double revolution. When the directing-surface of a hyperconical hypersurface consists of lines (as, for example, in the case of a conical surface), the hypersurface consists of planes or portions of planes, every point collinear with the vertex and a point of any one of these lines being a point of the hypersurface. If the entire planes are not included in this way, we can consider the hypersurface which does consist of the entire planes, defining it as consisting of these planes and calling the planes elements.

We can also form a hypersurface of planes through a fixed point O and the points of a plane curve, the planes being determined in some way so that they shall have only the point O common to any two of them and shall intersect the plane of the directing-curve only in the points of this curve. For example, the planes can be isocline to a given plane through O.

These various hypersurfaces should all be regarded as hyperconical hypersurfaces (see foot-note, p. 220).

We shall consider only the hypersurface generated by the rotation of one of two isocline planes around the other, the conical hypersurface of double revolution of Art. 112. O being the vertex (where the two planes meet), the plane through any other point of the hypersurface, absolutely perpendicular to the axis-plane, will intersect the hypersurface in a circle which can be taken for the directing-circle. As we have seen, there are two sets of planes in the hypersurface, and two generating planes, and the hypersurface rotates on itself in any double rotation around the given axis-plane and its absolutely perpendicular plane at O, or in any simple rotation around either one of these planes. Thus the hypersurface has a pair of axis-planes.

The hypersurface can also be described as consisting of all the half-lines drawn from O which make a given angle with a given plane through O. All other half-lines drawn from O are divided into two classes, those which make a smaller angle with the given plane, and those which make a smaller angle with its absolutely perpendicular plane, than do the half-lines of the hypersurface itself. The hypersurface, therefore, divides all the remaining points of hyperspace into two classes, one containing all the points except O of one of the axis-planes, and the other containing all the points except O of the other axis-plane.

We can pass around either axis-plane without passing through a point of the hypersurface, just as in a hyperplane we can pass around the axis-line of a conical surface of revolution without passing through a point of the surface. In the case of the hypersurface, however, each of the two regions into which it divides the rest of hyperspace is completely connected, so that in either one of these regions we can pass from any point to any other point without passing through a point of the hypersurface; while the axis of a conical surface of revolution in a hyperplane lies partly in one and partly in the other of two vertical regions that are completely separated.

III. THE HYPERSPHERE

119. Spheres and circles in a hypersphere. Tangent hyperplanes. A *hypersphere* consists of the points at a given distance from a given point. The terms *centre*, *radius*, *chord*, and *diameter* are used as with circles and spheres.

Theorem 1. *Any hyperplane section of a hypersphere is a sphere having for centre the projection of the centre of the hypersphere upon the hyperplane* (Art. 40, Th. 2).

When the hyperplane passes through the centre of the hypersphere the section is a *great sphere*. Other spheres of the hypersphere are *small spheres*.

THEOREM 2. *Four non-coplanar points of a hypersphere determine a sphere of the hypersphere, and three points not coplanar with the centre of the hypersphere determine a great sphere.*

THEOREM 3. *Any plane having more than one point in a hypersphere intersects the hypersphere in a circle having for centre the projection of the centre of the hypersphere upon the plane.*

This is proved by considering the hyperplane which contains the plane and the centre of the hypersphere.

A circle of a hypersphere is a *great circle* when its plane passes through the centre of the hypersphere.

THEOREM 4. *Three points of a hypersphere determine a circle, and two points not collinear with the centre of the hypersphere determine a great circle.*

THEOREM 5. *Two great circles on the same great sphere intersect, and two great circles which intersect lie on one great sphere* (Art. 22, Th., and Art. 20, Th. 2 (4)).

A great circle and a great sphere always intersect, intersecting in the extremities of a diameter, and two great spheres intersect in a great circle (Art. 27, Ths. 1 and 2).

Distance in a hypersphere between two points not the extremities of a diameter is always measured on the arc less than 180° of the great circle containing them. The distance between the extremities of any diameter is 180°.

THEOREM 6. *All the circles of a hypersphere which pass through a given point are perpendicular, that is, their tangents are perpendicular, to the radius of the hypersphere at this point. These tangent lines, therefore, all lie in the hyperplane which is perpendicular to the radius at this point.*

A hyperplane perpendicular to a radius of a hypersphere at its extremity is *tangent to the hypersphere.*

120. Spherical dihedral angles and spherical tetrahedrons. A great circle of a sphere, dividing the rest of the sphere into two hemispheres, may be called the *edge* of either of these hemispheres. Two hemispheres of great spheres in a hypersphere having a common edge form a figure somewhat like a double convex lens, and enclose a portion of the hypersphere, a definite volume. Along the edge we have a *spherical* * *dihedral angle*, which we can think of as consisting of a restricted portion of the edge and restricted portions of the hemispheres. The tangent half-planes which have a common edge tangent to the edge of the spherical dihedral angle form an ordinary dihedral angle whose measure can be taken as the measure of the former.

THEOREM 1. *A spherical dihedral angle has the same measure at all points of its edge.*

THEOREM 2. *The volume enclosed by the hemispheres of a spherical dihedral angle is to the volume of the hypersphere as the dihedral angle is to four right dihedral angles.*

The edge of a spherical dihedral angle has on each face a pole, and the arcs of great circles drawn through these poles from any point of the edge determine a spherical angle by which the spherical dihedral angle can be measured, just as the dihedral angle formed by two half-planes is measured by its plane angle. The spherical angle is itself measured by the distance between the two poles of the edge, so that this distance can be considered a measure of the spherical dihedral angle, and also, if we take corresponding units, as a measure of the volume enclosed by its hemispheres.

It is hardly necessary to define *spherical trihedral angle*

---

* We might have said hyperspherical, but we shall use the shorter word where there is no ambiguity.

P

and *spherical tetrahedron*. We shall suppose that the sides of a triangle and the edges of a tetrahedron are less than 180°. The four great spheres which contain the faces of a spherical tetrahedron determine a set of sixteen tetrahedrons, eight pairs, the two tetrahedrons of a pair being symmetrically situated with respect to the centre of the hypersphere, and therefore congruent (Art. 85, Th. 2). That half-hypersphere which lies on one side of any one of the four great spheres (on one side of the hyperplane of the great sphere) contains the interiors of eight tetrahedrons, one from each pair.

A spherical tetrahedron has six edges, each lying in the edge of a spherical dihedral angle whose interior contains the interior of the tetrahedron. The interior of one of these spherical dihedral angles contains also the interiors of three of the fifteen tetrahedrons associated with the given tetrahedron as explained above, and its volume is equal to the sum of the volumes of the four tetrahedrons whose interiors are within it.

Writing A' for the opposite point to A, the other extremity of the diameter to A, and so for other points, we let T denote the volume of the tetrahedron $ABCD$, T_1 the volume of $A'BCD$, T_{12} the volume of $A'B'CD$, and so on. $ABC'D'$ is congruent to $A'B'CD$, and we have $T_{34} = T_{12}$, etc.

The interior of the dihedral angle $C-AB-D$ contains the interiors of the four tetrahedrons whose volumes are T, T_1, T_2, and T_{12}. If θ_{12} is the measure of the dihedral angle AB in terms of a right dihedral angle, and if we take for unit of volume one-sixteenth of the volume of the hypersphere, we shall have the relation

$$T + T_1 + T_2 + T_{12} = 4\,\theta_{12}.$$

There are six of these equations, and in addition one equation expressing the fact that the sum of the eight different volumes is equal to the volume of a half-hypersphere, namely,

$$T + \Sigma\, T_1 + \Sigma\, T_{12} = 8.$$

These seven equations reduce to the following equivalent system:

$$T + T_1 \;= 2(\theta_{12} + \theta_{13} + \theta_{14} - 2),\; \text{etc., four equations,}$$
$$T - T_{12} = 2(\theta_{13} + \theta_{14} + \theta_{23} + \theta_{24} - 4),\; \text{etc., three equations.}$$

Given the volume of one tetrahedron, we can find the volumes of the others; but we have no simple formula for the volume of a single tetrahedron as we have for the area of a spherical triangle.*

121. Poles and polar circles. Duality in the hypersphere. The diameter of a hypersphere perpendicular to the hyperplane of any sphere of the hypersphere is called the *axis of the sphere*, and the extremities of the axis are the *poles of the sphere*.

THEOREM 1. *Each pole of a sphere of a hypersphere is equidistant from all the points of the sphere.*

The plane through the centre of a hypersphere absolutely perpendicular to the plane of any circle of the hypersphere is called the *axis-plane of the circle*, and the great circle in which this plane intersects the hypersphere is the *polar circle of the given circle*.

THEOREM 2. *Each point of the polar circle of a circle of a hypersphere is equidistant from all the points of the given circle.*

THEOREM 3. *A great circle of a hypersphere is itself polar to the great circle which is its polar, and the distance between any two points, one in each of two polar great circles, is a quadrant.*

* See Coolidge, *Non-Euclidean Geometry*, p. 181.

THEOREM 4. *A great sphere contains all the points at a quadrant's distance from either of its poles, and each of two polar great circles contains all points at a quadrant's distance from the other.*

THEOREM 5. *Great circles which pass through the poles of a sphere are perpendicular to the sphere, and any great circle perpendicular to a sphere passes through the poles of the sphere.*

If a point moves a given distance along an arc of a great circle, its polar great sphere will rotate around the polar great circle and generate a spherical dihedral angle whose measure is this same distance. If a great circle rotates on a great sphere through a given spherical angle around one of its points (and the opposite point), its polar great circle, lying on the polar great sphere of the given point and passing through the pole of the given great sphere, will rotate around the latter through the same angle. In fact, the rotation takes place in the hypersphere around the great circle (see Art. 124) determined by the two fixed points, and in hyperspace around the plane of this great circle.

We have a *principle of duality* in the hypersphere, points and great spheres corresponding to each other, and great circles to great circles, one great circle considered as made up of points and the other as common to a set of great spheres. Corresponding figures are called *reciprocal figures*. This correspondence can be realized by taking the relations of pole and polar as its basis.

The student may investigate the properties of polar spherical tetrahedrons.

122. Geometry of the hypersphere as an independent three-dimensional geometry. Starting with its points and great circles, and with certain fundamental theorems, we can build up the geometry of the hypersphere without further reference to the hyperspace in which it lies. These fundamental theorems play the part of axioms and we shall state them here as axioms.*

The points of this geometry are paired, the two points of a pair being called *opposites*. We express this as an axiom: namely,

AXIOM 1. *To each point there is one and only one opposite point.*

With any two non-opposite points A and B is associated a class of points as *points of the great circle AB*, a great circle determined by these two points. For great circles we have the following axioms:

AXIOM 2. *The great circle determined by any two nonopposite points of a given great circle is the given great circle itself* (Art. 10, Th. 2).

AXIOM 3. *All great circles which contain a given point contain also its opposite point.*

The points of a great circle are in cyclical order. In particular, any two pairs of opposite points separate each other (Art. 6).

A *spherical triangle* consists of three points not points of one great circle and all points between any two of them on that portion of a great circle which does not contain their opposites.

On a great circle containing one side of a spherical triangle, that portion which lies between one vertex and the opposite point to the other will be called the *side produced*, produced in one direction or the other as the case may be.

AXIOM 4. *A great circle intersecting one side of a spherical triangle and another side produced intersects the third side.*

* Compare the chapter on "Pure Spherics" in Halsted's *Rational Geometry* (chap. XVI of the second edition).

The two axioms of Art. 3 are included in Ax. 2, modified only by the term " non-opposite." Ax. 4 is the same as the Axiom of Pasch (Art. 7), with the restriction placed above on the phrase " side produced." It follows that in any portion of the hypersphere thus restricted the theorems of the first four sections of chap. I all hold true, if in place of the word " collinear " we use the phrase " on a great circle with," and for " line " say " great circle."

Certain other forms of expression, also, are changed as a matter of convenience. Thus we shall speak of a great circle as a *transversal to a triangle* when it contains at least two points of the triangle, and then we can speak of a point as *on a transversal to a triangle* where in chap. I we have said " collinear with a triangle." Again, in place of the word " plane " we must now say *great sphere*. This we define as consisting of the points that we get if we take three points not points of one great circle, all points on a great circle with any two of them, and all points on a great circle with any two non-opposite points obtained by this process.

We prove then that any point of the great sphere *A BC* is on a transversal to the triangle *A BC*, and that any three points of a great sphere, not points of one great circle, determine the same great sphere.

Now in order to confine our geometry to a single hypersphere we make this axiom:

AXIOM 5. *We get all the points of a hypersphere if we take four points not points of one great sphere, all points of the great circles determined by any two of them, and all points of the great circles determined by any two non-opposite points obtained by this process.*

Thus we see that the hypersphere is a space of three dimensions, and its geometry is a geometry of three dimensions.

Finally, we are able to consider the entire hypersphere, and determine its relation to the theory of parallels, by introducing the following axiom :

AXIOM 6. *Any two great circles of the same great sphere intersect.*

By passing a great sphere through a given great circle and a point of a given great sphere we prove from these axioms that the circle and sphere always intersect (Art. 22, Th.), and then that any two great spheres intersect in a great circle.

These " axioms," and such axioms as are necessary to establish the properties of points on a great circle (see Arts. 5 and 6), determine the nature of the hyperspherical geometry. The result we express in the following theorem :

THEOREM. *The geometry of the hypersphere is the same as the Double Elliptic Non-Euclidean Geometry of Three Dimensions,* the great circles and great spheres of the hypersphere being taken for lines and planes.*

---

* See the author's *Non-Euclidean Geometry*, chap. III. This book has been very properly criticised for giving only the Single Elliptic Geometry; but in any "restricted region" the two geometries are the same.

In the Double Elliptic Geometry two lines in the same plane intersect in two points, and a line meets any plane in which it does not lie in two points, the distance between the two points in each of these cases being one-half of the entire length of the line. The length of the line is most conveniently taken as 2π.

If we start at an intersection of two lines and follow one of them until we come again to the other, we shall come, not to the same intersection point, but to an "opposite" point. We have traversed only one-half of the line, and we arrive at the starting point only when we have gone the same distance further. The geometry of the sphere is the same as the Double Elliptic Geometry of Two Dimensions. In the Double Elliptic Geometry a line divides a plane in which it lies, and a plane divides space of three dimensions, into two entirely separate parts, which is not the case with the Single Elliptic Geometry. Symmetrical figures in the Single Elliptic Geometry can be made to coincide by moving one of them along the entire length of a line, but in the Double Elliptic Geometry a movement from intersection point to intersection point of two lines only puts a figure into the opposite region of space, and two symmetrical figures can never be made to coincide.

Two polar lines are still everywhere at a quadrant's distance from each other, and the locus of points at a given distance from a given line is also the locus of points

123. **Point Geometry the same as the geometry of the hypersphere.**

THEOREM. *The Point Geometry at the centre of a hypersphere is the same as the geometry of the hypersphere.*

PROOF. In the hypersphere points, great circles, and great spheres are its intersections with half-lines drawn from the centre and with planes and hyperplanes through the centre, and the distances and angles in the hypersphere are the same as the corresponding angles at the centre. Therefore the two geometries are the same.

In particular, to a great sphere of the hypersphere and its poles correspond at the centre a hyperplane and its perpendicular half-lines; to two polar great circles correspond two absolutely perpendicular planes; and two simply perpendicular planes correspond to two great circles intersecting at right angles.

The theorems of Point Geometry can, then, be stated as theorems of the geometry of the hypersphere. We shall mention only some of the more important results (Arts. 67, 68, 106, 107, and 109):

Any two great circles have a pair of common perpendicular great circles, two polar circles which intersect them at right angles.

When two great circles cut out equal arcs on a polar pair of common perpendicular great circles, they have an infinite number of common perpendicular great circles, on all of which they cut out the same arc.   Conversely, if two great circles have more than two common perpendicular great circles, the arcs not greater than a quadrant which they cut out on any one of them and on its polar circle are equal.

---

at the complementary distance from its polar line, namely, a surface of double revolution with the two polar lines for axes.   But a line intersecting the axes meets the surface in four points instead of two; and a plane through one axis, and so perpendicular to the other, cuts the surface in two circles instead of one.

There are two *distances between two great circles*, the distances not greater than a quadrant measured along a polar pair of common perpendicular great circles.

When the distances are equal the given circles are *parallel* in the sense used by Clifford.*   Parallel great circles, therefore, correspond to isocline planes of the Point Geometry.

There are two senses in which great circles can be parallel, and two great circles perpendicular to both of two parallel great circles (which are not polar) are themselves parallel in the opposite sense.   Through any point not a point of a given great circle nor a point of its polar great circle pass two great circles parallel in the two senses to the given circle and to its polar.   Two great circles parallel to a given great circle in the same sense are parallel to each other in this sense also ; and the set of all the great circles parallel to a given great circle in a given sense completely fills the hypersphere, one and only one such circle passing through each point.

We can prove in another way that the geometry of the hypersphere and the Double Elliptic Geometry of Three Dimensions are the same : †

The geometry of the hypersphere is the same as the Point Geometry at its centre.   But Point Geometry is the same whatever our theory of parallels, and therefore the geometry of the hypersphere is the same whatever our theory of parallels.

Now in the Double Elliptic Geometry of Four Dimensions all the lines perpendicular to a hyperplane meet in a pair of opposite points, the *poles of the hyperplane*.   This is true because any two of these lines lie in a plane (Art. 39, Th. 2) in which they are perpendicular to a line, and therefore they meet in two points each at a given distance on both

* See the author's *Non-Euclidean Geometry*, p. 68.
† See the author's *Non-Euclidean Geometry*, pp. 63 and 26.

of them. Thus the hyperplane is a particular case of a hypersphere having either pole as centre. Any point is one of the poles of a hyperplane, and the Point Geometry is the same as the hyperplane geometry: it is the Double Elliptic Non-Euclidean Geometry of Three Dimensions.

124. Rotation of the hypersphere.   The surface of double revolution.

Rotation of the hypersphere on itself is the same as the rotation of the Point Geometry at its centre. In any simple rotation a certain great circle, the axis of rotation, remains fixed in all of its points; while its polar great circle, the circle of rotation, rotates or slides on itself (Art. 81).*

Rotation around a great circle in the hypersphere is not a distorted rotation, such as we might have in the case of a flexible object rotated around a curved axis, but an actual hyperspace rotation around the plane of the great circle.

A *double rotation* is a combination of two simple rotations around two polar great circles. A double rotation can also be regarded as a double rotation along the two polar great circles, or as a *screw motion* along either one of them.

When the two rotations of a double rotation are equal it is a *parallel motion*, corresponding to an isocline rotation at the centre of the hypersphere. In a parallel motion all great circles parallel to the circles of rotation in the sense of the rotation rotate on themselves, and the motion can be regarded as a parallel motion along any polar pair taken

* A hypersphere can be moved freely on itself. Therefore, without attempting to define curvature in hyperspace, we can say that a hypersphere is a *space of constant curvature*. If our space were a hypersphere in Euclidean space of four dimensions we should realize the Elliptic Geometry. The Elliptic Geometry is therefore sometimes supposed to assume that our space is a space of constant curvature like a hypersphere, not a space of no curvature like a hyperplane. Elliptic Geometry of Three Dimensions, however, does not depend on any assumption of a Euclidean space of four dimensions. We might suppose our space to be an elliptic space lying in elliptic space of four dimensions and with no curvature whatever.

from this set of circles. We can also think of the motion as a parallel motion with respect to the set of circles, without thinking of any particular pair as the circles of rotation or as the axes of rotation (Art. 112).

THEOREM 1. *Any position of a hypersphere can be obtained from any other position with the same centre by a simple or a double rotation* (Art. 101, Th. 1).

THEOREM 2. *Two simple rotations are equivalent to a single simple rotation when and only when their axes intersect* (Art. 102, Ths. 1 and 2).

A *surface of double revolution* consists of the points of a hypersphere at a given distance from a given great circle, and so at the complementary distance from the polar great circle.* These two great circles are the axes and the two distances are the two *radii* of the surface. The surface is covered with two sets of parallel great circles, those of one set parallel in one sense and those of the other set parallel in the other sense. Through each point of the surface passes one and only one circle of each set, and the surface can be regarded as consisting of the circles of either one of these sets. Any great sphere containing one of the axes intersects the surface in a *meridian circle;* and any circle of either of the two sets of parallel great circles forms with the meridian circle at any point of it an angle equal to the corresponding radius of the surface (see proof of Th. 2 of Art. 107, or the author's *Non-Euclidean Geometry*, p. 67). The meridian circles with respect to one axis are the parallel circles of the surface regarded as a surface of revolution around the other axis; and two great circles, one from each

---

* See the author's *Non-Euclidean Geometry*, p. 68. The surface of double revolution is somewhat like the anchor ring of the ordinary geometry. This surface is of importance in the theory of functions of two complex variables. See Poincaré, " Sur les residus des intégrales doubles," *Acta Mathematica*, vol. 9, 1886–1887, p. 359.

of the two sets of parallel great circles, form at either of their two points of intersection two pairs of vertical angles, the angles of one pair the double of one radius of the surface, and the angles of the other pair the double of the other radius.

The surface of double revolution is the intersection of the hypersphere and a conical hypersurface of double revolution having its vertex at the centre of the hypersphere (Art. 118). When the two radii of the surface are equal, each being equal to $\dfrac{\pi}{4}$, the circles of each set of parallel great circles on the surface are perpendicular to the circles of the other set. They correspond to two conjugate series of isocline planes at the centre (Art. 105).*

---

* We have defined hyperconical hypersurface as consisting of lines through a point with a hyperplane directing-surface (Art. 33), and this is sufficient for any hypercone with a hyperplane base; but unless we make provision for certain special cases, like that of the conical hypersurface of double revolution, we should get a more general definition by making the hypersurface a "surface" of the three-dimensional Point Geometry, or by defining it as consisting of the half-lines drawn from the centre of a hypersphere through the points of any hyperspherical surface, together with the centre itself.

CHAPTER VI

EUCLIDEAN GEOMETRY. FIGURES WITH PARALLEL ELEMENTS

125. The axiom of parallels first introduced at this point. The development of the preceding chapters has been made independent of the axiom of parallels. They may be called chapters in *Pangeometry*.* We shall now make a study of parallels and of figures with parallel elements, confining ourselves, however, to the geometry of Euclid. In other words, we shall assume an axiom of parallels which it will be convenient to put in the following form:

Axiom. *Through any point not a point of a given line passes one and only one line that lies in a plane with the given line and does not intersect it.*

I. PARALLELS

126. Parallel lines and parallel planes. Lines and planes are *parallel* to one another as in the ordinary geometry: two lines when they lie in one plane and do not intersect, a line and a plane or two planes when they lie in one hyperplane and do not intersect.

Theorem 1. *Two lines perpendicular to the same hyperplane are parallel* (see Art. 39, Th. 2).

Theorem 2. *A hyperplane perpendicular to one of two parallel lines is perpendicular to the other.*

Theorem 3. *If two planes through a point are parallel to a given line they intersect in a parallel line.*

* A title used by Lobachevsky in 1855.

THEOREM 4. *If a hyperplane intersects one of two parallel planes and does not contain it, the hyperplane intersects the other plane also, and the two lines of intersection are parallel.*

For the hyperplane intersects the hyperplane of the parallel planes in a plane which intersects the parallel planes in parallel lines.

THEOREM 5. *If a plane meets one of two parallel planes in a single point, it will meet the other in a single point.*

THEOREM 6. *Two planes absolutely perpendicular to a third are parallel* (see Art. 45, Th.).

THEOREM 7. *A plane absolutely perpendicular to one of two parallel planes is absolutely perpendicular to the other.*

THEOREM 8. *Two planes parallel to a third are parallel to each other.*

For a plane absolutely perpendicular to the third is absolutely perpendicular to the first two, and they are parallel by Th. 6.

THEOREM 9. *If three parallel planes all intersect a given line, they all lie in one hyperplane.*

THEOREM 10. *Two planes absolutely perpendicular to two parallel planes are parallel, and two planes parallel respectively to two absolutely perpendicular planes are absolutely perpendicular.*

THEOREM 11. *If two planes intersect in a line, planes through any point parallel to them intersect in a parallel line and form dihedral angles equal to the dihedral angles formed by the two given planes.*

PROOF. The parallel planes are parallel to the line of intersection of the two given planes, and therefore intersect in a parallel line, by Th. 3. Now a hyperplane perpendicular to these parallel lines (see Th. 2) cuts the planes in lines which contain the sides of the plane angles of the various dihedral angles formed about the two parallel lines. Corresponding plane angles, and therefore corresponding dihedral angles,* are equal.

COROLLARY. *If two planes are perpendicular, planes through any point parallel to them are also perpendicular.*

THEOREM 12. *If two planes have a point in common, parallel planes through any other point make the same angles* (Art. 69).

PROOF. Let α and β be the two given planes having a point O in common, and let α' and β' be planes through a second point O' parallel respectively to α and β. The planes through O' parallel to the common perpendicular planes of α and β are themselves common perpendicular planes of α' and β' (Th. 11, Cor.). On each of these common perpendicular planes the same angles are cut out as on the corresponding planes at O, since the intersection of any two planes intersecting in a line at O' is parallel to the intersection of the parallel planes at O, and two intersecting lines at O' lie in a hyperplane with the parallel lines at O, forming angles equal to the angles formed by the latter.

COROLLARY. *A plane isocline to one of two parallel planes is isocline to the other and makes the same angle with both.*

THEOREM 13. *Two lines not in the same plane have only one common perpendicular line* (see Art. 62).

Since the two lines lie in a hyperplane this is always a theorem of geometry of three dimensions, and is proved as in the text-books.

THEOREM 14. *If a line and plane do not lie in one hyperplane, they have only one common perpendicular line.*

See proof of Th. 1 of Art. 63.

---

* *Corresponding dihedral angles* have corresponding faces. Two *corresponding faces* are parallel half-planes lying in their hyperplane on the same side of the plane determined by the two parallel lines.

127. Half-parallel planes. Two planes which do not lie in one hyperplane and do not intersect are said to be *half-parallel* or *semi-parallel*.

THEOREM 1. *The linear elements of two half-parallel planes are all parallel to one another* (see Art. 27).

THEOREM 2. *The linear elements which lie in one of two half-parallel planes are parallel to the other plane, and these are the only lines which lie in one plane and are parallel to the other.*

THEOREM 3. *Through any point passes one and only one hyperplane perpendicular to each of two half-parallel planes* (see Art. 53).

THEOREM 4. *Two half-parallel planes have one and only one common perpendicular plane.*

PROOF. There is one such plane, by Th. 3 of Art. 63. Suppose, then, we have given a plane perpendicular to each of two half-parallel planes. It will intersect these planes in linear elements, the edges of various right dihedral angles, each with one face in the perpendicular plane and one in one of the half-parallel planes. A perpendicular hyperplane intersects the planes in lines which contain the sides of the plane angles of these dihedral angles, that is, it intersects the perpendicular plane in the common perpendicular line of the lines in which it intersects the two half-parallel planes. There is only one such common perpendicular line, and the given plane is the plane determined as in Art. 63 by this common perpendicular line and the linear elements which it intersects.

THEOREM 5. *The only common perpendicular lines of two half-parallel planes are those which lie in the common perpendicular plane.*

The *perpendicular distance* or simply the *distance*, between two half-parallel planes is the distance between

the points where they are cut by a common perpendicular line. It is the same for all of these lines, since
the common perpendicular plane cuts the given plane in
parallel lines (Th. 1).

THEOREM 6. *The perpendicular distance between two
half-parallel planes is less than the distance measured along
any line which intersects both and is not perpendicular to both.*

PROOF. The perpendicular distance between two elements lying one in each of the two given planes is the distance measured along some line lying in a perpendicular
hyperplane, the distance measured along some line between
the intersections of the given planes and this hyperplane.
It is less than the distance between the two elements along
any line which does not lie in a perpendicular hyperplane.
But the intersections of the given plane and the perpendicular hyperplane have for common perpendicular only
the line in this hyperplane which is perpendicular to the two
given planes. Therefore the perpendicular distance between the two given planes is the perpendicular distance
between these two intersections, and is less than the distance between the two planes measured on any line that is
not perpendicular to both.

THEOREM 7. *Two planes through a point parallel respectively to two half-parallel planes intersect in a line which is
parallel to their linear elements.*

For the line through the point parallel to the linear elements is parallel to the two given planes, and therefore
lies in both of the two planes which are parallel to them
through the point.

THEOREM 8. *If a plane distinct from each of two parallel
planes intersects one in a line and does not intersect the other
in a line, it will be half-parallel to the second.*

Q

PROOF. If the given plane were in a hyperplane with the second parallel plane, this hyperplane, containing the line in which the given plane intersects the first parallel plane, must be the hyperplane of the parallel planes; or if the given plane intersected the second parallel plane in a point, it would lie entirely in the hyperplane of the parallel planes. Thus, in either case, we should have a plane lying in the hyperplane of the two parallel planes, intersecting one in a line, and therefore the other in a line. As the given plane does not intersect the second parallel plane in a line, it cannot lie in a hyperplane with it nor intersect it at all. They must, therefore, be half-parallel.

THEOREM 9. *If a plane perpendicular to one of two absolutely perpendicular planes does not contain their point of intersection, it is half-parallel to the other.*

PROOF. Let α and α' be two absolutely perpendicular planes intersecting in a point O, and let β be a plane perpendicular to α but not containing O. Then β cannot lie in a hyperplane with α', for such a hyperplane would intersect α only in a line through O. Nor can β intersect α' even in a point, for then it would contain the line through such a point perpendicular to α, and so contain the point O. β is therefore half-parallel to α'.

128. Lines and planes parallel to a hyperplane. Parallel hyperplanes. A line and a hyperplane, a plane and a hyperplane, or two hyperplanes, are *parallel* when they do not intersect.

THEOREM 1. *If a line, not a line of a given hyperplane, is parallel to a line of the hyperplane, it is parallel to the hyperplane; and if a plane, not a plane of a given hyperplane, is parallel to a plane of the hyperplane, it is parallel to the hyperplane.*

THEOREM 2. *If a line is parallel to a hyperplane, it is parallel to the intersection of the hyperplane with any plane through it or with any hyperplane through it; and if a plane is parallel to a hyperplane, it is parallel to the intersection of the hyperplane with any hyperplane through it.*

THEOREM 3. *If a line is parallel to a hyperplane, a line through any point of the hyperplane parallel to the given line lies wholly in the hyperplane; and if a plane is parallel to a hyperplane, a plane or line through any point of the hyperplane parallel to the given plane lies wholly in the hyperplane.*

THEOREM 4. *Two hyperplanes perpendicular to the same line are parallel.*

THEOREM 5. *If one of two parallel hyperplanes is perpendicular to a line, the other is also perpendicular to the line.*

THEOREM 6. *Through a point, not a point of a given hyperplane, can be passed one and only one parallel hyperplane.*

In general, we can pass through a point a hyperplane parallel to a given hyperplane, to a given line and plane, or to three given lines; through a line, a hyperplane parallel to a given plane or to two given lines; through a plane, a hyperplane parallel to a given line. In some cases, however, the construction will give us a hyperplane containing some or all of the given figures, and in some cases more than one hyperplane can be obtained.

THEOREM 7. *All the lines and planes in one of two parallel hyperplanes are parallel to the other, and all the lines and planes through a point, parallel to a hyperplane, lie in a parallel hyperplane.*

THEOREM 8. *If a plane intersects two parallel hyperplanes, or if a hyperplane intersects two parallel planes, the lines of intersection are parallel; and if a hyperplane intersects two parallel hyperplanes, the planes of intersection are parallel.*

THEOREM 9. *If three non-coplanar lines through a point are respectively parallel to three other non-coplanar lines through a point, the two sets of lines determine the same hyperplane or parallel hyperplanes; or if an intersecting line and plane are respectively parallel to another intersecting line and plane, they determine the same hyperplane or parallel hyperplanes.*

THEOREM 10. *Two trihedral angles having their sides parallel each to each and extending in the same direction* **from their vertices are congruent.*

For the corresponding face angles are equal.†

THEOREM 11. *If a line is parallel to a hyperplane, all points of the line are at the same distance from the hyperplane; or if a plane is parallel to a hyperplane, all points of the plane are at the same distance from the hyperplane.*

THEOREM 12. *Two parallel hyperplanes are everywhere equidistant.*

The student may prove the following theorem :

Let *ABCDE* be a pentahedroid cut by a hyperplane *α* so that the edge *AB* lies on one side of *α* and the face *CDE* on the other side. Then if *α* is parallel to the line *AB* and to the plane *CDE*, the section will be a prism; if *α* is parallel to the line but not to the plane, the section will be a truncated prism; if *α* is parallel to the plane but not to the line, the section will be a frustum of a pyramid; or if *α* is not parallel to the line nor to the plane, the section will be a truncated pyramid (see Art. 31, Th. 3).

---

* Two parallel half-lines extend in the same direction when in their plane they lie on the same side of the line determined by their extremities.

† The proof given in our text-books that the two dihedral angles are equal does not require that the trihedral angles shall lie in one hyperplane.

129. Projection from a plane upon an isocline plane produces similar figures.

THEOREM 1. *Any plane polygon and its projection upon an isocline plane are similar.*

PROOF. Let O be the point of intersection of the two isocline planes. Let A and B be any two points of the original polygon, and A' and B' their projections. OAA' and OBB' are two right triangles with equal acute angles at O (Art. 69). They are similar, and the sides OA and OB are proportional to the sides OA' and OB'. The angle AOB is also equal to the angle $A'OB'$ (same reference). Therefore the triangles OAB and $OA'B'$ are themselves similar triangles. Now if the triangles formed by joining the vertices of a plane polygon to a point O in its plane are respectively similar to the triangles formed in the same way from another polygon, the two polygons are similar. Therefore, the given polygon and its projection are similar.*

COROLLARY. *The projection of a circle upon a plane isocline to its plane is a circle.*

THEOREM 2. *Conversely, if a plane polygon is similar to its projection upon another plane, the two planes are isocline or parallel.*

PROOF. The planes (Art. 46) projecting a figure upon one of two parallel planes project the same figure upon the other (Art. 126, Th. 7), and the two projections are equal. We can then suppose that the plane of the projection passes through a vertex of the given polygon, and complete our proof by reversing the steps of the preceding proof and using the corollary to the second theorem of Art. 69.

---

* It can be proved in any case of projection of a plane polygon upon another plane that the area of the projection is equal to the area of the original polygon multiplied by $\cos \phi \cos \phi'$, where ϕ and ϕ' are the angles between the planes of the two figures.

II. THE "HYPERPLANE AT INFINITY"

130. The sense in which expressions in regard to infinity are used. Just as we sometimes speak of *points*, *lines*, and a *plane at infinity*, so now we can speak of *planes at infinity* in different hyperplanes, and of a *hyperplane at infinity*. This we shall regard only as a matter of language. We introduce these expressions without introducing any new elements into our geometry or a number " infinity " into our number-system. We express certain facts of parallelism as if they were matters of intersection, from which, indeed, they are derived by limiting processes. Thus, we say that two lines intersect at infinity only as another way of saying that they are parallel. These forms of expression appear to simplify the conception of parallelism, and they enable us to generalize certain theorems of intersection. We must be careful to remember, however, that from this point of view we are not really introducing any points, lines, and planes, nor a region to be called infinity, and that we are not really making any change in our conception of parallelism.*

Points at infinity are sometimes called *ideal points*, lines at infinity *ideal lines*, and so on.

We shall give a brief account of the geometry at infinity, and point out the relation to infinity of certain figures studied in the following pages; but the rest of this book will be entirely independent of the present section, and all reference to infinity can be omitted without disturbing the continuity of our chain of theorems.†

---

* It would be perfectly legitimate to assume points, lines, etc., at infinity, and a number *infinity*, just as we assume other points, lines, and numbers. Such a course may seem no more unreasonable than the assumptions which distinguish the Elliptic and Hyperbolic geometries from that of Euclid, or the assumption of a fourth dimension. But the point of view here presented is better for this geometry. See note by Professor Bôcher, *Bulletin of the American Mathematical Society*, vol. 5, 1898–1899, p. 182.

† The elements at infinity are made the basis of many of the proofs in the Geometry of Veronese.

131. The elements at infinity; all comprised in a single hyperplane. A line has a single *point at infinity*, its intersection with any parallel line. A plane has a *line at infinity*, its intersection with any parallel plane. The line at infinity of any plane is made up of the points at infinity of its lines, and is determined by any two of them.

In space of three dimensions, and so in any hyperplane, we have a *plane at infinity*, the intersection of the hyperplane with any parallel hyperplane. The plane at infinity of any hyperplane consists of the points at infinity of its lines, and contains the lines at infinity of its planes. Or, we can say that a plane at infinity consists of the points that we get if we take any three non-collinear points at infinity, all points collinear with any two of them, and all points collinear with any two obtained by this process.

Lines which intersect a given hyperplane, but do not lie in it, have points at infinity which do not lie in the plane at infinity of this hyperplane. That is, in space of four dimensions the points at infinity are not all points of a single plane at infinity. Thus we have a *hyperplane at infinity*.

A *hyperplane at infinity* consists of the points that we get if we take four non-coplanar points at infinity, all points collinear with any two of them, and all points collinear with any two obtained by this process.

THEOREM. *All points at infinity in space of four dimensions lie in a single hyperplane.*

PROOF. Through a given point O can be drawn a line parallel to any given line. Therefore, all points at infinity are the points at infinity of the lines through O. Through any point of hyperspace passes a line that goes through O and has a point at infinity.

Now we can get all the lines through O by taking four

of these lines which are not in one hyperplane, all coplanar
with any two of them, and all coplanar with any two obtained by this process (see last paragraph of Art. 64). But
any four non-coplanar points at infinity are the points at
infinity of four lines through O not in a hyperplane, and if
a line through O is coplanar with two others, its point at
infinity is collinear with their points at infinity. Therefore we can get all the points at infinity by taking four non-
coplanar points at infinity, all points collinear with any two
of them, and all points collinear with any two obtained by
this process. Hence all the points at infinity lie in a single
hyperplane.

132. Distance and angle at infinity. We can define
distance between two points at infinity as proportional to
the angle which they subtend at any point O which is not
a point at infinity. There are two supplementary angles
at O, and so two distances between two points at infinity.
We shall usually mean the smaller of these two distances
when they are not equal. Taking the entire length of a
line at infinity as equal to π, we shall give to all distances
at infinity the same measures as to the corresponding angles
at O.

Two lines in a plane at infinity are the lines at infinity
of two non-parallel planes in a hyperplane, and always intersect, intersecting in a single point. They divide the
rest of their plane into two separate regions, each a lune-
shaped region with the extremities coinciding and the two
angles actually vertical angles. A *half-line at infinity* is
the same as an entire line, but it will be more convenient
here to regard it as a " restricted " portion of a line, lying
in one direction from one of its points, the *extremity* of
the half-line. An *angle* will then be formed by two such
half-lines with a common extremity lying along different

lines. The lines through the points of such an angle and a point O not at infinity will determine a definite pair of vertical dihedral angles, and the measure of the angle at infinity will be the same as the measure of either of these dihedral angles, the sum of the angles around a point in a plane being always equal to 2π.

Two planes at infinity intersect in a line, and divide the rest of the hyperplane at infinity into two regions each somewhat like a double convex lens.* Along the edge of such a region we have what may be called a *dihedral angle at infinity*. We can think of a *half-plane at infinity* as a "restricted" portion of a plane lying on one side of a line, the *edge* of the half-plane, and think of a dihedral angle at infinity as formed by two such half-planes with a common edge but not lying in the same plane (compare Art. 120). To the dihedral angle will then correspond a hyperplane angle whose measure can be taken as the measure of the former.

Since two lines in a plane at infinity intersect in a single point, the geometry at infinity is the Single Elliptic Geometry (see foot-note, p. 215). This geometry is, indeed, the same as the Point Geometry of the half-lines from a point O, except that two opposite half-lines correspond to a single point at infinity. Thus all the theorems of Point Geometry can be stated as theorems of the geometry at infinity, just as they can be stated as theorems of the geometry of the hypersphere (Art. 123).†

133. Some generalizations now made possible. Intersection and perpendicularity. We will now show how

---

* The *volume* of one of these regions is to the entire *volume of the hyperplane at infinity* as the corresponding dihedral angle is to two right dihedral angles (not to four right dihedral angles, because the geometry at infinity is the Single Elliptic Geometry).

† We could have assumed that a line has two points at infinity, a separate point for each of two opposite half-lines. The geometry at infinity would then be the Double Elliptic Geometry. See Veronese, *Grundzüge*, Pt. I, Bk. I.

the forms of expression introduced in this section enable us to generalize certain theorems of geometry :

Two points determine a line, three non-collinear points determine a plane, and four non-coplanar points determine a hyperplane, even when some or all of the points are at infinity.

Two lines in a plane always intersect, and any two lines which intersect lie in a plane.   A line and a plane in a hyperplane intersect, and any line and plane which intersect lie in a hyperplane.   Thus a line and plane which do not lie in a hyperplane do not intersect even at infinity.

Two planes which lie in a hyperplane intersect in a line. Two planes which do not lie in a hyperplane intersect in a point; when the point is at infinity the planes are half-parallel.

A line and a hyperplane always intersect, intersecting in a point; a plane and a hyperplane always intersect, intersecting in a line; and two hyperplanes always intersect, intersecting in a plane.

A *dihedral angle at infinity* is the intersection of a hyperplane angle by the hyperplane at infinity.   A *polyhedral angle at infinity* is the intersection of a plano-polyhedral angle by the hyperplane at infinity.   The parts of the polyhedral angle have the same relation to the plano polyhedral angle as do those of any right section (Art. 75).

Two perpendicular lines, not lines at infinity, are lines whose points at infinity are at a quadrant's distance from each other.   A line and plane are perpendicular when their point and line at infinity are pole and polar in the plane at infinity of their hyperplane.   Two planes are absolutely perpendicular when their lines at infinity are polar lines.

When a line at infinity intersects both of two polar lines it is perpendicular to both.   Any two lines at infinity have two common perpendicular lines, and the *distances between two lines* are measured on these common perpendicular lines.

III. HYPERPRISMS

134. Prismoidal hypersurfaces. Their interiors. Sections. Axes. A *prismoidal hypersurface* consists of a system of parallel lines passing through the points of a given polyhedron but not lying in the hyperplane of the polyhedron. The polyhedron is called the *directing-polyhedron*, the parallel lines are the *elements*, and the elements which pass through the vertices are *lateral edges*. We shall assume that the directing-polyhedron is a simple convex polyhedron.

The elements which pass through the points of a face of the directing-polyhedron constitute the interior of a prismatic surface and a *cell* of the hypersurface. The elements which pass through the points of an edge of the directing-polyhedron constitute what may be called a *strip*, which is that portion of a plane that lies between two parallel lines. This strip is a *face* of the hypersurface, the common face of two adjacent prismatic surfaces.

The *interior of a prismoidal hypersurface* consists of the lines which pass through the points of the interior of the directing-polyhedron and are parallel to the elements. The hypersurface being convex, the interior of any segment whose points are points of the hypersurface will lie entirely in the interior of the hypersurface unless it lies entirely in the hypersurface itself, and a half-line drawn from a point of the interior and not parallel to the elements will intersect the hypersurface in one and only one point.

THEOREM I. *A hyperplane passing through a point of the interior of a prismoidal hypersurface and parallel to the elements intersects the hypersurface in a prismatic surface.*

For the hyperplane intersects the directing-polyhedron in a convex polygon, and intersects the hypersurface in the elements which pass through the points of this polygon.

THEOREM 2. *A hyperplane which is not parallel to the elements of a prismoidal hypersurface intersects the hypersurface in a polyhedron, and any such polyhedron can be taken as directing-polyhedron.*

Each element of the hypersurface, and, indeed, each line of hyperspace which is parallel to the elements, meets the hyperplane in a point. We have a correspondence between the points of the hyperplane and the lines which are parallel to the elements of the hypersurface, as also between the points of the intersection and the points of the given directing-polyhedron. Each cell of the hypersurface intersects the given hyperplane in a face, each face of the hypersurface in an edge, and each lateral edge in a vertex, of the given intersection.

A *right section* is a directing-polyhedron whose hyperplane is perpendicular to the elements.

THEOREM 3. *Directing-polyhedrons lying in parallel hyperplanes are congruent, and any two homologous points of two such polyhedrons lie in a line parallel to the elements.*

THEOREM 4. *If a prismoidal hypersurface has a parallelopiped for directing-polyhedron, it will have three pairs of equal opposite lateral cells lying in parallel hyperplanes, and all of its directing-polyhedrons will be parallelopipeds.*

PROOF. Any two opposite faces of the given parallelopiped are equal parallelograms lying in parallel planes. They are, then, directing-polygons of equal prismatic surfaces lying in parallel hyperplanes (Art. 128, Th. 9). Therefore, any directing-polyhedron will have three pairs of parallel opposite faces (Art. 128, Th. 8), and will be a parallelopiped.

THEOREM 5. *If any directing-polyhedron of a prismoidal hypersurface has a centre of symmetry, the line through this point parallel to the elements is an axis of symmetry, meeting the hyperplane of every directing-polyhedron in a point which is a centre of symmetry of this polyhedron. Each point of the line is, in fact, a centre of symmetry for the entire hypersurface, and the line as a whole is a line of symmetry.*

For this line lies mid-way between the two lines in which any plane containing it intersects the hypersurface, and any line intersecting it determines with it such a plane.

135. Hyperprisms. Interior of a hyperprism.   A *hyperprism* consists of that portion of a prismoidal hypersurface which lies between two parallel directing-polyhedrons, together with the directing-polyhedrons themselves and their interiors.

· The interiors of the directing-polyhedrons are the *bases*. In each hyperplane of the hypersurface we have a prism whose interior is one of the *lateral cells* of the hyperprism. The lateral faces and edges of these prisms are the *lateral faces* and *lateral edges* of the hyperprism. The lateral edges are all equal; the bases are congruent (Art. 134, Th. 3).

The *interior of a hyperprism* consists of that portion of the interior of the prismoidal hypersurface which lies between the bases. The hypersurface being convex, the interior of any segment whose points are points of the hyperprism will lie entirely in the interior of the hyperprism unless it lies entirely in the hyperprism itself, and a half-line drawn from a point of the interior will intersect the hyperprism in one and only one point.

A hyperprism is a *right hyperprism* when the lateral edges are perpendicular to the hyperplanes of the bases. When also the bases are the interiors of regular polyhedrons the hyperprism is *regular*.

We can cut apart a hyperprism, cutting it along its faces, sufficiently to spread it out into a single hyperplane. We can do this, for
example, so that the lateral prisms shall remain attached to one base,
while the other base rests upon one of them. The figure below represents a tetrahedroidal hyperprism cut apart and spread out in this
way. The four prisms rest upon the four faces of a tetrahedron, and
a second tetrahedron equal to the first (symmetrical in this hyperplane) rests on the other end of one of these prisms. Now in hyperspace we can turn these prisms around the faces of the tetrahedron
upon which they rest away from the hyperplane of this tetrahedron,

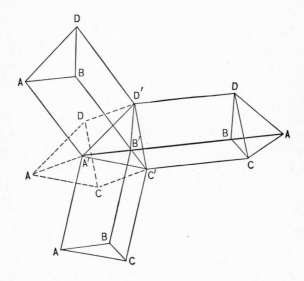

and the other tetrahedron around the face by which it is attached to
one of the prisms: we can do this without separating any of the
figures or distorting them in any way, until we bring them all together,
each prism with a lateral face resting upon a lateral face of each of
the others, and each of the four faces of the second tetrahedron resting upon one of the prisms. The figure will then enclose completely
a portion of hyperspace (see note in Art. 32).

The student may investigate the conditions necessary in order
that three given prisms and two tetrahedrons may be the lateral
prisms and tetrahedrons of a tetrahedroidal hyperprism.

136. **Special forms of hyperprisms.   Hyperparallelo-pipeds. The hypercube**. A hyperprism whose bases are the interiors of prisms can be regarded in two ways as a hyperprism of this kind; for the lateral prisms corresponding to the ends of the bases are parallel (Art. 128, Th. 9) and congruent, and the remaining lateral prisms are parallel-opipeds, which can be regarded as having their bases on this second pair of prisms and their lateral edges those edges which belong also to the first pair of prisms.   This figure is a particular case of a double prism, and will be studied in the next section (see Art. 144).

A *hyperparallelopiped* is a hyperprism whose bases are the interiors of parallelopipeds.   In a hyperparallelopiped there are four pairs of opposite equal parallel parallelopipeds whose interiors are the cells, and the interiors of any pair can be taken as bases.   There are four sets of eight parallel edges, each set joining the vertices of two opposite cells, becoming the lateral edges when these cells are taken as bases.   The section of a hyperparallelopiped made by a hyperplane intersecting all eight of the edges of a set will be a parallelopiped (Art. 134, Th. 4).

THEOREM 1.   *The diagonals of a hyperparallelopiped bisect one another, all passing through a point which is a centre of symmetry for the hyperparallelopiped.*

A right hyperparallelopiped whose base is a rectangular parallelopiped is a *rectangular hyperparallelopiped*.   The edges which meet at any vertex lie in the lines of a rectangular system (Art. 48).   The lengths of these four edges are the *dimensions* of the hyperparallelopiped.

THEOREM 2.   *The square of the length of a diagonal of a rectangular hyperparallelopiped is equal to the sum of the squares of the four dimensions.*

A *hypercube* is a rectangular hyperparallelopiped whose base is the interior of a cube and whose altitude is equal to the edge of the cube; that is, its four dimensions are all equal. The hypercube is a *regular polyhedron* (see Art. 166): it has eight equal cubical cells, twenty-four equal faces each a common face of two cubes, thirty-two equal edges, and sixteen vertices. There are four axes, lying in lines which also form a rectangular system.

THEOREM 3. *The diagonal of a hypercube is twice as long as the edge.*

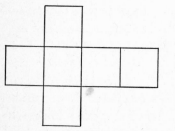

Six squares which can be folded so as to form a cube.

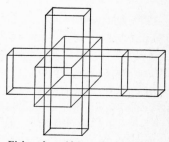

Eight cubes which can be folded so as to form a hypercube.

If we place six equal cubes upon the six faces of a cube, and one more outside of one of these, just as we put together four prisms and two tetrahedrons in the note in Art. 135, we can turn these cubes around the faces upon which they rest and bring them together so as to form a hypercube. This is analogous to the process of forming a cube by folding six squares together.

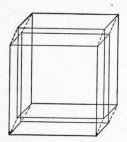

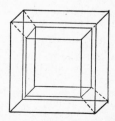

There are two ways of projecting a hypercube that will both assist us in forming some conception of it.   One is by an oblique projection, and the other is by projection from a point at a little distance from the hypercube in the line of one of its axes.   We can think of the first as representing the appearance of the hypercube when we stand a little to one side, and the second as we look down into it.   In each case we can pick out the projections of the eight cubes whose interiors form the cells of the hypercube.

The hypercube has become one of the most familiar of the figures of hyperspace.   The reader will find it mentioned in nearly all popular descriptions of the fourth dimension.   See, for example, *Fourth Dimension Simply Explained*, pp. 46, 72, 88, 92, and 113.

137. Relation of the prismoidal hypersurface to infinity. Taking the point of view explained in Art. 130, we can say that a prismoidal hypersurface is a polyhedroidal angle whose vertex is at infinity.

The eight hyperplanes of a hyperparallelopiped intersect the hyperplane at infinity in four planes which contain the faces of a tetrahedron.   Each vertex of this tetrahedron is the vertex of one of the prismoidal hypersurfaces connected with the hyperparallelopiped, and the opposite face of the tetrahedron is the plane of intersection of the hyperplanes of the corresponding pair of bases * (see Art. 145).

IV. DOUBLE PRISMS

138. Plano-prismatic hypersurfaces.   Sections.   We shall use the word *layer* to denote that portion of a hyperplane which lies between two parallel planes, and call the parallel planes the *faces of the layer*.

A *plano-prismatic hypersurface* consists of a finite number of parallel planes taken in a definite cyclical order, and the layers which lie between consecutive planes of this order.

* There are, indeed, four tetrahedrons at infinity, each of which has its vertices at these four points and its faces in these four planes, but we do not need to consider them here.

R

The parallel planes are *faces* and the layers are *cells* of the hypersurface. If α, β, γ, . . . are the faces in order, the cells can be described as the layers $\alpha\beta$, $\beta\gamma$, . . . , and the hypersurface as the plano-prismatic hypersurface $\alpha\beta\gamma$ . . . . The faces and all parallel planes within the layers are the *elements* of the hypersurface, and are in cyclical order (Art. 6).

The hypersurface is a *simple plano-prismatic hypersurface* when no plane occurs twice as an element. It is *convex* when, also, the hyperplane of each cell contains no element except those of this cell and the two which are its faces. We shall consider only hypersurfaces which are simple and convex.

THEOREM 1. *A hyperplane containing an element of a plano-prismatic hypersurface or any parallel plane will intersect the hypersurface in elements if at all* (Art. 128, Th. 1).

THEOREM 2. *A hyperplane intersecting but not containing an element of a plano-prismatic hypersurface will intersect the hypersurface in a prismatic surface.*

For the hyperplane intersects all the elements in parallel lines (Art. 126, Th. 4), and so the cells in strips (see Art. 134), which are the faces of a prismatic surface.

Thus the hypersurface can be regarded as a prismoidal hypersurface, with a directing prismatic surface instead of a directing-polyhedron.

THEOREM 3. *Two parallel prismatic sections of a plano-prismatic hypersurface are congruent.*

PROOF. The strips in which the hyperplanes of the two parallel sections intersect any one of the cells of the hypersurface lie in parallel planes (Art. 128, Th. 8) and between parallel planes (the faces of the cell), and are therefore of the same *width*. They lie also on the same side of either pair of corresponding edges, lying as they do in the same layer. Therefore corresponding dihedral angles of the two prismatic sections are equal (Art. 126, Th. 11; see also foot-note, p. 223), and the sections themselves are congruent.

139. Directing-polygons of a plano-prismatic hypersurface. Interior of the hypersurface.

THEOREM 1. *A plane which contains a line parallel to the elements of a plano-prismatic hypersurface, but is not itself parallel to them, will intersect in a line every element which it intersects at all.*

THEOREM 2. *A plane which does not contain a line parallel to the elements of a plano-prismatic hypersurface will intersect every element in a point, and will intersect the hypersurface, the latter being convex, in a convex polygon.*

PROOF. The plane will intersect each element in a point, by Th. 5 of Art. 126. In particular, it will intersect the faces in points which are the vertices of a polygon, and the layers in the sides of this polygon. The polygon is a simple convex polygon, since no two elements can intersect the same plane in the same point.

The polygon in which a plane containing no line parallel to the elements intersects the hypersurface can be called a *directing-polygon*, and the hypersurface can be described as consisting of a system of parallel planes passing through the points of a given polygon and intersecting the plane of the polygon only in these points. We can think of the polygon as *going around* the hypersurface.

THEOREM 3. *Through any line which is not parallel to the elements of a plano-prismatic hypersurface can be passed planes intersecting the hypersurface in directing-polygons.*

PROOF. Through a point A of the line pass a plane

parallel to the elements. The line intersects the plane only in this point, and the line and plane determine a hyperplane. Any plane through the line and a point which is not a point of the hyperplane will intersect the hyperplane only in the given line, and the plane which we have drawn parallel to the elements only in the point A : it will be the plane of a directing-polygon.

THEOREM 4. *Two parallel directing-polygons of a plano-prismatic hypersurface are congruent, and any two homologous points lie in one of the elements.*

In fact, their interiors are the bases of a prism whose lateral surface is cut out from the prismatic surface in which their hyperplane intersects the hypersurface.

THEOREM 5. *If a plano-prismatic hypersurface has a parallelogram for directing-polygon, it will have two pairs of equal opposite cells (layers of the same width) lying in parallel hyperplanes, and all of its directing-polygons will be parallelograms* (see Art. 128, Ths. 8 and 9).

We can study the properties of these hypersurfaces as a part of the two-dimensional geometry whose elements are a set of parallel planes. The theorems in chap. I which relate to triangles and convex polygons can all be interpreted as theorems concerning these hypersurfaces (compare this with Arts. 78 and 112). But we can also prove these theorems by means of a directing-polygon, making the elements and all parallel planes correspond to the points where they intersect the plane of the polygon.

Thus we have the *interior of the hypersurface* as consisting of those planes which correspond to the interior of the directing-polygon. The interior of any segment whose points are points of the hypersurface will lie entirely in the interior of the hypersurface unless it lies in the hypersurface itself, and a half-line drawn from a point of the

interior and not parallel to the elements will intersect the
hypersurface in one and only one point. Also, that portion
of a plane between two parallel lines of the hypersurface
(a strip, Art. 134), or a layer between any two elements,
lies entirely in the interior unless it lies entirely in the
hypersurface.

THEOREM 6. *When the layer between two elements of a
plano-prismatic hypersurface lies entirely in the interior of
the hypersurface, it separates the rest of the interior into two
portions lying on opposite sides of the hyperplane, and with
its faces and each of the two parts into which they separate
the rest of the hypersurface it forms a convex plano-prismatic
hypersurface* (see Art. 15, Ths. 2 and 3).

COROLLARY. *By taking the diagonal layers which have
in common one of the lateral faces of the hypersurface we can
form a set of triangular plano-prismatic hypersurfaces, their
interiors, together with the diagonal layers, making up the
interior of the given hypersurface.*

140. Right directing-polygons. Axis-planes. A directing-polygon whose plane is absolutely perpendicular to the
planes of the elements of a plano-prismatic hypersurface
is called a *right directing-polygon.**

THEOREM 1. *The projection of any directing-polygon
upon the plane of a right directing-polygon is the right directing-polygon itself* (see Art. 46).

THEOREM 2. *A plane isocline to the plane of a right directing-polygon, but not parallel to the elements, intersects the
hypersurface in a polygon similar to the right directing-polygon; and, conversely, any directing-polygon similar to a*

---

* We will not call it a right section, since it does not completely separate any
two parts of the hypersurface, nor even of a restricted portion of the hypersurface
(see foot-note, p. 65).

right directing-polygon lies in a plane which is isocline to the plane of the latter (see Art. 129, Ths. 1 and 2). *The right directing-polygon is the minimum of all these similar polygons.*

THEOREM 3. *If any directing-polygon of a plano-prismatic hypersurface has a centre of symmetry, the plane through this point parallel to the elements is an axis-plane of symmetry, meeting the plane of every directing-polygon in a point which is a centre of symmetry of this polygon. Each point of the plane is, in fact, a centre of symmetry for the entire hypersurface, every line of the plane is a line of symmetry, and the plane as a whole is a plane of symmetry.*

For the plane lies mid-way between the two planes in which any hyperplane containing it intersects the hypersurface, and any line intersecting it but not lying in it determines with it such a hyperplane.

141. Intersection of two plano-prismatic hypersurfaces. The two sets of prisms. When the elements of a plano-prismatic hypersurface intersect the elements of a second plano-prismatic hypersurface only in points, the intersection of the two hypersurfaces consists of the lateral surfaces of a set of prisms joined together in succession by their bases, together with the polygons whose interiors are these bases. In another way, also, the same intersection consists of the lateral surfaces of a set of prisms joined together by their bases, together with the polygons whose interiors are these bases.

In fact, the faces of the first hypersurface are parallel planes intersecting the second hypersurface in a set of equal parallel directing-polygons of the latter, and the cells of the first are layers, each layer intersecting the second in the lateral surface of a prism whose bases are interiors of two of these directing-polygons (see Art. 139, Th. 4).

In the same way the faces of the second hypersurface

are parallel planes intersecting the first hypersurface in a set of parallel directing-polygons, and each cell of the second intersects the first in the lateral surface of a prism whose bases are the interiors of two of these directing-polygons. Thus the entire intersection consists in two ways of the lateral surfaces of a set of prisms joined in succession by their bases, together with the polygons whose interiors are these bases.

The lateral faces of any prism of the first set are the interiors of parallelograms, and are the intersections of one particular cell of the first hypersurface with the different cells of the second. A set of corresponding faces of these prisms, one from each prism, are, then, the intersections of the different cells of the first hypersurface with one particular cell of the second. Thus the faces of any particular prism of either set form a set of corresponding faces of the different prisms of the other set, and every lateral face of a prism of one set is a lateral face of some prism of the other set. The lateral edges of the prisms of one set are the sides of the bases of the prisms of the other set, and the prisms of one set can be said to be joined crosswise by their lateral faces to the prisms of the other set. The interiors and the bases of the prisms of the first set lie in the first hypersurface and in the interior of the second, and the interiors and bases of the prisms of the second set lie in the second hypersurface and in the interior of the first. We can think of the first set of prisms as going around the first hypersurface, while any base or interior of a cross section of any of these prisms is a piece cut out of an element of the first hypersurface. In the same way the second set of prisms goes around the second hypersurface.

A *double prism* consists of the intersection of two plano-prismatic hypersurfaces whose elements intersect only in points, together with all that portion of each hypersurface which lies in the interior of the other; that is, it consists of all of the prisms of both sets described above and their interiors.

When the elements of one hypersurface are absolutely perpendicular to the elements of the other the double prism is a *right double prism*. When also the prisms of the two sets are regular the double prism is *regular*.

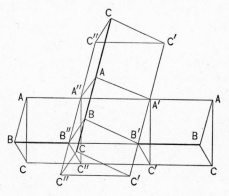

In a right double prism the prisms of each set can be put together in one hyperplane so as to form a single right prism with lateral edge equal to the perimeter of the base of the prisms of the other set. In forming the double prism these two single prisms are folded towards each other in such a way that the upper base of each occupies the same position as its lower base and the lateral surface of one coincides as a whole with the lateral surface of the other. Thus one single prism alone, folded in this way until the ends come together, gives us the other prism and the entire figure.

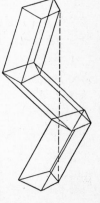

When we have an oblique double prism and spread out the prisms of one set in a single hyperplane, we have, not a prism, but a set of prisms with equal bases resting upon one another somewhat like a broken column. The upper base of the highest prism, however, and the lower base of the lowest prism will lie in parallel planes and will be so placed that each is the projection of the other.

142. Interior of a double prism. The directing-polygons.
The *interior of a double prism* consists of the points which are common to the interiors of its two hypersurfaces. A plane lying in the interior of one of the hypersurfaces parallel to its elements intersects the other in a directing-polygon whose interior belongs to the interiors of both, and so to the interior of the double prism. The vertices of this polygon are a set of corresponding points of the bases, and the sides lie in the interiors, of the prisms of the set which goes around the former hypersurface.

THEOREM 1. *Any plane through a point of the interior of a convex double prism intersects the double prism in a convex polygon.*

PROOF. The plane will intersect each hypersurface in a convex polygon, in two parallel lines, or not at all (Art. 139, Ths. 1 and 2). When the plane intersects each hypersurface in a pair of parallel lines the intersection with the double prism will be a parallelogram. In all other cases there will be at least one convex polygon, and by applying one or more times the second theorem of Art. 15 we can prove in all cases that the intersection of the double prism will be a convex polygon.

COROLLARY. *The interior of any segment whose points are points of a double prism will lie entirely in the interior of the double prism unless it lies entirely in the double prism, and a half-line drawn from a point of the interior will intersect the double prism in one and only one point.*

In a double prism the directing-polygons of each hypersurface whose planes are elements of the other are called *the directing-polygons of the double prism* (just as we say the vertex of a pyramid or hyperpyramid). Any two polygons intersecting in a single point and lying in planes which have only this point in common can be taken each as a directing-polygon with the plane of the other as element of a plano-prismatic hypersurface, and so the two together as the directing-polygons of a double prism.

We can say that the surface of intersection of the two hypersurfaces, the common lateral surfaces of the two sets of prisms as described in the preceding article, is generated by moving one of these polygons kept parallel to itself around the other. Each point of the polygon moves along the prisms of one set and around one of the prisms of the other set. The interior of the polygon generates the interiors of the prisms along which it moves. The interiors of the other prisms will be generated by the interior of the other polygon moving in the same way around the first. The surface of intersection is covered with the polygons of each set, the two sets forming on it a net.

143. Cutting a double prism so as to form two double prisms. Doubly triangular prisms.

THEOREM. *When a double prism is cut by a hyperplane passing through points of the interior and containing elements of one hypersurface, the intersection is a prism, and the rest of it is separated into two portions, which, each combined with the prism and its interior, form two double prisms whose interiors, with that of the prism, make up the whole interior.*

PROOF. The layer between the two elements of the hypersurface lies entirely in the interior of this hypersurface, and forms with it two hypersurfaces of the same kind (Art. 139, Th. 6). This layer and its faces intersect the other hypersurface in the lateral surface of a prism and two directing-polygons whose interiors are the bases of the prism. The polygons belong to both hypersurfaces, their interiors, the bases, belong to the first hypersurface and to the interior of the second, and the lateral surface belongs to the second hypersurface and to the interior of the first. The entire prism, therefore, belongs to the double prism, and is its intersection with the hyperplane of the layer, separating the rest of it into two portions which lie on opposite sides of this hyperplane. The prism and its interior form with these two portions two double prisms, whose hypersurfaces are the two hypersurfaces formed from the first given hypersurface each taken with the second given hypersurface. The interior of the prism lies entirely in the interior of the given double prism, and separates the rest of this interior into two portions which are the interiors of the two new double prisms.

The prisms of one set, the set which goes around the first hypersurface, are separated, some of them going to one of the two new double prisms and the rest to the other. One or two of them may be divided, cut into two shorter prisms, one of these shorter prisms going to each of the new double prisms. The prisms of the other set are all cut lengthwise, one part of each prism going to one of the new double prisms and the other part to the other.

COROLLARY. *By cutting a double prism diagonally we can form double prisms in which the prisms of one set are triangular, so that those of the other set are three in number; and then, cutting these in another way diagonally, we can form double prisms in which the prisms of both sets are triangular, the interiors of all of these double prisms together with the interiors of the prisms of intersection making up the whole interior.*

A double prism in which the prisms of both sets are triangular is a *doubly triangular double prism,* or simply a *doubly triangular prism.* Such a double prism is formed when any three hyperplanes intersecting by twos in three parallel planes are cut by three other hyperplanes which intersect by twos in three parallel planes, any plane of one set intersecting any plane of the other set only in a single point.

In Art. 163 it will be shown that a doubly triangular prism can be cut by hyperplanes so as to form six penta-hedroids.

144. Hyperprisms with prism bases as double prisms. Hyperparallelopipeds. Centre of symmetry. A hyper-prism whose bases are the interiors of prisms is a double prism, the two prisms of the bases and the two lateral prisms corresponding to their ends forming one of the two sets of prisms of the double prism, while the prisms of the other set are parallelopipeds (see Art. 136).

Conversely, a double prism in which the prisms of one set are parallelopipeds (and therefore the prisms of the other set are four in number, two pairs of opposites) can be regarded in two ways as a hyperprism, the bases in each case being the interiors of a pair of opposite prisms of the second set.

THEOREM 1. *When the prisms of both sets in a double prism are parallelopipeds, or, what is the same thing, when both sets of directing-polygons are parallelograms, the figure is a hyperparallelopiped. Indeed, the hyperparallelopiped can be regarded in three ways as a double prism, the parallel-opipeds of two pairs of opposite cells forming one of the sets of prisms and the other four parallelopipeds the other set.*

THEOREM 2. *When the two hypersurfaces of a double prism have axis-planes of symmetry, the point of intersection of these planes is a centre of symmetry of the double prism; and any hyperplane through this point intersects the double prism in a polyhedron which divides the rest of the double prism into two congruent parts* (Art. 85, Th. 2).

145. Relation of double prisms to infinity. Taking the point of view of Art. 130, we can say that a plano-prismatic hypersurface is a plano-polyhedral angle with vertex-edge at infinity.   Two such hypersurfaces give us a double prism when the vertex-edge of one does not intersect the vertex-edge of the other, both being lines at infinity.

When the prisms of one set in a double prism are parallelopipeds, so that the double prism can also be regarded in two ways as a hyperprism, there will be two points at infinity which are the vertices of two prismoidal hypersurfaces, and the line containing these two points will be the vertex-edge of a plano-prismatic hypersurface whose directing-polygons are parallelograms.

As stated in Art. 137, the eight hyperplanes of a hyperparallelopiped intersect the hyperplane at infinity in the planes of the faces of a tetrahedron whose vertices are the vertices of the four prismoidal hypersurfaces in which the hyperparallelopiped lies.   Each of the six edges of the tetrahedron lies in the vertex-edge of a plano-prismatic hypersurface, the three pairs of opposite edges corresponding to the three ways in which the hyperparallelopiped can be taken as a double prism.

The tetrahedron at infinity corresponding to a rectangular hyperparallelopiped is a rectangular tetrahedron.   Each vertex is the pole of the opposite face, opposite edges are polar lines, and at each vertex there is a trirectangular trihedral angle.

V. HYPERCYLINDERS

146. Hypercylindrical hypersurfaces.   Their interiors. Sections.   Axes.   A *hypercylindrical hypersurface* consists of a system of parallel lines passing through the points of a hyperplane surface, but not lying in the hyperplane of the surface.   The surface is called the *directing-surface*, and the parallel lines are the *elements*.

We shall consider only those cases in which the directing-surface is a surface of elementary geometry, a plane or a sphere, or a conical or cylindrical surface with directing-circle, or a part or combination of parts of such surfaces. A prismoidal hypersurface can also be regarded as a particular case of a hypercylindrical hypersurface.

Many of the properties of the hypersurface correspond to the properties of the directing-surface. In particular, the hypersurface has an interior when the directing-surface has an interior, the *interior of the hypersurface* consisting of the lines which pass through the points of the interior of the directing-surface and are parallel to the elements.

Sections of the hypersurface are like those of the prismoidal hypersurface: a hyperplane passing through a point of the interior and parallel to the elements intersects the hypersurface in a cylindrical surface, and a hyperplane which is not parallel to the elements intersects the hypersurface in a surface, or at least in a system of points, which can serve as directing-surface. A *right section* is a directing-surface whose hyperplane is perpendicular to the elements.

THEOREM. *Sections of a hypercylindrical hypersurface made by parallel hyperplanes not parallel to the elements are congruent.*

PROOF. The distance between any two points of one section is equal to the corresponding distance in the other section. Then any tetrahedron whose vertices are points of one section will be congruent to the corresponding tetrahedron in the other section (see Art. 72, Th. 1), and if we make these tetrahedrons coincide, every point of one section (forming a tetrahedron with three of these points) will coincide with the corresponding point of the other section (see proof of Th. 1 of Art. 98).

147. Hypercylinders. Special forms. Relation of the hypercylindrical hypersurface to infinity. A *hypercylinder* consists of that portion of a closed hypercylindrical hypersurface which lies between two parallel directing-surfaces, together with the directing-surfaces themselves and their interiors.

The interiors of the directing-surfaces are the *bases*, and that portion of the hypercylindrical hypersurface which lies between the directing-surfaces is the *lateral hypersurface* of the hypercylinder. The *interior of the hypercylinder* consists of that portion of the interior of the hypercylindrical hypersurface which lies between the bases.

A hypercylinder is a *right hypercylinder* when the elements are perpendicular to the hyperplanes of the bases.

A *spherical hypercylinder* is one whose bases are the interiors of spheres. The *axis of a spherical hypercylinder* is the interior of the segment whose points are the centres of the bases.

THEOREM 1. *When a spherical hypercylinder is cut by a hyperplane which passes through a point of the interior and is parallel to the elements, the intersection is a circular cylinder.*

THEOREM 2. *When a rectangle takes all positions possible with one side fixed, the vertices and the points of the other three sides make up a right spherical hypercylinder. The fixed side is the axis, the opposite side is an element, and the other two sides are radii of the bases.*

THEOREM 3. *If we pass a plane through the axis of a cylinder of revolution and rotate around this plane that portion of the cylinder which lies on one side of it, we shall form all of a right spherical hypercylinder except that portion which is the intersection of the cylinder and plane.*

A hypercylinder whose bases are the interiors of cylinders can be regarded in two ways as a hypercylinder of this kind; for there are two lateral cylinders corresponding to the ends of the bases, and these can be taken as the bases and the given bases as parts of the lateral hypersurface.

In fact, the two lateral cylinders are congruent and lie in parallel hyperplanes, with the elements of one parallel to the elements of the other and the planes of the bases of one parallel to the corresponding planes of the other. Moreover, those elements of the hypercylinder whose lines intersect any element of one of its bases lie in the interior of a parallelogram which bears the same relation to both pairs of cylinders. This figure is a particular case of a prism cylinder, and will be studied in the next section (see Art. 150).

Taking the point of view of Art. 130, we can say that a hypercylindrical hypersurface is a hyperconical hypersurface with vertex at infinity (see Art. 153).

VI. PRISM CYLINDERS AND DOUBLE CYLINDERS

148. Plano-cylindrical hypersurfaces. Sections. Right directing-curves. A *plano-cylindrical hypersurface* consists of a system of parallel planes passing through the points of a plane curve and intersecting the plane of the curve only in these points.* The curve is the *directing-curve*, and the planes are the *elements*. A plano-prismatic hypersurface can be regarded as a particular case of a plano-cylindrical hypersurface. Except for this, we shall consider only the case in which there is a directing-circle.

As the plano-cylindrical hypersurface is analogous to the plano-prismatic hypersurface, many of the theorems correspond. We shall only state some of them briefly (see Arts. 138–140) :

---

* If we had undertaken to give a definition and some of the properties of curves, we might have followed the analogy of the plano-prismatic hypersurface and defined this hypersurface independently of any directing-curve, as a part of the two-dimensional geometry of a system of parallel planes (see Art. 138).

We have the *interior of the hypersurface* consisting of those planes parallel to the elements which pass through the points of the interior of the directing-curve, with the usual theorems in regard to the interior. The section made by a hyperplane containing an element will be one or two elements, but the section made by a hyperplane which does not contain an element will be a cylindrical surface, so that the hypersurface can also be regarded as a hypercylindrical hypersurface with a directing cylindrical surface. Likewise, as in the case of the plano-prismatic hypersurface, a plane which does not contain a line parallel to the elements will intersect every element in a point, and the hypersurface in a curve which can be taken as directing-curve; and directing-curves which lie in parallel planes are congruent.

A directing-curve whose plane is absolutely perpendicular to the planes of the elements is called a *right directing-curve;* and any plane isocline to the plane of a right directing-curve but not parallel to the elements, or, what is the same thing, any plane isocline to the elements, intersects the hypersurface in a curve which is similar * to the right directing-curves.

When the hypersurface has a directing-circle, the plane through its centre parallel to the elements is an *axis-plane of the hypersurface*, and every point of it is a centre of symmetry. When the right directing-curve is a circle, the hypersurface can be generated by the rotation of one of the elements around the axis-plane, that is, by the rotation of one of two parallel planes around the other. It is then a *plano-cylindrical hypersurface of revolution*. For such a hypersurface we can say that any plane isocline to the elements, or to the axis-plane, intersects the hyper-

---

* Two curves are *similar* when they can be placed in positions where they cut proportionally all half-lines which intersect them from a given point.

s

surface in a circle; and through any line which is not perpendicular nor parallel to the elements pass two such
planes (Art. 107, Th. 1).

THEOREM. *Any directing-curve of a plano-cylindrical
hypersurface of revolution is a directing-curve of a circular
cylindrical surface.**

PROOF. Through some line of the plane of the directing-curve pass a plane isocline to the planes of the elements,
and so intersecting the hypersurface in a circle. This
plane and the given plane lie in a hyperplane, and the directing-curves in which they intersect the hypersurface are
directing-curves of the cylindrical surface in which the
hyperplane intersects the hypersurface. Since one of
these is a circle, the surface is a circular cylindrical surface;
and the given directing-curve is a directing-curve of a
circular cylindrical surface.

149. **Intersection of a plano-prismatic hypersurface and
a plano-cylindrical hypersurface**. When the elements of a
plano-prismatic hypersurface intersect the elements of a
plano-cylindrical hypersurface only in points, the intersection of the two hypersurfaces consists of the lateral surface of a set of cylinders lying in the cells of the prismatic
hypersurface and joined together by their bases, together
with the curves whose interiors are these bases.

In fact, the faces of the prismatic hypersurface are parallel
planes intersecting the cylindrical hypersurface in a set
of equal parallel directing-curves of the latter, and the
cells of the prismatic hypersurface are layers, each layer
intersecting the cylindrical hypersurface in the lateral
surface of a cylinder whose bases are the interiors of two
of these directing-curves. The interiors of the bases of
the cylinders lie in the prismatic hypersurface and in the

---

* And is therefore a circle or ellipse.

interior of the cylindrical hypersurface. A set of corresponding elements of the cylinders, one from each cylinder, are the sides of a polygon which is a directing-polygon of the prismatic hypersurface; and the interiors of these polygons lie in the cylindrical hypersurface and in the interior of the prismatic hypersurface. We can think of the set of cylinders as going around the prismatic hypersurface, while any base or interior of a cross section of any of these cylinders is a piece cut out of an element of the prismatic hypersurface.

A *prism cylinder* consists of the intersection of a plano-prismatic hypersurface and a plano-cylindrical hypersurface whose elements intersect only in points, together with all that portion of each hypersurface which lies in the interior of the other.

The *interior of a prism cylinder* consists of the points which are common to the interiors of its two hypersurfaces. A plane lying in the interior of the cylindrical hypersurface parallel to its elements intersects the prismatic hypersurface in a directing-polygon whose interior belongs to the interiors of both hypersurfaces, and so to the interior of the prism cylinder. The vertices of this polygon are a set of corresponding points of the bases, and the sides lie in the interiors, of the set of cylinders described above.

When the elements of one hypersurface are absolutely perpendicular to the elements of the other the prism cylinder is a *right prism cylinder*. When also the cylinders are cylinders of revolution, and when any set of corresponding elements, one from each cylinder, form a regular polygon, the prism cylinder is *regular*.

In a right prism cylinder the cylinders of the surface of intersection of the two hypersurfaces can be put together in one hyperplane so as to form a single right cylinder. On the other hand, if this surface is cut along a set of corresponding elements of the cylinder, and so along a directing-polygon of the prismatic hypersurface, it can be spread out so as to form a single right prism. The cylinder and prism will each have their elements equal to the perimeters of the bases of the other. In forming the prism cylinder this single right cylinder is folded on the planes of certain cross sections until the ends are brought together, and the prism is bent around the cylinder. The two are linked together, the lateral surface of one coinciding as a whole with the lateral surface of the other (see note to Art. 141).

150. Directing-polygons and directing-curves. Triangular prism cylinders. Prism cylinders of revolution.

In a prism cylinder the directing-polygons of the prismatic hypersurface whose planes are elements of the cylindrical hypersurface, and the directing-curves of the cylindrical hypersurface whose planes are elements of the prismatic hypersurface, are called the *directing-polygons* and *directing-curves of the prism cylinder*.

We can say that the surface of intersection of the two hypersurfaces is generated by moving the polygon around the curve, or by moving the curve around the polygon. In the first case each point of the polygon moves around one of the cylinders; in the second case each point of the curve moves along them all. The interior of the curve generates the interiors of the cylinders; the interior of the polygon generates that portion of the prism cylinder which belongs to the cylindrical hypersurface and to the interior of the prismatic hypersurface. The surface of intersection is covered with the polygons and with the curves, the two sets forming on it a net.

THEOREM I. *When a prism cylinder is cut by a hyperplane passing through points of the interior and containing elements of the prismatic hypersurface, the intersection is a cylinder, and the rest of it is separated into two portions, which, each combined with the cylinder and its interior, form two prism cylinders whose interiors, with that of the cylinder, make up the whole interior.*

The proof is the same as that of Art. 143, with only such changes in the terms used as are necessary because the second hypersurface is cylindrical and not prismatic.

The cylinders of the prism cylinder are separated, some of them going to one of the two new prism cylinders and some to the other. The other portion of the prism cylinder, that portion which goes around the cylindrical hypersurface, is cut lengthwise, one part going to each of the new prism cylinders.

COROLLARY. *By cutting a prism cylinder diagonally we can form prism cylinders in which the directing-polygons are triangles and the cylinders, three in number, triangular prism cylinders.*

A hypercylinder whose bases are the interiors of cylinders is a prism cylinder; and a prism cylinder in which the directing-polygons are parallelograms (and therefore the cylinders are four in number) can be regarded in two ways as a hypercylinder.

When the two hypersurfaces of a prism cylinder have axes-planes of symmetry, the point of intersection of these planes is a centre of symmetry (as in Art. 144, Th. 2).

THEOREM 2. *If we rotate a right prism around the plane of one base, the rest of the prism will generate a right prism cylinder having circles for its directing-curves. The lateral edges generate the bases of the cylinders of the prism cylinder, each lateral face generates the interior of one of these cylinders, and the moving base generates that portion of the prism cylinder which lies in the cylindrical hypersurface and in the interior of the prismatic hypersurface. The fixed base and the interior of the prism belong to the interior of the prism cylinder.*

151. Intersection of two plano-cylindrical hypersurfaces.
When the elements of a plano-cylindrical hypersurface intersect the elements of a second plano-cylindrical hypersurface only in points, each element of one hypersurface intersects the other hypersurface in a directing-curve, and

the surface of intersection * consists of the curves of either one of these sets. The interiors of the curves of each set lie in one of the hypersurfaces and in the interior of the other.

A *double cylinder* consists of the intersection of two plano-cylindrical hypersurfaces whose elements intersect only in points, together with that portion of each which lies in the interior of the other. The directing-curves of each hypersurface whose planes are elements of the other are called the *directing-curves of the double cylinder*.

The *interior of a double cylinder* consists of the points which are common to the interiors of its two hypersurfaces. A plane lying in the interior of one hypersurface parallel to its elements intersects the other hypersurface in a directing-curve whose interior belongs to the interior of the double cylinder.

When the elements of one hypersurface of a double cylinder are absolutely perpendicular to the elements of the other the double cylinder is a *right double cylinder*.

The surface of intersection of the two hypersurfaces is generated by moving a directing-curve of one system around a directing-curve of the other. If this surface is cut along a directing-curve, it can be spread out in a hyperplane, and in the case of a right double cylinder it will then form the lateral surface of a right cylinder. This can be done in two ways, and in the double cylinder we have two cylinders bent around each other, the lateral surface of one coinciding as a whole with the lateral surface of the other, and this common surface, together with the interiors and bases of the two cylinders, making up the double cylinder. When the two bases of a single cylinder come together, any two corresponding points of these bases and the points which were on a line between them become the points of a directing-curve whose interior belongs to the interior of the double cylinder.

---

* Without defining surface in general, we assume that the intersection of two hypersurfaces is a surface.

152. Cylinders of double revolution.

THEOREM 1. *If we rotate a cylinder of revolution around the plane of one base, the rest of the cylinder will generate a right double cylinder with directing-circles; and the double cylinder can be generated in two ways by the rotation of a cylinder of revolution around one of its bases.*

The right double cylinder with directing-circles is therefore called a *double cylinder of double revolution*, or simply a *cylinder of double revolution*.

THEOREM 2. *In a cylinder of double revolution the intersection of the two hypersurfaces lies in a hypersphere, and in this hypersphere it is a surface of double revolution* (Art. 124).

PROOF. Any point of the intersection, its projection upon one of the axis-planes, and the centre of the double cylinder, are the vertices of a right triangle whose legs are radii of directing-circles of the two systems. The hypothenuse, therefore, and the angle which it makes with the axis-plane are the same for all points of the intersection, so that the intersection lies entirely in a hypersphere, and in this hypersphere is a surface of double revolution whose axis-circles are the two great circles in which the axis-planes of the double cylinder intersect the hypersphere.

A plane passing through the hypothenuse of the triangle just considered, and isocline to the axis-planes of the double cylinder, intersects the hypersurfaces in the same circle. The system of all these planes forms the conical hypersurface of double revolution whose intersection with the hypersphere is this same surface of double revolution.

THEOREM 3. *Conversely, any surface of double revolution in a hypersphere is the surface of intersection of the two hypersurfaces of a cylinder of double revolution.*

For the points of this surface, being all at the same distance from each of the axis-circles of the surface, are in hyperspace all at the same distance from each of the planes of these circles, and lie, therefore, in two plano-cylindrical hypersurfaces of revolution which have these planes for axis-planes.

The cylinder of double revolution can be regarded as inscribed in the hypersphere.

153. **Relation of prism cylinders and double cylinders to infinity**. Taking the point of view explained in Art. 130, we can say that a plano-cylindrical hypersurface is a plano-conical hypersurface with vertex-edge at infinity. We have a prism cylinder or double cylinder when the vertex-edge of one hypersurface does not intersect the vertex-edge of the other. We have a right prism cylinder or double cylinder when one vertex-edge is polar to the other.

When the bases of a hypercylinder are cylinders there are two points at infinity, the vertices of two hypercylindrical hypersurfaces which we get by taking the figure in two ways as a hypercylinder. The line determined by these two points is the vertex-edge of the plano-cylindrical hypersurface which belongs to the figure regarded as a prism cylinder. The other vertex-edge in this case is the line of intersection of the planes of the bases of the four cylinders.

CHAPTER VII

MEASUREMENT OF VOLUME AND HYPERVOLUME IN HYPERSPACE

I. VOLUME

154. Lateral volumes of hyperprisms and hyperpyramids. Volume of the double prism. The cells of the polyhedroids that we have studied are polyhedrons of three-dimensional geometry, and it is only necessary to state the theorems which concern their volumes.

THEOREM 1. *The lateral volume of a hyperprism is equal to the area of a right section multiplied by the lateral edge.*

The lateral volume of a right hyperprism is equal to the area of the surface of the base * *multiplied by the altitude.*

THEOREM 2. *The lateral volume of a regular hyperpyramid is equal to the area of the surface of the base multiplied by one-third of the slant height, the common altitude of the lateral pyramids.*

THEOREM 3. *The lateral volume of a frustum of a regular hyperpyramid is equal to the sum of the surface areas of the bases plus a mean proportional between them, multiplied by one-third of the slant height.*

THEOREM 4. *In a double prism the total volume of one set of prisms is equal to the common area of their bases multiplied by the perimeter of a right directing-polygon of the hypersurface around which the set of prisms extends.*

---

* Area of the polyhedron whose interior is the base. Many forms of expression commonly used in mensuration will be employed freely in this chapter.

PROOF. Any prism of the given set has its bases in the two faces of a cell of the hypersurface around which this set of prisms extends, and its altitude is the distance between these two faces. Now a right directing-polygon of the hypersurface is a polygon whose plane is absolutely perpendicular to the elements, and the side which lies in this cell is perpendicular to the faces and measures the distance between them. Therefore the volume of this prism is equal to the area of its base multiplied by this side of the right directing-polygon of the hypersurface, and the total volume of the given set of prisms is equal to the common area of their bases multiplied by the perimeter of the right directing-polygon.

COROLLARY. *The total volume of a right double prism is equal to the area of one directing-polygon multiplied by the perimeter of the other, plus the area of the second multiplied by the perimeter of the first.*

155. Lateral volumes of cylindrical and conical hypersurfaces. In the case of curved hypersurfaces we have to employ the theory of limits or some other equivalent theory, and, in fact, to extend our definition of volume. Without going into details, we state the following theorems:

THEOREM 1. *The lateral volume of a right spherical hypercylinder is equal to the area of the base multiplied by the altitude. It is given by the formula*

$$4 \pi R^2 H,$$

R being the radius and H the altitude.

THEOREM 2. *The lateral volume of a right spherical hypercone is equal to the area of the base multiplied by one-third of the slant height. Its formula is*

$$\tfrac{4}{3} \pi R^2 H',$$

H' being the slant height.

THEOREM 3. *The lateral volume of a frustum of a right spherical hypercone is given by the formula*

$$\tfrac{4}{3}\,\pi\,H'(R^2 + Rr + r^2),$$

r being the radius of the upper base.

THEOREM 4. *In a right prism cylinder with directing-circles the total volume is equal to the area of the directing-polygon multiplied by the circumference of the directing-circle, plus the area of the directing-circle multiplied by the perimeter of the directing-polygon.*

The total volume of a cylinder of double revolution is equal to the area of one directing-circle multiplied by the circumference of the other, plus the area of the second multiplied by the circumference of the first. It is given by the formula

$$2\,\pi^2 R R'(R + R'),$$

R and R' being the radii of the two circles.

156. Volume of the hypersphere.

THEOREM. *The volume of a hypersphere is given by the formula*

$$2\,\pi^2 R^3,$$

R being the radius.

PROOF. Let AB be a quadrant of a great circle. Two hyperplanes perpendicular to the radius OB cut the hypersphere in two spheres, whose interiors are the bases of a frustum of a hypercone inscribed in the hypersphere. Let H' be the slant height of this frustum, and r_1 and r_2 the radii of the bases. H' is the length of a chord of the great circle. The lateral volume of the frustum is given by the formula

$$\tfrac{4}{3}\,\pi\,H'(r_1^2 + r_1 r_2 + r_2^2).$$

Let H be the altitude of the frustum, and K the distance from O to the middle point of the chord which represents H'. From similar triangles we have

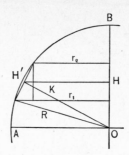

$$\frac{H'}{K} = \frac{H}{\frac{1}{2}(r_1 + r_2)},$$

or

$$r_1 + r_2 = \frac{2\,KH}{H'}.$$

Also, from right triangles,

$$H'^2 = H^2 + (r_1 - r_2)^2,$$

and

$$R^2 = K^2 + (\tfrac{1}{2}H')^2.$$

Therefore

$$\tfrac{4}{3}(r_1{}^2 + r_1 r_2 + r_2{}^2) = (r_1 + r_2)^2 + \tfrac{1}{3}(r_1 - r_2)^2$$

$$= (4\,R^2 - H'^2)\frac{H^2}{H'^2} + \tfrac{1}{3}(H'^2 - H^2)$$

$$= 4\,R^2\frac{H^2}{H'^2} + \tfrac{1}{3}H'^2 - \tfrac{4}{3}H^2.$$

For an inscribed hypercone with vertex at B and r_1 the radius of the base, we have only to make $r_2 = 0$ in all of these expressions.

If we take two arcs symmetrically situated on the arc AB with respect to P, the middle point of this arc, we shall have two right triangles with hypothenuse equal to H' symmetrically situated with respect to the radius OP, and therefore equal. But the legs denoted by H are non-homologous sides in the two triangles, and so the sum of

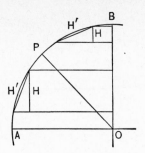

their squares is H'^2. Therefore, if we write down the formula given above for each of two divisions of AB symmetrically situated with respect to P, the sum of the two expressions will be

$$4\,R^2 - \tfrac{2}{3}\,H'^2\,;$$

and the sum of the volumes of the frustums corresponding to the two arcs will be

$$4\,\pi R^2 H' - \tfrac{2}{3}\pi H'^3.$$

Now if we divide the arc AB into $2\,n$ equal parts, we shall have a hypercone and frustum, and $n-1$ pairs of frustums, all inscribed in a half-hypersphere; and when n is increased indefinitely the sum of their lateral volumes will have for limit the volume of the half-hypersphere.*
This sum is

$$4\,n\pi R^2 H' - \tfrac{2}{3}\,n\pi H'^3.$$

But

$$\lim_{n\,=\,\infty} n H' = \text{arc } AP = \frac{\pi R}{4},$$

and

$$\lim_{n\,=\,\infty} n H'^3 = \lim_{n\,=\,\infty}\frac{(n H')^3}{n^2} = 0.$$

---

* Here again we omit details involving essentially a definition of the volume of the hypersphere.

Thus the volume of the half-hypersphere is

$$4 \pi R^2 \cdot \frac{\pi R}{4},$$

and the volume of the hypersphere is

$$2 \pi^2 R^3.$$

COROLLARY. *The volume of a cylinder of double revolution circumscribed about a hypersphere is twice the volume of the hypersphere.*

II. HYPERVOLUME

157. The terms hypersolid and hypervolume. We shall use the term *hypersolid* for that portion of hyperspace which constitutes the interior of a polyhedroid or of a simple closed hypersurface such as a hypercone, hypersphere, or double cylinder. A hypersolid is supposed to have *hypervolume*, which can be computed from the measurements of certain segments and angles, and which can be expressed in terms of the hypervolume of a given hypercube taken as a unit. The theory of hypervolume is exactly the same as the theory of volume in the ordinary geometry. We shall omit all discussion of this matter, and, as in the preceding section, we shall use freely the forms of expression commonly employed in mensuration. The distinction between hypersurface and hypersolid is important, but we shall often use these terms interchangeably, speaking, for example, of the hypervolume of a given hypersurface, and, on the other hand, of the vertices, edges, faces, or cells of a hypersolid.

By the *ratio of two hypersolids* we mean the ratio of their hypervolumes. Thus the ratio of any hypersolid to the unit hypercube is the same as the hypervolume of the hypersolid. Two hypersolids which have the same hypervolume are *equivalent;* and if a hypersolid is divided into two or more parts, the hypervolume of the whole is equal

to the sum of the hypervolumes of the parts. Two hypersolids which are congruent are equivalent.

158. Congruent and equivalent hyperprisms.

THEOREM 1. *Two right hyperprisms are congruent when
they have congruent bases and equal altitudes.*

PROOF. A given base of one can be made to coincide
with either base of the other, and in one of these two
positions the hyperprisms will lie on the same side of the
hyperplane of the coinciding bases and will coincide throughout.

THEOREM 2. *An oblique hyperprism is equivalent to a
right hyperprism having for its base a right section and for
its altitude a lateral edge of the oblique hyperprism.*

COROLLARY. *Any two hyperprisms cut from the same
prismoidal hypersurface with equal lateral edges are equivalent.*

159. Hypervolume of a hyperparallelopiped.

THEOREM 1. *The hypervolume of a rectangular hyperparallelopiped is equal to the product of its four dimensions.*

PROOF. In the first place, two rectangular hyperparallelopipeds having congruent bases are to each other
as their altitudes. This we can prove when the altitudes
are commensurable and then when the altitudes are incommensurable.

Then we prove that when they have two dimensions in
common they are to each other as the products of the other
two dimensions; when they have one dimension in common they are to each other as the products of the other
three dimensions; and, finally, in any case, they are to
each other as the products of their four dimensions.

From the last statement, by taking for the second hyperparallelopiped the unit hypercube, we have the theorem
as stated.

THEOREM 2. *The hypervolume of any hyperparallelopiped is equal to the volume of any base multiplied by the corresponding altitude.*

PROOF. We shall prove the theorem by proving that we can construct an equivalent rectangular hyperparallelopiped with base equivalent to the base and altitude equal to the altitude of the given hyperparallelopiped.

We shall speak of a pair of opposite cells and the eight edges which join the vertices of one to the vertices of the other as a *corresponding pair of bases and set of edges* (Art. 136).

We produce a set of edges and cut off an equivalent hyperparallelopiped by two hyperplanes perpendicular to these edges (Art. 158, Th. 2). The set of edges which are produced are taken on the same lines in the two hyperparallelopipeds, and are of equal lengths. The other three sets of edges of the given figure are replaced by edges perpendicular to the set produced. If the edges of any set were already perpendicular to the edges produced, they are replaced by a set of edges parallel and equal to them, and if the edges of any set were perpendicular to the corresponding bases, and so to all of the other edges, the same will be true of the edges by which they are replaced. The pair of bases corresponding to the edges produced is replaced by a pair of bases perpendicular to these lines. The bases of the other three pairs are parallelopipeds replaced by equivalent right parallelopipeds lying in the same hyperplanes.

Starting with the second hyperparallelopiped, we produce a second set of edges, forming a third hyperparallelopiped in the same way; and, finally, from the third hyperparallelopiped, producing a third set of edges, we form a fourth hyperparallelopiped, the four being all equivalent.

The edges of the first set in all four hyperparallelopipeds

are equal and parallel, and in the second, third, and fourth they are perpendicular to the corresponding bases, and therefore to all the other edges. The edges of the second set in the second, third, and fourth hyperparallelopipeds are equal and parallel, and in the third and fourth they are perpendicular to the corresponding bases, and therefore to all the other edges. The edges of the third set in the third and fourth hyperparallelopipeds are equal and taken along the same lines, and in the fourth they are perpendicular to the corresponding bases.

Therefore, in the fourth hyperparallelopiped the edges of each set are perpendicular to the edges of all the other sets, and the hyperparallelopiped is rectangular.

Now the hyperplanes of the fourth pair of bases remain the same throughout this process, and with these bases the four hyperparallelopipeds all have the same altitude (Art. 128, Th. 12). Moreover, these bases do not differ in volume, and in the last two they are congruent; they are, in fact, parallelopipeds formed by this same process of producing successively different sets of edges.

We have constructed an equivalent rectangular hyperparallelopiped with base equivalent to the base and altitude equal to the altitude of the given hyperparallelopiped, and this is sufficient to prove the theorem.

160. Hypervolume of any hyperprism.

THEOREM 1. *The hypervolume of a hyperprism whose base is the interior of a prism is equal to the volume of its base multiplied by its altitude.*

PROOF. As any prism can be divided into triangular prisms,* it is only necessary to prove the theorem when the base is a triangular prism.

---

* We are using the term prism here for the solid (see Art. 157); we mean that a set of triangular prisms can be formed whose volumes together make up the volume of the given prism.

T

On a triangular prism we can build a parallelopiped by joining an equal triangle to its base so as to form a parallelogram, and drawing a fourth lateral edge. We join to the given prism a second triangular prism, and the two are symmetrically situated with respect to the centre of the parallelopiped, and therefore equal (Art. 84, Ths. 2 and 4). On the hyperprism we can, then, build a hyperparallelopiped having this parallelopiped as base. We join to the given hyperprism a second hyperprism, and the two hyperprisms are indeed congruent, since the centre of symmetry of the hyperparallelopiped lies in the diagonal hyperplane along which the two prisms are joined (Art. 136, Th. 1, and Art. 85, Th. 2). The hypervolume of the given hyperprism is therefore equal to one-half of the hypervolume of the hyperparallelopiped, and so to the volume of its own base multiplied by its altitude.

THEOREM 2. *Two right hyperprisms are equivalent if they have equal altitudes and if their bases are the interiors of tetrahedrons which can be so placed that as triangular pyramids they shall have equivalent bases and equal altitudes.*

PROOF. The lateral cells are the interiors of triangular prisms. We will rest the hyperprism upon one of these cells, which may be called a *prismatic base*. The opposite lateral edge will then be a *vertex-edge*, and the *altitude* will be the distance of the vertex-edge from the prismatic base.

The original base is now at one end, and is itself the interior of a triangular pyramid with one of the ends of the prismatic base for its base, and for its altitude the altitude of the hyperprism in its present position.

Looking at the hyperprism in this way, we have a series of theorems analogous to the theorems by which we determine the volume of a pyramid in geometry of three dimensions:

(1) A hyperplane section parallel to the prismatic base is itself a prism of the same length as the prismatic base, and its end is a section of the end-pyramid parallel and similar to the base of the pyramid. The volume of this parallel hyperplane section is, then, proportional to the square of its distance from the vertex-edge.

(2) If two right hyperprisms with tetrahedral ends, when placed as explained above, have equivalent prismatic bases and equal altitudes, hyperplane sections parallel to the prismatic bases and at the same distance from the vertex-edges are equivalent.

(3) Given the two hyperprisms just considered, we divide the common altitude into equal parts and construct a series of inscribed and circumscribed prisms to the pyramids at the ends, and so a series of hyperprisms having these prisms for ends, inscribed and circumscribed to the original hyperprisms. The hypervolume of either of the given hyperprisms is the limit of the sum of the hypervolumes of the hyperprisms inscribed or of the hyperprisms circumscribed to it, when the number of subdivisions of the altitude is increased indefinitely. Any inscribed or circumscribed hyperprism of one figure is equivalent to the corresponding hyperprism of the other figure, and therefore the two given hyperprisms must be equivalent.

Now when two right hyperprisms have equal altitudes, and for bases the interiors of triangular pyramids with equivalent bases and equal altitudes, the hyperprisms satisfy the conditions of (3) and are equivalent.

THEOREM 3. *The hypervolume of any hyperprism is equal to the volume of its base multiplied by its altitude.*

PROOF. As any polyhedron can be divided into tetrahedrons, it is only necessary to prove the theorem when the base is a tetrahedron.

On a tetrahedron we can build a triangular prism by joining to it two other equivalent tetrahedrons, and so on the given hyperprism we can build a hyperprism with a triangular prism for base, composed of three hyperprisms with tetrahedral bases. If we produce the lateral edges, we can form a right hyperprism with a triangular prism for base, composed of three right hyperprisms with tetrahedral bases, the four right hyperprisms equivalent respectively to the hyperprisms from which they were produced (Art. 158, Th. 2). The three tetrahedral bases of the right hyperprisms are equivalent, and any two of them can be so placed that as triangular pyramids they shall have equivalent bases and equal altitudes. Hence the three right hyperprisms with tetrahedral bases are equivalent, and the first three hyperprisms with tetrahedral bases are equivalent. The hypervolume of the given hyperprism is, therefore, equal to one-third of the hypervolume of the hyperprism with triangular prism for base of which it forms a part, and so it is equal to the volume of its own base multiplied by its altitude.

COROLLARY. *The hypervolume of a hyperprism is equal to the volume of a right section multiplied by the lateral edge.*

161. Hypervolume of a hyperpyramid. For the hypervolume of a hyperpyramid we have, as in the proof of Th. 2 of the preceding article, a series of theorems analogous to the theorems by which we determine the volume of a pyramid in geometry of three dimensions:

THEOREM 1. *A hyperplane section of a hyperpyramid parallel to the base is similar to the base, and its volume is proportional to the cube of its distance from the vertex.*

THEOREM 2. *If two hyperpyramids have equivalent bases and equal altitudes, hyperplane sections parallel to the bases and at the same distance from the vertices are equivalent.*

THEOREM 3. *Two pentahedroids are equivalent if they can be so placed that as hyperpyramids they shall have equivalent bases and equal altitudes.*

PROOF. Dividing the altitude into some number of equal parts, we can construct a series of inscribed and circumscribed hyperprisms and prove that the hypervolume of either pentahedroid is the limit of the sum of the hypervolumes of the set of hyperprisms inscribed or circumscribed to it when the number of subdivisions of the altitude is increased indefinitely. Thus we prove our theorem in the same manner as we prove the corresponding theorem in geometry of three dimensions.

THEOREM 4. *The hypervolume of any hyperpyramid is equal to the volume of its base multiplied by one-fourth of its altitude.*

PROOF. As any polyhedron can be divided into tetrahedrons, it is only necessary to prove the theorem when the base is the interior of a tetrahedron, that is, to prove it for pentahedroids.

On a pentahedroid taken as a hyperpyramid we can build a hyperprism having the same base and one lateral edge the same. In doing this we join to the given pentahedroid a hyperpyramid with a triangular prism for base, a hyperpyramid which can be divided into three pentahedroids, the triangular prism being divided into three tetrahedrons. One of these pentahedroids can then be proved equivalent to the given pentahedroid, so that the four pentahedroids are all equivalent.

Let $A-A'B'C'D'$ be the given pentahedroid. Drawing lines through B', C', and D' parallel to $A'A$, and a hyperplane through A parallel to the hyperplane of the tetrahedron $A'B'C'D'$, we have a hyperprism $ABCD-A'B'C'D'$ composed of the given pentahedroid and the hyperpyramid

$A-BCDB'C'D'$. This hyperpyramid we divide into three equivalent pentahedroids by dividing the prism $BCD-B'C'D'$ into three equivalent tetrahedrons, the common altitude of the three pentahedroids being the distance of the vertex A from the hyperplane of the triangular prism. Now of these three pentahedroids one can be regarded as having $ABCD$ as its base, and as its vertex one of the points B', C', or D' of the lower base of the hyperprism. Regarded in this way it is seen to be equivalent to the original pentahedroid, since the bases of the two are the bases of the hyperprism, and their common altitude is the altitude of the hyperprism.

The given pentahedroid is, therefore, one of four equivalent pentahedroids which go to make up the hyperprism; and its hypervolume is one-fourth of the hypervolume of the hyperprism, and so equal to the volume of its own base multiplied by one-fourth of its altitude.

The figure on page 238 represents the cells of the hyperprism spread out into a single hyperplane. Dividing the three prisms on the left by the planes $AB'C'$, $AB'D'$, and $AC'D'$, we have all the cells except the common cell $AB'C'D'$ of the given pentahedroid and of the hyperpyramid $A-BCDB'C'D'$.

162. Hypervolume of a frustum of a hyperpyramid.

THEOREM. *The hypervolume of a frustum of a hyperpyramid is given by the formula*

$$\tfrac{1}{4} H(B + B^{\frac{2}{3}}b^{\frac{1}{3}} + B^{\frac{1}{3}}b^{\frac{2}{3}} + b),$$

where B and b are the volumes of the bases and H is the altitude.

PROOF. Let B be the volume of the lower base, and let r be the ratio of an edge of the upper base to the corresponding edge of the lower base, so that we have $b = Br^3$. The formula of the theorem can, then, be written

$$\tfrac{1}{4} HB(1 + r + r^2 + r^3).$$

By dividing the bases into tetrahedrons we can divide the frustum into frustums of pentahedroids,* in all of which H and r have the same values. Therefore, it is only necessary to prove the theorem when the bases are the interiors of tetrahedrons, that is, for a frustum of a pentahedroid.

Now the frustum of a pentahedroid is of the same general form as a hyperprism with tetrahedral bases, and can be divided into four pentahedroids in the same way that the hyperprism of the preceding proof is divided into four pentahedroids.† Then it can be proved that the hyper-volumes of these four pentahedroids form a geometrical progression in which the ratio is r and the first term $\frac{1}{4} HB$, the hypervolume of the pentahedroid whose base is the lower base of the frustum.

Let the given frustum be $ABCD$–$A'B'C'D'$, $ABCD$ being the upper base and $A'B'C'D'$ the lower base. We divide this into four pentahedroids by the three hyperplanes

$$AB'C'D', \ ABC'D', \text{ and } ABCD';$$
namely, into

$$AA'B'C'D', \ ABB'C'D', \ ABCC'D', \text{ and } ABCDD'.$$

The first hyperplane, cutting off the pentahedroid $AA'B'C'D'$, leaves the hyperpyramid A–$BCDB'C'D'$. That is, the last three of the four pentahedroids together form a hyperpyramid with vertex at A and base the frustum BCD–$B'C'D'$ of a tetrahedron. When the hyperpyramid is divided into three pentahedroids this frustum is divided into three tetrahedrons whose volumes are proportional to 1, r, and r^2. Therefore, the hypervolumes of the three pentahedroids are proportional to 1, r, and r^2.

---

* See Art. 157, and foot-note, p. 273.

† A truncated pentahedroid is divided in this way by Sylvester in the memoir, "On the Centre of Gravity of a Truncated Triangular Pyramid" (p. 172), referred to on p. 5.

Similarly, the first three pentahedroids form a hyper-pyramid with vertex at D' and base the frustum $ABC-A'B'C'$ of a tetrahedron, and their hypervolumes are proportional to 1, r, and r^2.

In other words, the hypervolumes of the four pentahe-droids are proportional to 1, r, r^2, and r^3.

But the hypervolume of the first pentahedroid is $\frac{1}{4} HB$. Therefore the hypervolume of the given frustum is

$$\tfrac{1}{4} HB(1 + r + r^2 + r^3).$$

The formula can also be derived algebraically by sub-tracting from the hypervolume of a hyperpyramid the hypervolume of a smaller hyperpyramid cut off so as to leave a frustum.

163. Hypervolume of a double prism.

THEOREM 1. *The hypervolume of a doubly triangular prism is equal to six times the hypervolume of the pentahe-droid whose vertices are the points obtained by taking the vertices of a base in one of the two sets of prisms together with the vertices of a base in the other set* (Art. 141).

PROOF. We shall prove this theorem by dividing the double prism into two hyperpyramids with triangular prisms for bases, and then into six equivalent pentahedroids. Certain of these pentahedroids will be found to have among their faces a base from each of the two sets of prisms of the double prism.

Let the nine vertices of the double prism be

$$
\begin{array}{ccc}
A & B & C \\
A' & B' & C' \\
A'' & B'' & C'',
\end{array}
$$

where the three lines as written represent three equal parallel triangles, and the three columns represent three

equal parallel triangles. Any two triangles of either set
lie in a hyperplane, and their interiors are the bases of a
prism.

The point A and the plane of the parallelogram $B'C'B''C''$
determine a hyperplane which divides the double prism
into two hypersolids. We can indicate this by writing
their vertices

$$
\begin{array}{ccccccc}
A & B & C & \text{and} & A & & \\
 & B' & C' & & A' & B' & C' \\
 & B'' & C'' & & A'' & B'' & C''.
\end{array}
$$

The hyperplane cannot contain any of the points B, C, A',
or A''; for it contains at least one vertex of each of the
six triangles, and if it contained any one of these triangles,
it would contain the two triangles parallel to it and so all
the nine vertices of the double prism. Now the hyperplane intersects the hyperprism $ABC-A'B'C'$ in the plane
$AB'C'$ which separates B and C from A', and it intersects
the hyperplane of the prism $ABC-A''B''C''$ in the plane
$AB''C''$ which separates B and C from A''. Therefore
B and C are separated in hyperspace from A' and A'' by
this hyperplane (Art. 28).

The two hypersolids are hyperpyramids, each having
its vertex at A and a triangular prism as base. Each of
these hyperpyramids can be divided into three equivalent
pentahedroids, the base being divided into three equivalent
tetrahedrons. This can be done in such a way that one
of the pentahedroids of the first set shall be the pentahedroid $ABCC'C''$, and one of the pentahedroids of the
second set the pentahedroid $AA'A''B''C''$. We write
these

$$
\begin{array}{ccccccc}
A & B & C & \text{and} & A & & \\
 & & C' & & A' & & \\
 & & C'' & & A'' & B'' & C''.
\end{array}
$$

We will take the first pentahedroid as a hyperpyramid with vertex at C' and its base as a pyramid with vertex at C'', and the second pentahedroid as a hyperpyramid with vertex at A' and its base as a pyramid with vertex at A. The two pyramids will then have equal bases, ABC and $A''B''C''$, and equal altitudes, the distance between the planes of these bases. In fact, they are two of the three equivalent tetrahedrons into which the prism ABC–$A''B''C''$ can be divided. The altitudes of the two hyperpyramids will be equal to the distance of the plane $A'B'C'$ from the hyperplane of this prism, to which it is parallel. Therefore, these two hyperpyramids are equivalent pentahedroids; that is, the six pentahedroids into which the double prism has been divided are all equivalent, and the hypervolume of the double prism is equal to six times the hypervolume of any one of these pentahedroids, for example, of the pentahedroid $ABCC'C''$, which has among its faces the triangles ABC and $CC'C''$.

The figure on page 248 represents the cells of the double prism spread out in a single hyperplane. Dividing the prisms on the right and left by the planes $AB'C'$ and $AB''C''$, and the upper two prisms in front by the planes $AB'B''$ and $AC'C''$, we have all the cells except the common cell $AB'C'B''C''$ of the two hyperpyramids into which we first divide the double prism.

THEOREM 2. *The hypervolume of a double prism is equal to the area of a base of any of the prisms of either set, multiplied by the area of a right directing-polygon of the hypersurface around which this set of prisms extends.*

PROOF. We can divide the bases of the prisms of the given set into triangles, the given prisms into triangular prisms, and the double prism into double prisms having each a set of triangular prisms for the given set of prisms. The hypersurface around which these prisms extend is the same for the given double prism and for all of the double

prisms into which it is divided (Art. 143, Th. and Cor.).
Therefore it is only necessary to prove the theorem for
double prisms in which the given set of prisms is a set of
triangular prisms.

Again, taking a double prism with a given set of triangular
prisms for one of its sets of prisms, we can divide the right
directing-polygons of the hypersurface around which these
prisms extend into triangles. The diagonals which divide
one of these directing-polygons into triangles, together
with the faces of the hypersurface at their extremities,
determine layers which form, with the parts into which
they divide the hypersurface, triangular hypersurfaces,
and so divide the double prism into doubly triangular
prisms. If the theorem is true of doubly triangular prisms,
it is true of any double prism in which the given set of
prisms is a set of triangular prisms. Therefore, it is only
necessary to prove the theorem for doubly triangular prisms.

Proceeding as in the proof of Th. 1, we have a pentahedroid $ABCC'C''$, one of six equivalent pentahedroids
into which the double prism can be divided. The volume
of the tetrahedron $ABCC''$ is equal to the area of the
triangle ABC multiplied by one-third of the distance of
C'' from the plane of this triangle; and the hypervolume
of the pentahedroid is equal to the volume of the tetrahedron $ABCC''$ multiplied by one-fourth of the distance of C'
from the hyperplane of this tetrahedron. That is, the
hypervolume of the pentahedroid is equal to the area of
the triangle ABC multiplied by one-twelfth of the product
of these two distances.

Now the plane absolutely perpendicular to the plane ABC
intersects the hypersurface which has this plane for one
of its faces in a right directing-triangle. One side of this
triangle measures the distance between the planes ABC
and $A''B''C''$, and the corresponding altitude of the

triangle measures the distance of the plane $A'B'C'$ from the hyperplane of the other two planes. The area of the triangle, that is, of the right directing-triangle of the hypersurface which has the plane ABC for one of its faces, is then equal to one-half of the product of these two distances; and the hypervolume of the pentahedroid $ABCC'C''$ is equal to one-sixth of the product of the areas of the two triangles.

But the hypervolume of the pentahedroid is also one-sixth of the hypervolume of the double prism. Therefore, the latter is exactly equal to the product of the areas of the two triangles, that is, to the area of a base in one set of prisms multiplied by the area of a right directing-triangle of the hypersurface around which this set of prisms extends.

COROLLARY. *The hypervolume of a right double prism is equal to the product of the areas of its two directing-polygons.*

164. Hypervolumes of cylindrical and conical hypersurfaces. For the hypercylinder, hypercone, prism cylinder, and double cylinder we have the following theorems, derived from the corresponding theorems of the preceding articles:

THEOREM 1. *The hypervolume of a spherical hypercylinder is equal to the volume of the base multiplied by the altitude. It is given by the formula*

$$\tfrac{4}{3}\pi R^3 H,$$

R being the radius of the base and H the altitude, as in Art. 155.

THEOREM 2. *The hypervolume of a spherical hypercone is equal to the volume of the base multiplied by one-fourth of the altitude. It is given by the formula*

$$\tfrac{1}{3}\pi R^3 H.$$

THEOREM 3. *The hypervolume of a frustum of a spherical hypercone is given by the formula*

$$\tfrac{1}{3}\,\pi\,H(R^3 + R^2r + Rr^2 + r^3),$$

or

$$\tfrac{1}{3}\,\pi\,H(R + r)(R^2 + r^2).$$

THEOREM 4. *The hypervolume of a right prism cylinder with directing-circle is equal to the product of the areas of the directing-polygon and directing-circle.*

The hypervolume of a cylinder of double revolution is equal to the product of the areas of its directing-circles. It is given by the formula

$$\pi^2 R^2 R'^2.$$

165. Hypervolume of the hypersphere.

THEOREM. *The hypervolume of a hypersphere is equal to its volume multiplied by one-fourth of its radius.*

PROOF. We use the construction and notation of Art. 156. We inscribe a frustum of a hypercone entirely on one side of the centre O, and on each base we place a hypercone with vertex at O. The figure formed by adding to the frustum the hypercone with larger base and then taking away the hypercone with smaller base is a hypersolid which we can use to determine the hypervolume of the hypersphere. If we divide the arc AB into some number of equal parts and form these figures for all the chords H', we shall have a set of hypersolids fitting together within the half-hypersphere, and the limit of the sum of their hypervolumes we assume to be the hypervolume of the half-hypersphere.

Let x denote the distance from O of the nearer base of the inscribed frustum, and let this be the base whose radius is r_1. The hypervolumes of the two hypercones are then

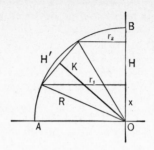

$$\tfrac{1}{3}\,\pi x r_1{}^3 \text{ and } \tfrac{1}{3}\,\pi(x + H)r_2{}^3,$$

and the hypervolume of the frustum is

$$\tfrac{1}{3}\,\pi H(r_1 + r_2)(r_1{}^2 + r_2{}^2).$$

Adding to this last the hypervolume of the first hypercone and substracting the hypervolume of the second, we have

$$\tfrac{1}{3}\,\pi\,\{\,H(r_1 + r_2)(r_1{}^2 + r_2{}^2) + x r_1{}^3 - (x + H)r_2{}^3\,\}.$$

Now

$$R^2 = x^2 + r_1{}^2 = (x + H)^2 + r_2{}^2.$$

Hence

$$2\,xH = r_1{}^2 - r_2{}^2 - H^2,$$
$$2(x + H)H = r_1{}^2 - r_2{}^2 + H^2,$$

and

$$2\,\{\,x r_1{}^3 - (x + H)r_2{}^3\,\}\,H = (r_1{}^2 - r_2{}^2)(r_1{}^3 - r_2{}^3) - H^2(r_1{}^3 + r_2{}^3).$$

That is,

$$x r_1{}^3 - (x + H)r_2{}^3$$
$$= \frac{r_1 + r_2}{2\,H}\,\{\,(r_1 - r_2)^2(r_1{}^2 + r_1 r_2 + r_2{}^2)$$
$$-\,H^2(r_1{}^2 - r_1 r_2 + r_2{}^2)\,\}.$$

But

$$r_1 + r_2 = \frac{2\,K H}{H'}, \text{ and } (r_1 - r_2)^2 = H'^2 - H^2 \text{ (Art. 156)}.$$

Hence, finally, our hypervolume becomes

$$\frac{\pi K}{3 H'} \{ 2 \ H^2(r_1^2 + r_2^2)$$
$$+ (H'^2 - H^2)(r_1^2 + r_1 r_2 + r_2^2)$$
$$- H^2(r_1^2 - r_1 r_2 + r_2^2) \}$$
$$= \tfrac{1}{3} \pi K H'(r_1^2 + r_1 r_2 + r_2^2).$$

Now the lateral volume of the frustum is

$$\tfrac{4}{3} \pi H'(r_1^2 + r_1 r_2 + r_2^2),$$

so that the hypervolume of our hypersolid is equal to the lateral volume of the frustum multiplied by $\tfrac{1}{4} K$.

Consider now all the subdivisions of the arc AB. When the number of subdivisions is increased indefinitely the sum of the hypervolumes will, as we have assumed, approach as limit the hypervolume of the half-hypersphere, the sum of the lateral volumes will approach what we have called the volume of the half-hypersphere, and K will approach R. Therefore, passing to the limit and expressing the result for the entire hypersphere, we have the hypervolume of the hypersphere equal to its volume multiplied by one-fourth of the radius.

COROLLARY 1. *The hypervolume of the hypersphere is given by the formula*

$$\tfrac{1}{2} \pi^2 R^4.$$

COROLLARY 2. *The hypervolume of a hypersphere is equal to one-half the hypervolume of the circumscribed double cylinder, and twice the hypervolume of the inscribed double cylinder with equal radii. It is equal to the hypervolume of any inscribed double cylinder plus the hypervolumes of two hyperspheres whose radii are the radii of the double cylinder.*

The student may investigate the hypervolume of a pentahedroid in elliptic hyperspace, following the analogy of Art. 120. He will find that there are eleven equations connecting the sixteen different hypervolumes of a set of associated pentahedroids with the measures of the five hyperplane angles. If he introduces also what we may call the hypervolumes of the five tetrahedroidal angles, he will have five more equations, so that he can express the hypervolume of the pentahedroid in terms of the hyperplane angles and the tetrahedroidal angles.* But a tetrahedroidal angle is like a spherical tetrahedron: we cannot measure it directly, and we have no simple formula for its hypervolume.

---

* M. Dehn, "Die Eulersche Formel in Zusammenhang mit dem Inhalt in der Nicht-Euklidische Geometrie," *Mathematische Annalen*, vol. 61, 1905, pp. 561–586, in particular, pp. 583–584.

CHAPTER VIII

THE REGULAR POLYHEDROIDS *

I. THE FOUR SIMPLER REGULAR POLYHEDROIDS

166. Definition of regular polyhedroid. The regular pentahedroid. A *regular polyhedroid* † consists of equal regular polyhedrons together with their interiors, the polyhedrons being joined by their faces so as to enclose a portion of hyperspace, and the hyperplane angles formed at the faces by the half-hyperplanes of adjacent polyhedrons being all equal to one another.

We have already had two regular polyhedroids, the regular pentahedroid (Art. 114) and the hypercube (Art. 136).

The interior of the segment which measures the altitude of a regular pentahedroid is one leg of a right triangle whose hypothenuse is the edge of one of its cells and whose other leg is the radius of the sphere circumscribed about the cell. The radius of the hypersphere circumscribed about the pentahedroid is equal to four-fifths of the altitude, and the radius of the inscribed hypersphere is equal to one-fifth of the altitude. These theorems are proved in the same way that the corresponding theorems are proved for the regular tetrahedron and the triangle.

Radii perpendicular to the cells of a regular pentahedroid meet the circumscribed hypersphere in five points which are the vertices of a second regular pentahedroid symmetri-

---

* This subject is treated by I. Stringham, "Regular Figures in n-dimensional Space," *American Journal of Mathematics*, vol. 3, 1880, pp. 1–14.

† That is, a *regular convex polyhedroid*. We shall consider only convex polyhedroids in this chapter.

cally situated to the first with respect to the centre, and therefore equal to it (Art. 85, Th. 2).

The pentahedroid has

5 vertices, 10 edges, 10 faces, and 5 cells.

167. The hypercube. The hypercube can be generated by the motion of a cube in a direction perpendicular to its hyperplane through a distance equal to its edge. The centre of the cube generates the interior of a segment whose middle point is the centre of the hypercube, equally distant from all of the sixteen vertices. The distance of the centre from any cell (the radius of the inscribed hypersphere) is equal to one-half of the edge, the radius of the circumscribed hypersphere is equal to the edge, and the diagonal of the hypercube (the diameter of the circumscribed hypersphere) is twice the edge (Art. 136, Th. 3).

The hypercube has

16 vertices, 32 edges, 24 faces, and 8 cells.

As the regular polyhedroids are usually named from the number of cells, the hypercube is also called a *regular octahedroid*.

We can fill all hyperspace with a set of hypercubes and their interiors, sixteen hypercubes coming together at any vertex. Moreover, the centres of these hypercubes are themselves the vertices of a second set of hypercubes of the same kind, and the two sets are in this way reciprocally related. Two hypercubes of one set whose centres are the extremities of an edge of the other set have in common a cube, and the centre of the cube is the projection upon its hyperplane of the centres of the two hypercubes. The edge and the cube lie, therefore, in a perpendicular line and hyperplane, intersecting at a point which is the middle point of the edge and the centre of the cube.

our hypercubes of one set whose centres are the vertices
a face of the other set have in common a square. The
hypercubes are in cyclical order around the plane of this
quare, and the centre of the square is the projection upon
s plane of the centres of the four hypercubes. More-
ver, the vertices of this square are in turn the centres of
ur hypercubes of the second set, arranged in cyclical
der around the plane of the given face of this set. The
lanes of the two faces are therefore absolutely perpendic-
ar, intersecting at a point which is the centre of both
ee Arts. 46 and 179).

A set of polyhedroids filling hyperspace without over-
pping is called a *net:* every point of hyperspace is either
point of two or more of the polyhedroids or a point of
e interior of only one. The two sets of hypercubes just
escribed are *reciprocal nets*.

168. The hexadekahedroid or 16-hedroid.

If we lay
f a given distance in both directions on each of four
utually perpendicular lines intersecting at a point O,
e eight points so obtained are the vertices of a regular
olyhedroid which has four diagonals along the four given
nes. In fact, the rectangular system contains sixteen
ctangular tetrahedroidal angles, and the four vertices
hich lie on the edges of one of these angles are the ver-
ces of a regular tetrahedron congruent to the tetrahedron
hose vertices lie on the edges of any other one of these
etrahedroidal angles (see Art. 72, Th. 1). Thus the sixteen
etrahedrons together with their interiors form a polyhe-
roid and enclose a portion of hyperspace about the point
. Now any face of this polyhedroid can be taken as the
ase of each of the two tetrahedrons which have this face
common and lie in the cells of a hyperplane angle of the
olyhedroid. Thus the opposite vertices of these two tet-

rahedrons lie in the plane angle at the centre of the given face, and as they lie also in one of the four lines of the rectangular system, they and the centre of the given face are the vertices of an isosceles triangle whose sides and angles are the same whatever face be taken. The hyperplane angles of the polyhedroid are, therefore, equal,* and the polyhedroid is regular. As there are sixteen cells the polyhedroid is called a *hexadekahedroid*, or as we shall usually write it, a 16-*hedroid*.

Each tetrahedron has four faces, and each face is common to two tetrahedrons. The number of faces of the 16-hedroid is therefore

$$\frac{16 \times 4}{2} = 32.$$

Each vertex, being one extremity of a diagonal, is a common extremity of six of the edges. The other extremities of these edges are the extremities of the other three diagonals. The number of edges is therefore

$$\frac{8 \times 6}{2} = 24.$$

Thus the regular 16-hedroid has

   8 vertices, 24 edges, 32 faces, and 16 cells.

The diagonals of the 16-hedroid are also called its *axes*.

169. Reciprocal relation of the hypercube and the 16-hedroid. When a hypercube is inscribed in a hypersphere, the radii perpendicular to the hyperplanes of its eight cells are the radii to the eight vertices of a regular 16-hedroid inscribed in the same hypersphere, the two polyhedroids having their axes along the same lines. Each vertex of the 16-hedroid and the centre of the hypersphere are sym-

---

* They are, in fact, angles of 120°.

metrically situated with respect to the hyperplane of a cube, and the vertex is at a distance r from each of the eight vertices of the cube, r being the radius of the hypersphere. We shall speak of the vertex as *corresponding* to the cube.

This relation is reciprocal. At a vertex of the hypercube there are four cubes lying in hyperplanes perpendicular respectively to the four axes; and the four vertices of the 16-hedroid corresponding to these four cubes are the vertices of one of its tetrahedrons. These four vertices are at a distance r from the vertex of the hypercube, and the radius to the latter point is perpendicular to the hyperplane of the tetrahedron, passing through its centre. Therefore, the radii perpendicular to the hyperplanes of the sixteen cells of a 16-hedroid are the radii to the sixteen vertices of a hypercube. The hypercube and the 16-hedroid are said to be *reciprocal polyhedroids* (see Art. 177).

170. The diagonals of the hypercube and the 16-hedroid forming three rectangular systems. The hypercube has eight diagonals joining the eight vertices of any one cube to the eight vertices of the opposite cube. Since any vertex of a 16-hedroid is at a distance r from each of the eight vertices of the corresponding cube, the radius to the former makes an angle of 60° with each of the eight radii to the latter.

Now the eight radii to the vertices of a cube can be associated in two sets of four each; for on a cube the common vertex of three adjacent squares and the three opposite vertices of these squares are the vertices of a tetrahedron whose edges are diagonals of the six faces of the cube, one in each face, while the other four vertices of the cube are the vertices of a second tetrahedron of the same kind. The diagonal of a square subtends a right angle at the centre of the hypersphere, and the four radii of a set are mutually perpendicular. Two radii taken, one from each set, are radii to the extremities of an edge or to the extremities of a diagonal of the cube. Now an edge subtends an angle of 60° at the centre, and a diagonal, its length being $r \sqrt{3}$, subtends an angle of 120°. Therefore, any radius of one set makes an angle of 60° with three of the radii of the other set, and with the fourth an angle of 120°. In fact, the radius opposite to this fourth radius goes to the other extremity of the fourth edge of the hypercube at the given point. Thus we can say that the radii to the extremities of the four edges which go out from a vertex of a hypercube are a set of four mutually perpendicular radii.

Putting these results together, we find that the four diagonals of the 16-hedroid and the eight diagonals of the hypercube lie in three sets of four mutually perpendicular lines, each line of one set making with each line of the other two sets the two supplementary angles of 60° and 120°. The lines of any one of these three sets can be taken as the axis-lines of a hypercube, and the eight lines of the other two sets will pass through its vertices, for there are only eight lines that can make angles of 60° and 120° with the four lines of a rectangular system. A half-line making an angle of 60° with a half-line of a rectangular system will make an angle of 30° with the hyperplane to which the latter is perpendicular, and the point at a distance r on it will be at a distance $\dfrac{r}{2}$ from the hyperplane. But there are just sixteen points at the distance $\dfrac{r}{2}$ from each of the four hyperplanes of a rectangular system, the sixteen points of intersection of four pairs of parallel hyperplanes, and so the sixteen vertices of a hypercube which has its axes along the four lines of the rectangular system.

Associated with the twelve lines described above, there are, therefore, three hypercubes and three regular 16-hedroids.

171. The 24-hedroid associated with a hypercube and a 16-hedroid. Given a hypercube and a regular 16-hedroid inscribed in the same hypersphere and with their axes lying in the same rectangular system, let P and P' be two vertices of the latter corresponding to the two cubes which have in common the square $ABCD$. Let O' be the centre of the square. Since P is at the distance r from each of the four vertices of the square, it determines with the square one-half of a regular octahedron. The same is true of the point P', and indeed it is also true of the centre O of the hypersphere. The altitude $O'P$ of the pyramid P–$ABCD$ is equal to $\dfrac{r}{\sqrt{2}}$, and $O'P'$ is of the same length.

But the segment PP' subtends at O an angle of 90°, and is of twice this length. Hence the line PP' passes through O', and the points P and P', together with the square, lie in one hyperplane, and are the vertices of a regular octahedron with centre at O'.

From a cube can be formed six equal pyramids having a common vertex at the centre of the cube and the six faces of the cube as bases. The interior of the square $ABCD$ is the common base of two such pyramids, one from each of the two cubes which have this square in common. These two pyramids do not lie in one hyperplane, nor does either of them belong to a regular octahedron, but the two pyramids of the octahedron PP' are the projections of these pyramids upon the hyperplane of the octahedron, projected from the centre of the hypersphere. At a vertex P there are six quadrangular pyramids, belonging to six regular octahedrons, and the projections of the six pyramids which have a common vertex at the centre of the corresponding cube. The interiors of these six pyramids at P are the lateral cells of a hyperpyramid whose base is the interior of the cube, that is, a cell of the hypercube.

From the cubes of the hypercube are formed in all twenty-four pairs of pyramids, the two pyramids of a pair having a common base. The interiors of these pyramids and their bases can be projected as above from the centre O into the interiors of the twenty-four regular octahedrons, the cells of a polyhedroid which can be built up by placing a hyperpyramid as described above upon each cell of the hypercube. This polyhedroid is called an *ikosatetrahedroid* or *24-hedroid*. Its vertices are the sixteen vertices of the hypercube and the eight vertices of the 16-hedroid, twenty-four in all. This polyhedroid can be built up from any one of the three hypercubes associated with a set of twelve lines such as is described in the preceding article, and it has the same number and arrangement of parts at a vertex of the hypercube that it has at a vertex of the 16-hedroid.

To get the plane angle of a hyperplane angle of the 24-hedroid we draw half-lines through the centres of two adjacent octahedrons from the centre of their common face. One common vertex of the two octahedrons can be taken as the point P, and their centres are the centres of two adjacent squares of the cube to which P corresponds. These two points and the centre of the common face of the octahedrons are the vertices of an isosceles triangle whose sides are equal respectively to the sides of the isosceles triangle formed in the same way from any other pair of adjacent octahedrons. Therefore the hyperplane angles of the polyhedroid are all equal,* and the polyhedroid is regular.

---

* These are angles of 120°, like those of the 16-hedroid.

The octahedron has eight faces. The number of faces of the 24-hedroid is therefore

$$\frac{24 \times 8}{2} = 96.$$

Eight edges meet at a vertex, and the number of edges is likewise 96.

Thus the regular 24-hedroid has

24 vertices, 96 edges, 96 faces, and 24 cells.

172. Reciprocal 24-hedroids. There are twenty-four points O', the centres of the twenty-four octahedrons, the centres of the twenty-four squares of the hypercube, and the middle points of the twenty-four edges of the 16-hedroid. These twenty-four points lie on twelve lines through O.

Since the points O' are the middle points of the edges of a 16-hedroid, the half-lines OO' bisect the twenty-four right angles formed by the four axes of this 16-hedroid. Now these right angles lie in three pairs of absolutely perpendicular planes, and the half-lines which bisect the eight right angles in any one of these three pairs of planes are themselves the half-lines of a set of four mutually perpendicular lines. Our twelve lines, therefore, consist of three sets of four mutually perpendicular lines.

If two right angles lie in perpendicular planes and have a common side along the intersection of these planes, their bisectors form an angle of 60°. Now any two of the six planes of a rectangular system, if not absolutely perpendicular, are perpendicular, intersecting in one of the four lines. Therefore each of the bisectors of the four right angles in one of these planes makes with each of the bisectors of the four right angles in the other an angle of 60° or an angle of 120°.

This proves that a line in any one of our three sets of four mutually perpendicular lines makes with each of the eight lines of the other two sets the supplementary angles of 60° and 120°, and that the radii of the hypersphere drawn through the points O' meet the hypersphere in twenty-four points which are the vertices of a second regular 24-hedroid. The two 24-hedroids are related in the same way as a hypercube and a 16-hedroid whose axes lie along the same four lines; namely, the radii perpendicular to the hyperplanes of the cells of one are the radii to the vertices of the other (Art. 169). The two 24-hedroids are said to be *reciprocal* (see Art. 177).

173. The reciprocal nets of 24-hedroids and 16-hedroids. The interior of a cube of a hypercube is the base of a hyperpyramid with vertex at the centre O, congruent to the hyperpyramid built upon the same base with vertex at the corresponding point $P *$. From the hypercube can be formed eight such hyperpyramids, and therefore eight polyhedroidal angles like that of the 24-hedroid at P can be placed together with a common vertex so as to fill the hyperspace about this vertex. In other words, eight 24-hedroids can be placed together at a point with their interiors filling the hyperspace about this point, and we have in hyperspace a net of 24-hedroids like the net of hypercubes described in Art. 167. The centres and vertices of the 24-hedroids are, indeed, the centres and vertices of a net of hypercubes. The eight polyhedroidal angles at O have their axes lying in the axis-lines of the hypercube. Therefore, the eight 24-hedroids put together at any point have axis lines through this point forming a rectangular system, and their centres are the vertices of a 16-hedroid whose centre is this point.

---

* The two hyperpyramids are symmetrically situated with respect to the centre of the cube, and are congruent. Thus the hypervolume of the 24-hedroid is twice that of the hypercube.

Let us suppose that the given 24-hedroid with centre at
O is one of eight 24-hedroids put together at a vertex P,
so that P is the centre of the 16-hedroid and one of its
vertices is at O. The edges of the 16-hedroid pass through
the centres of certain cells of the 24-hedroids. In particular, the edges which come to O pass through points
which we have called O', through those six which lie on
the cube corresponding to P. Now the points O' which
lie on a single cube lie on radii to the vertices of a single
cell of the reciprocal 24-hedroid constructed in the preceding article. This cell is therefore the base of a hyperpyramid with vertex at O whose polyhedroidal angle at O
is the polyhedroidal angle at this point of the 16-hedroid
just mentioned. Therefore, twenty-four such polyhedroidal angles, and so twenty-four 16-hedroids, can be
put together at a point with their interiors filling the hyperspace about this point; and we have in hyperspace a
net of 16-hedroids reciprocal to the net of 24-hedroids.

Two adjacent 24-hedroids have in common an octahedron PP', with its centre O' the projection upon its hyperplane of the centres of the two 24-hedroids. These
centres are the extremities of an edge in the net of 16-he-
droids. Thus the edges of the 16-hedroids correspond to
the cells of the 24-hedroids, an edge and a cell lying in a
perpendicular line and hyperplane, and intersecting at a
point which is the middle point of the edge and the centre
of the cell. Three 24-hedroids whose centres are the vertices of a face of the net of 16-hedroids are in cyclical order,
each having a cell in common with the next, and the hyperplanes of the three cells, being perpendicular to the sides
of the given face at their middle points, pass through the
centre and intersect in the plane absolutely perpendicular
to its plane at this point. In other words, the three 24-
hedroids have in common a triangle and the face which is

the interior of this triangle. The vertices of this triangle are in turn the centres of three of the 16-hedroids having the given face in common, and arranged in cyclical order around the plane of this face. Each of these three 16-hedroids has in common with the next a cell whose centre is the projection upon its hyperplane of the centres of the two 16-hedroids, so that each edge of the net of 24-hedroids and the corresponding cell of the net of 16-hedroids lie in a perpendicular line and hyperplane, and intersect at a point which is the middle point of the edge and the centre of the cell (see Art. 179).

II. THE POLYHEDROID FORMULA

174. Extension of the polyhedron formula. In a simple polyhedron the number of vertices and faces taken together is 2 more than the number of edges.* This relation can be expressed very conveniently in the form

$$1 - N_0 + N_1 - N_2 + 1 = 0,$$

where N_0 is the number of vertices, N_1 the number of edges, and N_2 the number of faces.

For the five regular polyhedrons this formula becomes

for the tetrahedron $\qquad 1 - 4 + 6 - 4 + 1 = 0,$
" hexahedron or cube $\quad 1 - 8 + 12 - 6 + 1 = 0,$
" octahedron $\qquad\quad 1 - 6 + 12 - 8 + 1 = 0,$
" dodekahedron $\qquad 1 - 20 + 30 - 12 + 1 = 0,$
" ikosahedron $\qquad\quad 1 - 12 + 30 - 20 + 1 = 0.$

* This theorem was discovered by Euler about 1750 and usually goes by his name. It was known to Descartes more than a century earlier — at least it follows directly from formulæ in a manuscript, "De Solidorum Elementis," left by Descartes. This memoir was not published, however, until 1860, a copy having been found only a few years earlier among the papers of Leibnitz (*Œuvres inédites de Descartes*, par M. le Comte Foucher de Careil, Paris, 1860, vol. II, p. 214. See communication by Prouhet in the *Comptes Rendus*, vol. 50, 1860, p. 779, and several by E. de Jonquières in vol. 110, 1890).

In the first three cases the first members of these equations are the expansions of

$$(1 - 1)^4, \quad 1 - (2 - 1)^3, \quad \text{and} \quad (1 - 2)^3 + 1.$$

The polyhedrons take their names from the numbers N_2.

The above formula can be generalized so as to apply to certain more complicated figures and to polyhedroids in space of four dimensions.

For a simple polygon we can write a similar formula, namely,

$$1 - N_0 + N_1 - 1 = 0.$$

In proving the formula for a polyhedron we think of the polyhedron as built up by putting together a set of polygons, taking them in succession in such order that each is joined to those already taken by a side or by two or more sides forming a single broken line. As long as we have not completely enclosed any portion of space and formed a polyhedron we have the relation

$$1 - N_0 + N_1 - N_2 = 0.$$

In the same way we can build up a polyhedroid by putting together a set of polyhedrons. We take them in succession in such order that each is joined to those already taken by a set of polygons like the incomplete polyhedron. At each stage of the process we add to the number of vertices, edges, and faces already obtained the number of vertices, edges, and faces of the new polyhedron, and to the number of cells we add 1 ; and we subtract the number of vertices, edges, and faces of the connecting figure, which otherwise would be counted twice.

Assuming that the figure had an equation of the form

$$1 - N_0 + N_1 - N_2 + N_3 = 0,$$

where N_3 is the number of cells, we add all but the first term of the equation of the new polyhedron, and then subtract all but the first term of the equation of the connecting figure. Thus we prove by induction that as long as the polyhedroid is incomplete its equation is of the form assumed.

When we come to the last polyhedron there are no new vertices, edges, or faces. Only the number N_3 is increased by 1, and the equation will be true if we write it

$$1 - N_0 + N_1 - N_2 + N_3 - 1 = 0.$$

This equation is true for a simple polyhedroid, and we shall call it the *polyhedroid formula*. The relation can be stated as a theorem in the following words:

THEOREM. *In a simple polyhedroid the number of cells plus the number of edges is equal to the number of faces plus the number of vertices.*[*]

For the four regular polyhedroids already considered the polyhedroid formula becomes

for the pentahedroid $\quad 1 - 5 + 10 - 10 + 5 - 1 = 0,$
" hypercube $\qquad 1 - 16 + 32 - 24 + 8 - 1 = 0,$
" 16-hedroid $\qquad 1 - 8 + 24 - 32 + 16 - 1 = 0,$
" 24-hedroid $\qquad 1 - 24 + 96 - 96 + 24 - 1 = 0.$

In the first three cases the first numbers of these equations are the expansions of

$$(1 - 1)^5, \quad 1 - (2 - 1)^4, \text{ and } (1 - 2)^4 - 1.$$

In all cases the name of the polyhedroid comes from the number N_3.

---

[*] An interesting discussion of this law and its extension to geometry of higher dimensions is given in Schoute's *Mehrdimensionale Geometrie*, vol. II, § 2. The corresponding law for simple polyhedroids of any number of dimensions is proved by Stringham in the article referred to on p. 289. The theorem will not be used in proving the existence of any regular polyhedroid, nor even in computing the number of any of its elements. Its proof may be omitted by the student, but we have in the formula itself a convenient mode of expressing these numbers.

III. RECIPROCAL POLYHEDROIDS AND RECIPROCAL NETS OF POLYHEDROIDS

175. Reciprocal polyhedrons and nets of polyhedral angles. In geometry of three dimensions a regular polyhedron can always be inscribed in a sphere. This is proved in the same way that it is proved for tetrahedrons, and the proof holds also in the Elliptic Non-Euclidean Geometry, and so in the geometry of the hypersphere. The vertices of the polyhedron are the vertices of a *net* of equal regular spherical polygons, a net of spherical polygons being a set covering the sphere so that every point of the latter is either a point of two or more of the polygons or a point of the interior of only one. Conversely, the vertices of a net of equal regular spherical polygons are always the vertices of a regular polyhedron inscribed in the sphere. Since the sphere is the same in the Elliptic Geometry, the regular polyhedrons of this geometry are of the same types as those of Euclidean Geometry.*

When we have a net of equal regular spherical polygons, the centres and vertices of these polygons are the vertices and centres of a second net of equal regular polygons *reciprocal* to the first. And so when a regular polyhedron is inscribed in a sphere, radii perpendicular to the planes of the faces are radii to the vertices of a second regular polyhedron. Two polyhedrons which can be so placed that half-lines from the centre perpendicular to the planes of the faces of one are half-lines from the centre through the vertices of the other, are said to be *reciprocal polyhedrons*.

---

* It can also be proved in the Hyperbolic Geometry that a regular polyhedron can be inscribed in a sphere, and that we have just the same types of regular polyhedrons. But in the Hyperbolic Geometry we have also boundary-surfaces and equidistant-surfaces on which we can form other nets of polygons; and the vertices of such a net are the vertices of an infinite broken surface formed of equal regular polygons and their interiors, like a regular polyhedron.

They have the same number of edges, and the number of
vertices of one is the same as the number of faces of the
other.   The polyhedron formula of one is the polyhedron
formula of the other written backwards.

Half-lines from the centre of a regular polyhedron
through the vertices are the edges of equal regular polyhedral angles forming a *net of polyhedral angles* in the two-
dimensional Point Geometry at this point, every half-
line element of the Point Geometry being either a half-line
of two or more of the polyhedral angles, or a half-line of
the interior of only one.   Corresponding to two reciprocal
polyhedrons and to two reciprocal nets on the sphere we
have two *reciprocal nets of polyhedral angles*, the edges of
the polyhedral angles of one net being the axes of the
polyhedral angles of the other net.   Conversely, a net of
equal regular polyhedral angles in a hyperplane intersects
any sphere of the hyperplane with centre at the vertex of
the net in a net of equal regular spherical polygons, and
the edges of the polyhedral angles pass through the vertices of a regular inscribed polyhedron which corresponds
to the net.

176. Reciprocal nets of polyhedrons.   In a net of equal
regular spherical polygons the angles at a vertex P are
equal, vertices adjacent to P are vertices of a regular
spherical polygon, and the corresponding inscribed polyhedron has a regular polyhedral angle at P.   If, then, a
set of equal regular polyhedrons with their interiors fills
a three-dimensional space about a point so that their
polyhedral angles at this point form a net, the centres of
the polyhedrons, lying at a given distance on the axes
of these polyhedral angles, are themselves the vertices
of a regular polyhedron, reciprocal to the polyhedron which
corresponds to the net.   With any given net of regular

polyhedrons is associated a reciprocal net, the vertices of the polyhedrons of one net being the centres of the polyhedrons of the other. Any edge of a polyhedron of one net, joining the centres of two polyhedrons of the other net, and the common face of these two polyhedrons, lie in a perpendicular line and plane and intersect at a point which is the middle point of the edge and the centre of the face. The number of vertices in a polyhedron of one net is equal to the number of polyhedrons of the other net at a vertex. The polyhedrons of two reciprocal nets are not, in general, reciprocal polyhedrons.

Now the polyhedral angles of the polyhedrons of a net must be such as occur in a net of polyhedral angles at the centre of a regular polyhedron. Thus we have

at the centre of	a tetrahedron	4	trihedral angles,
"	a cube	6	tetrahedral "
"	an octahedron	8	trihedral "
"	a dodekahedron	12	pentahedral "
"	an ikosahedron	20	trihedral "

The polyhedral angles of the five regular polyhedrons are as follows:

in the	tetrahedron	trihedral angles,
"	cube	" "
"	octahedron	tetrahedral "
"	dodekahedron	trihedral "
"	ikosahedron	pentahedral "

Therefore the only sets of regular polyhedrons that can be used to form nets are

4	tetrahedrons, cubes, or dodekahedrons at a point,
8	" " " "
20	" " " "
6	octahedrons "
12	ikosahedrons "

x

In two reciprocal nets the number of vertices in a poly-hedron of one net is equal to the number of polyhedrons of the other net at a point. These nets of polyhedrons are associated, therefore, as follows:

    4 cubes   reciprocal to 8 tetrahedrons,
    4 dodekahedrons   "   20   "
    8   "   "   20 cubes;
also

    4 tetrahedrons reciprocal to a net of the same kind,
    8 cubes   "   "   "
    20 dodekahedrons "   "   "
    6 octahedrons   "   "   "
    12 ikosahedrons   "   "   "

These theorems are true of the Non-Euclidean Geometries as well as of Euclidean Geometry, but in the Hyperbolic Geometry the angles of a regular polyhedron are smaller, and in the Elliptic Geometry they are larger, than they are in Euclidean Geometry. Moreover, we can make the angles in the first case as small as we please, and in the second case as large as we please up to 180°, by taking the figures sufficiently large. Thus any of these combinations is possible in one of the three geometries, at least for a restricted portion of space, and two reciprocal nets must occur in the same kind of geometry. Any combination which more than fills the part of Euclidean space about a point belongs to Hyberbolic Geometry, and any combina-tion which does not fill the part of Euclidean space about a point belongs to Elliptic Geometry.

Now in Euclidean Geometry we have a net of cubes, eight at a point. Then eight dodekahedrons, twenty cubes, or twenty dodekahedrons would more than fill Euclidean space, and nets of these types must belong to the Hyper-bolic Geometry; while nets with four cubes, four tetrahedrons, or eight tetrahedrons will belong to the Elliptic Geometry. We can also prove that the polyhedral angles of a regular octahedron in Euclidean Geometry are smaller than those of a net at the centre of a cube, so that the net of octahedrons, six at a point, belongs to Elliptic Geometry. For example, the faces of the octahedron are equilateral triangles, while the centre and two adjacent vertices of a cube are the vertices of an isosceles triangle in which the legs, each being the half of a diagonal, are shorter than the base.

There remains to be considered the net of ikosahedrons, twelve at a point, and the reciprocal nets of four dodekahedrons and twenty tetrahedrons. In the net of twelve pentahedral angles and in the net of four trihedral angles there are three of these angles around an edge, and the dihedral angles must all be angles of 120°. Therefore in the net of ikosahedrons and in the net of dodekahedrons the dihedral angles must be angles of 120°. Thus we have

to determine in which geometry the dihedral angles of the ikosahedron, and in which geometry the dihedral angles of the dodekahedron, are angles of 120°.

Let ABC be a spherical triangle of the net corresponding to the ikosahedron, O its centre (on the sphere), and D the

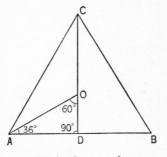

middle point of the arc AB. Then 2 OD is the supplement of the dihedral angle of the ikosahedron, and 2 AD is the supplement of the dihedral angle of the dodekahedron, the dodekahedron being reciprocal to the ikosahedron. Now two sides of the triangles ABC on opposite sides of the sphere lie on a great circle which also crosses four of these triangles. Hence, we have four arcs equal to OD, four equal to AD, and four equal to AO on such a circle. Therefore,

$$OD + AD + AO = 90°.$$

But in the triangle AOD the angles are 36°, 60°, and 90°,

$$OD < AD < AO,$$

and $$OD < 30°.$$

Again, in the triangle ACD the angles are 72°, 36°, and 90°, and

$$CD < AC.$$

That is, $$OD + AO < 2\,AD,$$

and therefore $$AD > 30°.$$

It follows that in the Euclidean Geometry the dihedral angles of the ikosahedron are greater than 120°, and the net of ikosahedrons belongs to Hyperbolic Geometry; but the dihedral angles of the dodekahedron are less than 120°, so that the net of dodekahedrons and the reciprocal net of tetrahedrons belong to Elliptic Geometry.*

Summing up we find that

Euclidean space can be filled with cubes, eight at a point;

Hyberbolic space can be filled with dodekahedrons, eight at a point or twenty at a point, with cubes, twenty at a point, or with ikosahedrons, twelve at a point; and

Elliptic space, or at least any restricted portion of elliptic space, can be filled with tetrahedrons, four at a point, eight at a point, or twenty at a point, with cubes, four at a point, with dodekahedrons, four at a point, or with octahedrons, six at a point.

---

* In the net of twenty trihedral angles the dihedral angles are angles of 72°, and it can be proved that the dihedral angles of the tetrahedron in Euclidean Geometry are less than 72°, so that the net of twenty tetrahedrons at a point belongs, indeed, to the Elliptic Geometry.

177. Reciprocal polyhedroids. A regular polyhedroid can always be inscribed in a hypersphere. For the perpendiculars to the hyperplanes of the cells at the centres of the cells all pass through a point which is at the same distance on each of them, and, therefore, at the same distance from all the vertices of the polyhedroid. This is proved in the same way that it is proved for pentahedroids (see Art. 113, Th. 1). Since the hyperplane angles are all equal, no two adjacent cells lie in the same hyperplane, and the perpendiculars to the hyperplanes of two adjacent cells cannot be parallel and must therefore intersect.*

When a regular polyhedroid is inscribed in a hypersphere, its vertices are the vertices of a net of equal regular hyperspherical polyhedrons. For the vertices of any polyhedron of the polyhedroid lie on a sphere which lies entirely in the hypersphere, and so they are the vertices of a regular hyperspherical polyhedron of the same type. The polyhedrons are equal, for the spheres are equal, and with their interiors they completely fill the hypersphere. They can, indeed, be regarded as the projections of the polyhedrons of the given polyhedroid, projected by radii from the centre of the hypersphere. Conversely, the vertices of a net of equal regular hyperspherical polyhedrons are always the vertices of a regular polyhedroid inscribed in the hypersphere. The vertices of any one of the polyhedrons lie on a sphere and are the vertices of a regular hyperplane polyhedron in the hyperplane of the sphere. These hyperplane polyhedrons are all equal, with their interiors they enclose a portion of hyperspace, and the hyperplane angles formed by the hyperplanes of any two which are adjacent are all equal.

When a regular polyhedroid is inscribed in a hypersphere,

---

* The theorem is true in Elliptic Geometry of four dimensions, since any two lines in a plane of Elliptic Geometry intersect. It can also be proved in Hyperbolic Geometry.

so that its vertices are the vertices of a net of equal regular hyperspherical polyhedrons, radii perpendicular to the hyperplanes of its cells will be radii to the centres of these hyperspherical polyhedrons; that is, they will be radii to the vertices of the reciprocal net, to points which are, therefore, the vertices of a second regular polyhedroid. The relation of the two polyhedroids is reciprocal; and two regular polyhedroids which can be so placed that half-lines from the centre perpendicular to the hyperplanes of the cells of one are half-lines from the centre through the vertices of the other, are called *reciprocal polyhedroids*. The number of vertices of one is equal to the number of cells of the other, and the number of edges of one is equal to the number of faces of the other. The polyhedroid formula of one is the polyhedroid formula of the other written backwards. Moreover, the number of cells at a vertex of one equals the number of vertices to a cell of the other, the number of edges at a vertex of one equals the number of faces to a cell of the other, and so on. Whenever we have constructed a regular polyhedroid, or proved its existence, we have proved the existence of a reciprocal polyhedroid. The two may, however, be polyhedroids of the same type.

The hypercube and the regular 16-hedroid are reciprocal polyhedroids. The regular pentahedroid and the regular 24-hedroid are self-reciprocal. These cases correspond to the two reciprocal nets of four cubes at a point and eight tetrahedrons at a point, and to the two self-reciprocal nets of four tetrahedrons at a point and six octahedrons at a point. Now we have found that in Elliptic space of three dimensions, or at least in a restricted portion of such space, and so in the hypersphere or in a restricted portion of the hypersphere, there exists another pair of reciprocal nets, nets with four dodekahedrons at a point and twenty tetrahedrons at a point; and so in Euclidean space of four dimensions there can be at most only two types of regular polyhedroids besides the four which we have already found. In the next section we shall construct a regular polyhedroid with twenty tetrahedrons at a point and a regular polyhedroid with four dodekahedrons at a point, one of these constructions being necessary to complete the proof of the existence of the two.

Assuming that these polyhedroids exist, we know that they are reciprocal and that the polyhedroid equation of one is the polyhedroid equation of the other written backwards. Let us suppose that the second polyhedroid has N cells, that is, that it contains N dodekahedrons, and call it an N-*hedroid*. Each dodekahedron has twenty vertices, and at each vertex there are four dodekahedrons. Therefore the number of vertices is

$$\frac{20\,N}{4} = 5\,N.$$

The first polyhedroid is, then, a $5\,N$-*hedroid*, containing $5\,N$ tetrahedrons.

The dodekahedron has twelve faces, and in the N-hedroid each face is common to two dodekahedrons. Therefore the number of faces in the N-hedroid is

$$\frac{12\,N}{2} = 6\,N.$$

In the same way the number of faces in the $5\,N$-hedroid is found to be

$$\frac{4 \times 5\,N}{2} = 10\,N.$$

Thus the polyhedroid formulæ of the two are

$$1 -\quad N +\quad 6N - 10N + 5N - 1 = 0,$$

and $\quad 1 - 5N + 10N -\quad 6N +\quad N - 1 = 0.$

178. Regular polyhedroidal angles. A *regular poly-hedroidal angle* is one subtended at the centre of a hyper-sphere by a regular hyperspherical polyhedron whose circumscribed sphere is not a great sphere. But the hy-perspherical polyhedron is the projection from the centre of the hypersphere of a hyperplane polyhedron which has the same vertices, and through the vertices of a given hyper-plane polyhedron we may pass a hypersphere having its centre at any point in the line perpendicular at the centre of the polyhedron to its hyperplane. Therefore the polyhe-droidal angle subtended by a regular polyhedron at any point in the line drawn through the centre of the polyhe-dron perpendicular to its hyperplane, except at the centre itself, is a regular polyhedroidal angle. The polyhedroidal angle at the vertex of a regular hyperpyramid is a regular polyhedroidal angle.

The half-line drawn from the vertex of a regular poly-hedroidal angle through the centre of the subtending poly-hedron, or, in the case of a regular hyperpyramid, the half-line which contains the axis of the hyperpyramid, is the *axis* of the polyhedroidal angle.

Let P be the vertex of a regular polyhedroidal angle and O' the centre of the subtending polyhedron. If we project the polyhedroidal angle by orthogonal projection upon the hyperplane of the polyhedron, the vertex will be projected at the centre O', and the polyhedroidal angle will be pro-jected into the net of equal regular polyhedral angles at this point. Take a point O on PO' produced, and with O as centre construct a hypersphere passing through P. Radii from O will project the polyhedroidal angle into a net of equal regular hyperspherical polyhedral angles at P congruent to the net at O'. The polyhedral angles at P in the hypersphere can be regarded as in the tangent hyperplane at P. Any one of the half-lines from P in this hyperplane, and the corresponding half-line from O', lie in the intersections of a projecting plane * through O with two parallel hyperplanes, and are parallel (Art. 128, Ths. 4 and 8). Conversely, suppose we have a net of equal regular hyperspherical polyhedral angles at P. If we project these by radii upon a hyperplane perpendicular to OP at some point O' between O and P, we shall have a congruent net at O', and any sphere in this hyperplane with centre at O' will intersect the edges of the polyhedral angles in the vertices of a regular polyhedron which subtends at P a regular polyhedroidal angle.

A regular polyhedroid is projected by radii upon the circumscribed hypersphere in a net of equal regular hyperspherical polyhedrons, and the edges of the polyhedroid which come to a vertex P are projected into arcs which lie in the edges of the hyperspherical polyhedral angles of the net at P. Now these edges are of the same length, their extremities are the vertices of a regular polyhedron, and the polyhedroidal angle at P of the given polyhedroid is a regular polyhedroidal angle subtended by this polyhedron. In other words, the polyhedroidal angles at the vertices of a regular polyhedroid are regular polyhedroidal angles.

The half-line from a vertex of a regular polyhedroid through the centre is the axis of the polyhedroidal angle at the vertex.

Half-lines drawn from the centre of a regular polyhedroid through the vertices are the edges of a set forming a *net of polyhedroidal angles* in the Point Geometry at this point, every half-line of the Point Geometry being a half-line of two or more of the polyhedroidal angles or a half-line of the interior of only one. Corresponding to two reciprocal nets of polyhedrons in the hypersphere, we have two *re-*

* See foot-note, p. 84.

ciprocal nets of polyhedroidal angles, the edges of the polyhedroidal angles of one net being the axes of the polyhedroidal angles of the other net. Conversely, a net of equal
regular polyhedroidal angles intersects any hypersphere
with centre at the vertex of the net in a net of equal regular polyhedrons, and the edges of the polyhedroidal angles
pass through the vertices of a regular inscribed polyhedroid which corresponds to the net.

179. Reciprocal nets of polyhedroids. If a set of equal
regular polyhedroids having a common vertex at P, with
their interiors, fill the part of hyperspace about this point
so that their polyhedroidal angles at P form a net, the
centres of the polyhedroids, lying at a given distance from P
on the axes of these polyhedroidal angles, are themselves
the vertices of a regular polyhedroid with centre at P,
reciprocal to the polyhedroid which corresponds to the
net. With any given *net of regular polyhedroids* is associated a *reciprocal net*, the vertices of the polyhedroids of
one net being the centres of the polyhedroids of the other.
Any edge of a polyhedroid of one net, joining the centres
of two polyhedroids of the other net, and the common cell
of these two polyhedroids, lie in a perpendicular line and
hyperplane, and intersect at a point which is the middle
point of the edge and the centre of the cell. Those polyhedroids of one net whose centres are the vertices of a face
of the other net, have in common a face in a plane absolutely perpendicular to the plane of the given face at a
point which is the centre of both faces. The vertices of
the second face are in turn the centres of polyhedroids of
the other net which have the given face in common (see
Arts. 167 and 173). The number of vertices in a polyhedroid of one net is equal to the number of polyhedroids
of the other net at a vertex. The polyhedroids of two

reciprocal nets are not, in general, reciprocal polyhedroids. Whenever we have constructed a net of equal regular polyhedroids, or proved the existence of such a net, we have proved the existence of a reciprocal net.

Now the polyhedroidal angles of the polyhedroids of a net must be such as occur in a net of polyhedroidal angles at the centre of a regular polyhedroid. Thus we have

at the centre of	a pentahedroid	5	tetrahedroidal angles,
"	a hypercube	8	6-hedroidal "
"	a 16-hedroid	16	tetrahedroidal "
"	a 24- "	24	8-hedroidal "
"	a $5N$- "	$5N$	tetrahedroidal "
"	an N- "	N	12-hedroidal "

The polyhedroidal angles of the six regular polyhedroids are as follows:

in the pentahedroid	tetrahedroidal angles,
" hypercube	" "
" 16-hedroid	8-hedroidal "
" 24- "	6- " "
" $5N$- "	20- " "
" N- "	tetrahedroidal "

Therefore the only sets of regular polyhedroids that can be used to form nets are

5	pentahedroids, hypercubes, or N-hedroids at a point,
16	" " " "
$5N$	" " " "
8	24-hedroids "
24	16- " "

The number of vertices in a polyhedroid of one of two reciprocal nets is equal to the number of polyhedroids of the other at a point. These nets of polyhedroids are associated, therefore, as follows:

    5 hypercubes reciprocal to 16 pentahedroids,
    5 N-hedroids   " $5N$ "
  16 N-   "   " $5N$ hypercubes,
    8 24-   "   "   24 16-hedroids;

also

    5 pentahedroids reciprocal to a net of the same kind,
   16 hypercubes   "   "   "
   $5N$ N-hedroids   "   "   "

These theorems are true of the Non-Euclidean Geometries as well as of Euclidean Geometry.   As in the case of poly-hedrons (Art. 176), those combinations which more than fill the part of Euclidean hyperspace about a point belong to Hyperbolic Geometry, and those which do not fill the part of Euclidean hyperspace about a point belong to Ellip-tic Geometry.

Now in Euclidean Geometry we have a net of hyper-cubes, sixteen at a point (Art. 167).   Then sixteen N-he-droids, or $5N$ of either of these polyhedroids, would more than fill the Euclidean hyperspace, and nets of these types must belong to Hyperbolic Geometry; while nets with five hypercubes, five pentahedroids, or sixteen pentahe-droids, will belong to Elliptic Geometry.

We have also in Euclidean hyperspace the reciprocal nets of eight 24-hedroids and twenty-four 16-hedroids (Art. 173).   There remain, therefore, to be considered only the reciprocal nets of five N-hedroids and $5N$ pentahe-droids.   We shall find when we have constructed the $5N$-hedroid that its edge subtends an angle of 36° at the centre (see Art. 182), and therefore the hyperplane angles of the N-hedroid in Euclidean hyperspace are the supplements of 36°, or 144°, the N-hedroid being reciprocal to the $5N$-hedroid.   But in a net of five N-hedroids there are four of these around any face, and the hyperplane angles

PLATE I.

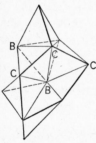

FIG. 1.

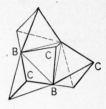

FIG. 2.

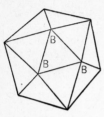

FIG. 3.

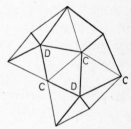

FIG. 4.

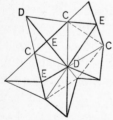

FIG. 5.

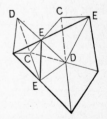

FIG. 6.

must be angles of 90°. Therefore these reciprocal nets belong to the Hyperbolic Geometry. Or, we may say that the face angles of the pentahedroid in Euclidean hyperspace are angles of 60°, so that $5N$ pentahedroids would more than fill Euclidean hyperspace about a point.

Summing up, we find that

Euclidean hyperspace can be filled with hypercubes, sixteen at a point, with 24-hedroids, eight at a point, or with 16-hedroids, twenty-four at a point;

Hyperbolic hyperspace can be filled with N-hedroids, five at a point, sixteen at a point, or $5N$ at a point, with pentahedroids, $5N$ at a point, or with hypercubes, $5N$ at a point; and

Elliptic hyperspace, or at least any restricted portion of elliptic hyperspace, can be filled with pentahedroids, five at a point, or sixteen at a point, or with hypercubes, five at a point.*

IV. CONSTRUCTION OF THE REGULAR 600–HEDROID AND THE REGULAR 120–HEDROID

180. First half of the 600-hedroid : proving its existence. We shall construct in a hypersphere a net of equal regular tetrahedrons, twenty at a point, with their interiors completely filling the hypersphere. We have already proved that we can in this way fill the part of the hypersphere about a point, and so any " restricted " portion of the hypersphere, with tetrahedrons. What we have to show now is that a certain number of these tetrahedrons will fill the entire hypersphere without overlapping.

* Thus in space of five dimensions there are only three possible types of regular (convex) figures:

the *simplex*, corresponding to the tetrahedron and pentahedroid,

the *orthogonal*, corresponding to the cube and hypercube, and

the figure reciprocal to the latter, constructed on a set of mutually perpendicular diagonals and corresponding to the octahedron and 16-hedroid.

The hypersphere is a three-dimensional space (Art. 122), and by fixing our attention at any one time upon a sufficiently small portion of it we can carry on our processes as if it were the space of our experience. We shall use the language of the ordinary three-dimensional geometry and say "line" and "plane" instead of "great circle" and "great sphere."

We start with a regular ikosahedron made up of twenty tetrahedrons (Plate I, fig. 1). Let A be the centre and B any one of the vertices. The radii AB, as well as the edges BB, are edges of the tetrahedrons. About each edge there are five tetrahedrons.

Two adjacent tetrahedrons form a double triangular pyramid,* the common face of the two tetrahedrons being the interior of what we may call a cross section of the double pyramid.

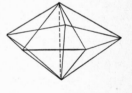

Five tetrahedrons about an edge form a double pentagonal pyramid* with this edge as axis. The cross section is a pentagon whose sides and vertices are edges and vertices of the tetrahedrons.

Let α denote any one of the component tetrahedrons of the ikosahedron. We have

20 tetrahedrons α,

1 vertex A and 12 vertices B,

12 edges AB "   30 edges BB,

30 faces ABB "   20 faces BBB.

---

* The term double pyramid is not used here in the technical sense defined in Art. 32. However, this may be regarded as a limiting case, obtained by rotating the end-pyramids around the plane of their common base until they come into a hyperplane with their vertices on opposite sides of this plane.

To each face BBB attach a tetrahedron β (Fig. 2). The α and β which have this face in common form a double triangular pyramid. We have a new vertex C, three new edges BC, and three new faces BBC. We have added

20 tetrahedrons β,
20 vertices C,
60 edges BC,
and   60 faces BBC.

Along an edge BB we have now two tetrahedrons α and two tetrahedrons β. Along such an edge, therefore, we can put one more tetrahedron γ (fig. 3). This gives us a new edge CC and two new faces BCC. The vertices C and the edges CC are the vertices and sides of a set of pentagons like those on the original ikosahedron. The pentagons of the ikosahedron, however, overlap, while these form a regular dodekahedron. We have added

30 tetrahedrons γ,
30 edges CC,
and   60 faces BCC.

Along an edge BC we have now one tetrahedron β and two tetrahedrons γ. At a vertex B we have five tetrahedrons α, five tetrahedrons β, and five tetrahedrons γ. We can fill the space about B by inserting a double pentagonal pyramid made up of five new tetrahedrons δ (fig. 4). We have a new vertex D. The axis forms an edge BD, a continuation of AB, and there are five new edges CD. There are five faces BCD between the tetrahedrons of the double pyramid, and five faces CCD coming to the point D. We have added

60 tetrahedrons δ,
12 vertices D,
12 edges BD and 60 edges CD,
60 faces BCD " 60 faces CCD.

Along CC we have one tetrahedron γ and two tetrahedrons δ. Along this edge there is room, therefore, for two more tetrahedrons ϵ forming a double triangular pyramid (fig. 5). This gives us a new vertex E, two new edges CE, and two new edges DE. There is one new face CCE between the two tetrahedrons, and there are four new faces CDE coming to the point E. We have added now

$$
\begin{aligned}
&\text{60 tetrahedrons } \epsilon, \\
&\text{30 vertices } E, \\
&\text{60 edges } CE \quad \text{and} \quad \text{60 edges } DE, \\
&\text{30 faces } CCE \quad `` \quad \text{120 faces } CDE.
\end{aligned}
$$

Along CD we have two tetrahedrons δ and two tetrahedrons ϵ. Along CD there is room, therefore, for one more tetrahedron ζ, with one new edge EE and two new faces CEE and DEE (Fig. 6). The vertices E and the edges EE are the vertices and sides of a third set of pentagons like the two sets already mentioned. These pentagons, however, touch only at their vertices, and are separated by triangles. We have added

$$
\begin{aligned}
&\text{60 tetrahedrons } \zeta, \\
&\text{60 edges } EE, \\
&\text{60 faces } CEE \text{ and 60 faces } DEE.
\end{aligned}
$$

Along each edge CE we have two tetrahedrons ϵ and two tetrahedrons ζ, and along each edge DE we have one tetrahedron ϵ and two tetrahedrons ζ.

Now the pentagons and triangles just mentioned lie all in one plane.* If at C we insert a tetrahedron η having the interior of the triangle EEE for face, and at D the half of a double pentagonal pyramid formed by taking a half of each of five tetrahedrons θ, with the interior of the

---

* We say plane instead of great sphere, as explained at the beginning of this article.

pentagon for base, we shall have along the edge EE one tetrahedron ζ, one tetrahedron η, and a half of a tetrahedron θ, forming dihedral angles whose sum is just equal to two right dihedral angles. Therefore it is not necessary to continue our process. We have a plane completely filled with triangles and pentagons and their interiors, and the half of space on one side of this plane completely filled with the tetrahedrons which we have taken, and their interiors. If we continued our process we should have the same figure on the other side of the plane, and the two together would completely fill the elliptic space.

There are

20 tetrahedrons η and 60 tetrahedrons θ.

The total number of tetrahedrons in the entire figure will be the number of each of the kinds α, β, . . . η counted twice, and the number of the tetrahedrons θ counted once. That is, it will be

$$2(20 + 20 + 30 + 60 + 60 + 60 + 20) + 60 = 600.$$

This construction in the hypersphere of 600 equal regular tetrahedrons, which, with their interiors, fill the hypersphere, determines in space of four dimensions a regular polyhedroid containing 600 equal regular tetrahedrons. Its name is *hexakosioihedroid*, or *600-hedroid*.

We can count the number of vertices, edges, and faces, but from any one of these numbers the other three can be computed directly. In fact, the "N" of Art. 177 is 120, and the polyhedroid formula of this polyhedroid is

$$1 - 120 + 720 - 1200 + 600 - 1 = 0.$$

181. Completion of the 600-hedroid. Although it is not necessary to do so, we shall complete the figure by the process employed for the first half. The different parts,

Y

as we come to them, will correspond to the parts already formed for the first half, and we shall denote them by the same letters with accents.

After adding the tetrahedrons ζ we had a figure (Fig. 6) on which were triangular cavities at the points C and pentagonal cavities at the points D. In the former we insert double triangular pyramids each made up of two tetrahedrons η and η', and at each point D we put a double pentagonal pyramid formed by taking five tetrahedrons θ (Plate II, fig. 7). The double triangular pyramid gives us a new vertex C', three new edges EC', a new face EEE separating the two tetrahedrons, and three faces EEC' coming to C'. The double pentagonal pyramid gives us a new vertex D', an axis edge DD' in a line with AB and BD, and five new edges ED' coming to D'. It gives us five faces DED', common faces of successive tetrahedrons around the axis, and five faces EED' coming to D'. Corresponding to themselves in the two halves of the figure are the tetrahedrons θ, the vertices E, the edges EE and DD', and the faces EEE and DED'.

Along EE there is room for one tetrahedron ζ', with a new edge $D'C'$ and two new faces $ED'C'$ (fig. 8).

At the point E we can still insert a double triangular pyramid (fig. 9), corresponding to the one which first produced the vertex E (fig. 5). This is formed of tetrahedrons ϵ', giving us the new edge $C'C'$, a dividing face $EC'C'$, and two new faces $D'C'C'$. The points C' are the vertices of twelve pentagons forming a regular dodekahedron, outside of which our figure lies.

At the point D' we insert a double pentagonal pyramid (fig. 10), corresponding to that which first produced the vertex D. This is composed of five tetrahedrons δ'. We have a new vertex B', a new edge, the axis $D'B'$, and five new edges $C'B'$. We have five new faces $D'C'B'$, common

faces of successive tetrahedrons around the axis, and five
new faces $C'C'B'$ coming to the point B'.

Along the edge $C'C'$ we have two tetrahedrons ϵ' and
two tetrahedrons δ'. We have room, here, then, for one
more tetrahedron γ', giving us one new edge $B'B'$ and two
new faces $C'B'B'$ (fig. 11).

At the point C' we can still insert one tetrahedron β',
with the face $B'B'B'$ (fig. 12).

Our figure now encloses a regular ikosahedron like that
with which we started. It contains twenty tetrahedrons
α', with one new vertex A', twelve new edges $B'A'$, and
thirty new faces $B'B'A'$ (fig. 13).

On the following page is a table of all the parts of the
regular 600-hedroid.

**182. The seventy-two dekagons in a 600-hedroid.
The angle subtended at the centre by an edge.** We have
noticed that the edges AB, BD, and DD' lie along the
same line. From A to A' one of these lines contains five
edges, and the entire line must contain ten edges; the ten
edges and their extremities make up the entire line. In the
complete figure there are seventy-two such lines, each line
running along ten of the 720 edges.

In the hypersphere there are seventy-two great circles;
and in hyperspace there are seventy-two planes through
the centre of the 600-hedroid, each intersecting the polyhedroid in a regular dekagon whose sides are all edges of
the polyhedroid. An edge of the 600-hedroid, therefore,
subtends an angle of 36° at the centre; and a set of regular pentahedroids, 600 at a point, having as they do face
angles of 60°, with their interiors would more than fill the
part of Euclidean hyperspace about the point, so that
such a set must belong to Hyperbolic Geometry (see
Art. 179).

Tetrahedrons		Vertices		Edges		Faces	
α	20	A	1	AB	12	ABB	30
		B	12	BB	30	BBB	20
β	20	C	20	BC	60	BBC	60
γ	30			CC	30	BCC	60
δ	60	D	12	BD	12	BCD	60
			45	CD	60	CCD	60
			2				
			90				
ϵ	60	E	30	CE	60	CCE	30
				DE	60	CDE	120
					324		
					2		
					648		
ζ	60			EE	60	CEE	60
						DEE	60
							560
							2
							1120
η	20					EEE	20
	270						
	2						
	540						
θ	60			DD'	12	DED'	60
	600		120		720		1200

183. Construction of the 120-hedroid. In the manner in which we have constructed the regular 600-hedroid we can construct a regular polyhedroid with four dodekahedrons at a point.

Starting with a dodekahedron α, we attach a dodeka-hedron β to each face (Plate III, fig. 14). About any vertex A of α we have three new dodekahedrons, with a common edge which extends outwards from A to a vertex B. The face common to two adjacent β's has for its vertices two A's, two B's, and a vertex C, the highest

PLATE II.

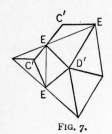

FIG. 7.

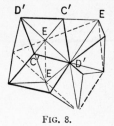

FIG. 8.

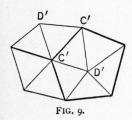

FIG. 9.

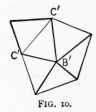

FIG. 10.

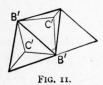

FIG. 11.

FIG. 12.

FIG. 13.

point of this face. Each dodekahedron β has at the top a face DD. . . .

At B we have now a triangular cavity in which we can insert a dodekahedron γ (Fig. 15). Each γ is attached to three others. The face common to two adjacent γ's has for vertices one C, two D's, and two new vertices E. The two γ's form a figure with a neck across which this face cuts. Each γ has three new vertices F, and at the very top one new vertex G.

The outer face of the dodekahedron β now becomes the base of a pentagonal cavity in which we can insert a dodekahedron δ (Fig. 16). Each δ has at the top a face with five new vertices H. Two δ's resting above two adjacent faces of the original dodekahedron α are separated by the neck joining two adjacent γ's. The upper edge of this neck, EE, is now at the base of a cavity in which we can insert a dodekahedron ϵ edgewise.

If instead of a dodekahedron ϵ we take a half, cut off by the plane of two opposite edges, we shall have along the edge HH one dodekahedron δ and a half of a dodekahedron ϵ, forming dihedral angles whose sum is just equal to two right dihedral angles (Fig. 17). The section of the ϵ will lie in a plane with the upper face of the δ, and the half of space on one side of this plane will be filled.* The plane contains a set of regular pentagons, and a set of hexagons with two sides equal to the sides of a pentagon and four sides equal to the altitudes of a pentagon, the pentagons and hexagons with their interiors filling the plane.

The highest point of a dodekahedron γ does not appear in this plane, being at a distance equal to one-half of the edge beneath the point common to three adjacent hexagons.

We have one dodekahedron α, twelve β's, twenty γ's,

* See foot-note, p. 320.

and twelve δ's, making forty-five besides the half-dodeka-
hedrons ε, of which there are thirty. Thus the total
number in the entire figure will be

$$2 \times 45 + 30 = 120.$$

The name of the figure is *hekatonikosahedroid* or 120-*hedroid*,
and its polyhedroid formula is

$$1 - 600 + 1200 - 720 + 120 - 1 = 0.$$

Below is a table for the 120-hedroid, corresponding to
the table on p. 324.

DODECAHEDRONS		VERTICES		EDGES		FACES	
α	1	A	20	AA	30	AA . . .	12
β	12	B	20	AB	20	AA . . C	30
		C	30	BC	60	B . . DD	60
		D	60	CD	60	DD . . .	12
				DD	60		
γ	20	E	60	DE	60	C . . EE	30
		F	60	EE	30	DD . . F	60
		G	20	EF	120	EE . . G	60
			270	FG	60		
			2				
			540				
δ	12	H	60	FH	60	E . . HH	60
	45				560		324
	2				2		2
	90				1120		648
				HH	60	HH . . .	12
ε	30			GG′	20	G . . G′	60
	120		600		1200		720

PLATE III.

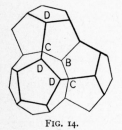

FIG. 14.

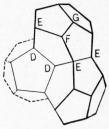

FIG. 15.

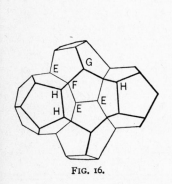

FIG. 16.

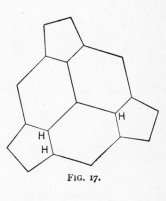

FIG. 17.

TECHNICAL TERMS

In this list are some of the terms of four-dimensional geometry not used in the text and of *n*-dimensional geometry, also terms equivalent to some that are used, and the principal abbreviations. In most cases a reference is added. For terms used or explained in the text, see Index.

The following are the authors most frequently mentioned, many of the references being given in full in the preceding pages: Cayley, *Math. Papers* (p. 5); Clifford, *Math. Papers* (p. 5); Cole (p. 142); Dehn (p. 288); Enriques, *Encyclopédie*, vol. III₁ (p. 15); Jouffret (p. 9); Loria (p. 9); Pascal, *Repertorium der höheren Mathematik*, Ger. trans. by Schepp, vol. II, Leipzig, 1902; Poincaré, *Proc. London Math. So.*, vol. 32 (p. 12); Riemann (p. 6); Schläfli (p. 22); Schoute (p. 9); Stringham (p. 289); Sylvester, 1851 and 1863 (p. 5); Veronese, *Grundzüge*, etc. (p. 9); Wilson and Lewis (p. 12).

The numbers refer always to pages.

Achtzell, Z_8, reguläre, *hypercube;* —-netz; Schoute, II, 202, 242. See *Zell.*

Allomorph, *allomorphic,* two polyhedrons having the same number of vertices and edges, and the same number of faces of each kind that they have; similarly of polyhedroids; Schoute, II, 22–23. See *Isomorph.*

Ankugel, Ankugelraum, Anradius, see *Kugel.*

Apothema (of a hypercone), *slant height,* Schoute, II, 302.

Arête, *edge,* Jouffret, 96.

Axe (of a plano-polyhedral angle), *vertex-edge,* see *Kant.*

Basis, *base,* of a pyramid, hyperpyramid, etc., Schoute, II, 35; —-raum, Schoute, II, 242; used also of the base of a linear system of spaces (*e.g.,* the line common to the linear system formed from the equations of three hyperplanes in R_4), Schoute, I, 141.

Bildraum, the space of the figure of descriptive geometry, the space in which all the different projections are placed together, Schoute, I, 88, 124.

Bipiano (Ital.), R_{n-2} in R_n, Pascal, 577.

C^5, C^8, C^{16}, C^{24}, C^{120}, C^{600}, the six regular polyhedroids, Jouffret, 103.

Case, *cell;* hypercase, corresponding term in space of five dimensions; Poincaré, 278. See Jouffret, 96, 103.

Cell, *case, Grenzraum, Seitenraum, Zell;* (of a hyperplane angle) *Schenkelraum.*

-cell, *-hedroid,* Maschke, *Am. Jour. Math.*, vol. 18, 181.

Configuration, Cayley-Veronese (p. 5), Carver, *Trans. Am. Math. So.*, vol. 6, 534.

Confine, *polyhedroid of n dimensions;* face of a —, $(n-1)$-*boundary;* prime —, *simplex;* rectangular prime —, with edges at one vertex equal and perpendicular to one another; Clifford, 603.

Cylinderraum, $(Cy)_k$, of k dimensions, *hypercylinder;* sphärisch, with spherical bases; — zweiter Stufe, with cylinders for bases (Art.

147); *s*-ter Stufe $(k + s)$-ter Dimension, $Cyl[(\overline{Po})_k, RV(s)]$, what a prism of this kind becomes when the bases, $(Po)_k$, are no longer entirely linear (see *Prisma*); Schoute, II, 293. Kreiscylinder *plano-cylindrical hypersurface with right directing-circle* (Art. 148), Veronese, 557.

Decke, *vertex-face*, analogous to vertex-edge, Schoute, II, 4.

Demi-, *half-*; — espace, *half-hyperplane;* Jouffret, 60.

Dièdre d'espaces, *hyperplane angle*, Jouffret, 60.

Ditheme, *surface*, see *Theme*.

Differentielle, géométrie métrique, *restricted geometry*, see *Restreint*.

Dreikant, *trihedral angle*, see *Kant*.

Droite-sommet, *vertex-edge*, Jouffret, 92.

Eben, *flat;* Ebene, *plane;* used by Pascal for an $(n - 1)$-dimensional flat, E_{n-1}, the same as R_{n-1}, 577; Dreieben, vierdimensionale Ebentripel, *plano-trihedral angle*, Schoute, II, 8, 4.

Eigentlich, *proper*, not at infinity, see *Uneigentlich*, Schoute, I, 20.

Entendue, *hyperspace* (of four dimensions), Jouffret, 1.

Entgegengesetzte Punkte, *opposite points* (of the Double Elliptic Geometry), see *Gegen-Punkte*.

Espace, *hyperplane*, Jouffret, 2.

Face: — à deux dimensions, *face angle* (of a tetrahedroidal angle), *half-plane* (of a plano-trihedral angle); — à trois dimensions, *dihedral angle;* — à quatre dimensions, *hyperplane angle;* Jouffret, 62–63.

First, *vertex-edge*, Schoute, II, 4.

Flat noun and adjective), *linear*, *homaloid* (or *omaloid*), eben, *flach*.

Fluchtpunkt (of a line), the point at

infinity (the "vanishing point" of perspective), Schoute, I, 2; Fluchtraum (of R_n), Schoute, I, 124.

Fold: two-fold, *n*-fold, applied to figures, angles, boundaries, spheres, etc., to indicate the number of their dimensions, Stringham; see *Manifold*. A *k*-fold relation in space of *m* dimensions gives an $(m - k)$-dimensional locus, Cayley, VI, 458; see *Omal*.

Fünfzell, Z_5, *pentahedroid*, Schoute, II, 4; see *Zell*.

g_∞, *line at infinity*, Schoute, I, 21.

Gegen-Punkte or entgegengesetzte Punkte, *opposite points* (as in the Double Elliptic Geometry, see footnote, p. 215), Veronese, 237.

Gegenüber, *opposite* (as in a trihedral angle each edge is opposite the face which contains the other two), Veronese, 449; see also Schoute, I, 268.

Gemischt, having both proper and improper points; gemischtes Simplex, $S_\rho(d)$; Schoute, I, 29.

Gerade, *right*, Schoute, II, 108, 293; schief when not gerade.

Gleichwinklige Ebene, *isocline planes*, Veronese, 539.

Grad von Parallelismus, Orthogonalitätsgrad, see *Parallel*, *Orthogonal*.

Grenzraum, *cell*, Schoute, I, 10; Grenztetraeder, Schoute, II, 218.

Half-, *semi-*, *demi-*, *halb-*.

Hécatonicosaédroïde, C^{120}, *120-hedroid*, Jouffret, 105, 169.

-hedroid, Stringham.

Hexacosiédroïde, C^{600}, *600-hedroid*, Jouffret, 105, 169.

Hexadécaédroïde, C^{16}, *16-hedroid*, Jouffret, 105, 128.

Homaloid, *flat*, represented by an equation or by equations of the first degree, Sylvester, 1851; written also omaloid; see *Theme*.

Huf, polyhedron in which two faces

are polygons of the same number of sides with one side in common (Ferse) and the remaining sides of one connected with the remaining sides of the other by two triangles and by quadrilaterals; in R_n a polyhedroid formed in a similar way. Particular cases are the Prismenkeil and the Pyramidenkeil. Schoute, II, 26, 41, 43.

Hundertzwanzigzell, Z_{120}, *120-hedroid*, Schoute, II, 213.

Hyper-: hyperlocus, Sylvester, 1851, 8, 12; — plane, — planar,— pyramid, — pyramidal, — geometry, — theory, — ontological, Sylvester, 1863, 172–177; Ital. iper-.

Hypercone, *hypercone de première espèce*, *Kegelraum*.

Hypercone de première espèce, *hypercone;* de seconde espèce, *double cone;* Jouffret, 92.

Hypercube, *tesseract, octaédroïde, Achtzell, Masspolytop, Oktaschem* (see *-schem*).

Hypercylinder, *Cylinderraum.*

Hyperebene, R_{n-1} (or E_{n-1}, Pascal, 577).

Hyperparallelopiped, *parallélépipède à quatre dimensions, Parallelotop, Paralleloschem* (see *-schem*).

Hyperplane, *lineoid, quasi-plane, espace, plan, Hyperebene, Raum.*

Hyperplane angle, *dièdre d'espaces, Raumwinkel.*

Hyperprism, *Prisma.*

Hyperpyramid, *Pyramide.*

Hypersolid, *Confine, Polytop.*

Hyperspace, *4-space, l'entendue, Hyperraum* (Pascal, 577).

Hypersphere, *quasi-sphere, Kugelraum, n-Sphäre, Polysphäre.*

(Hyper)$^{p-3}$ surface, of $p - 1$ dimensions in space of p dimensions; *e.g.*, in space of five dimensions, hyper-hyper-surface. H. R. Greer, "Question 2503," *Math. Questions from the Educational Times*, vol. 10: 100.

Icosatétraédroïde, C^{24}, *24-hedroid*, Jouffret, 105, 137.

Ideal, *improper, uneigentlich.*

Inkugel, see *Kugel.*

Ineunt points, the points of a locus, Cayley, VI, 469. In the same way he uses the expression, "tangent omals of an envelope."

Inhalt, *volume, hypervolume*, etc., Schoute, II, 94.

Iper- (Ital.), *hyper-*, Loria, 302.

Isocline planes, *plans d'angles égaux, plans à une infinité d'angles, gleichwinklige Ebene.*

Isomorph, *isomorphic*, allomorphic polyhedrons or polyhedroids are isomorphic when faces or cells which come together in one always correspond to faces or cells which come together in the other. Schoute, II, 22–23. See *Allomorph.*

Isomorphic geometries are different interpretations of the same abstract geometry (see p. 15).

K_k, *Kugelraum*, see this word.

Kant, *edge*, Schoute, I, 9; Dreikant, *trihedral angle*, Schoute, I, 271; Vierkant, *tetrahedroidal angle*, Schoute, I, 267; *n*-Kant, Vielkant, Schoute, I, 279, 286; Scheitelkant, *vertex-edge*, Schoute, I, 268; Dreikant zweiter Art, *plano-trihedral angle*, Axe, its *vertex-edge*, Veronese, 540, 544; reguläre *m*-Kant *p*-ter Art, Schoute, II, 140.

Kantenwinkel (of a Vierkant), *face angle*, Schoute, I, 268.

Kegel: Kreiskegel erster Art, *plano-conical hypersurface of revolution;* zweiter Art, *conical hypersurface of double revolution* (Art. 112), Veronese, 557.

Kegelraum, $(Ke)_k$, of k dimensions, *hypercone;* — zweiter Stufe, *double cone, s*-ter Stufe $(k + s)$-ter Dimension, $Ke[(\overline{Po})_k, S(s)]$, what a pyramid of this kind becomes when the base, $(Po)_k$, is no longer entirely linear (see *Pyramide*) ; the Kegelraum (of any kind) is sphärisch, if the base is spherical, gerade if also the centre of the base is the projection of the entire vertexsimplex upon the space of the base, reguläre if, further, the vertexsimplex is regular and its centre is the projection upon its space of the centre of the base, schief if not gerade; Schoute, II, 292–293.

Keil, *dihedral angle*, Veronese, 444; *hyperplane angle* (Keil von vier Dimensionen), Veronese, 544; *plano-polyhedral angle*, Dehn, 571. *Prismenkeil, Pyramidenkeil*, see these words.

Kiste, $(Ki)_k$, of k dimensions, *rectangular parallelopiped* or *hyperparallelopiped*, Schoute, II, 94.

Kontinuum, the aggregate of all solutions of an equation or of a system of equations, *locus* or *spread*, Schläfli, 6.

Kreiscylinder, Kreiskegel, see *Cylinder, Kegel*.

Kreuzen, used of lines not parallel and not intersecting, also of other spaces; often used with senkrecht, Schoute, I, 43–44.

Kugel, *hypersphere* (of any number of dimensions), Veronese, 592. With Veronese Kugel denotes the interior, Kugeloberfläche the hypersurface; see *Kugelraum;* — -netz, net of regular polygons on a sphere, Schoute, II, 154; Ankugel, sphere tangent to the edges of a regular polyhedron, Inkugel, *inscribed sphere,·* Umkugel, *circumscribed sphere;* Ankugelraum, Anradius, etc.; Schoute, II, 151, 199, 245.

Kugelraum, K_{n-1} or K_n, *hypersphere*, Schoute, I, 127. With Schoute

Kugelraum is the hypersurface, not the interior. In space of n dimensions it is of $n - 1$ dimensions, and he writes K_{n-1}, but later he writes K_n, the subscript denoting the number of dimensions of the space. See foot-note, II, 263.

Leit-, *directing-;* — strahl, — kurve, — raum; Schoute, I, 98, 117, 199, etc.

Linear, *flat*, spaces as defined in Art. 2, represented by equations of the first degree.

Lineoid, *hyperplane*, Cole, 192; collineoidal, Keyser, *Bull. Am. Math. So.*, vol. 9: 86.

Lösung, *point*, used by Schläfli to denote a set of values of the variables satisfying given equations, and then for any set of values, like Cauchy's "analytical point" (p. 6), Schläfli, 6.

Lot, *perpendicular line*, Schoute, I, 44; Letvieleck, *simplex with all angles right angles* (in Elliptic Geometry), Schoute, I, 47.

Manifold, *space of any number of dimensions, variety, Mannigfaltigkeit*, Grassmann, Riemann, and others.

Mantel, *lateral boundary*, of a hyperpyramid, etc., Schoute, II, 35.

Masspolytop, *hypercube*, Schoute, II, 93.

Monotheme, *line*, Sylvester; see *Theme*.

Netz, Achtzellnetz, etc., Schoute, II, 242.

Normal, *perpendicular;* (of planes) *absolutely perpendicular;* stereometrisch normale Ebenen, *perpendicular in a hyperplane;* Schoute, I, 70–72; see *Senkrecht*.

Oberfläche, *Inhalt of the boundary*, Schoute, II, 95, 263.

Octaédroïde, C^8, *hypercube*, Jouffret, 83, 118.

Omal or omaloid (both noun and adjective), *line, plane*, etc., *linear,* the same as *homaloid*. If the relation is linear or omal, the locus is a k-fold or $(m - k)$-dimensional (in space of m dimensions) omaloid. Omaloid is used absolutely to denote the onefold or $(m - 1)$-dimensional omaloid, Cayley, VI, 463.

Operationsraum, R_n, the space in which all the figures considered are supposed to lie, as if there were no space of higher dimensions (see Art. 26), Schoute, I, 4.

Opposite, *gegenüber, entgegengesetzte*.

Order, *Richtung, Sinne*.

Orthogonal, teilweise, Orthogonalitätsgrad, Schoute, I, 49; see *Senkrecht*.

Orthogonal figure, *cube, hypercube*, etc., Stringham, 5.

P_∞, *point at infinity*, Schoute, I, 21.

Parallel: planes are parallel "von der ersten Art" if they have the same line at infinity, "von der zweiten Art" if they have only a point in common and this point is at infinity, Veronese, 516; planes are "parallèles suivant le premier mode ou incomplètement parallèles" if their lines at infinity have a single point in common, "parallèles suivant le deuxième mode ou complètement parallèles" if their lines at infinity coincide, Jouffret, 31 (we should notice that these two writers use "first" and "second" in opposite senses); teilweise parallel or halb parallel are terms used by Schoute; in a space of more than four dimensions lower spaces may be "ein Viertel, zwei Viertel or drei Viertel parallel," etc., Schoute, I, 34.

Parallélépipède à quatre dimensions, Jouffret, 82.

Paralleloschem, *hyperparallelopiped*, see *-schem*.

Parallelotop, $(Pa)_k$, of k dimensions, *hyperparallelopiped*, Schoute, II, 39.

Pentaédroïde, C^5, *pentahedroid*, Jouffret, 105, 132.

Perpendicular, absolutely, simply, Cole, 195, 198; simplement ou incomplètement perpendiculaires, absolument ou complètement —, Jouffret, 34; see *Normal, orthogonal, senkrecht*.

Plagioschem, *spherical simplex*, see *-schem*.

Plan (Fr.), *plane;* used by Cayley in 1846 for hyperplane, demi-plan for ordinary plane (I, 321), see also plane; plans d'angles égaux ou plans à une infinité d'angles, *isocline planes*, Jouffret, 77.

Plane, used by Cayley in five-dimensional geometry for a space of four dimensions: "In five-dimensional geometry we have: space, surface, subsurface, supercurve, curve, and point-system according as we have between the six coördinates, o, 1, 2, 3, 4, or 5 equations: and so when the equations are linear, we have: space, plane, subplane, superline, line, and point," IX, 79.

Plano-trihedral angle, *trièdre de seconde espèce*, Dreieben (see *Eben*).

Planoid, *hyperplane*, Wilson and Lewis, 446.

Point: *r* point (Fr.), the space of $r - 1$ dimensions determined by r independent points (Art. 2); bipoint, *line*, d'Ovidio, *Math. Annalen*, vol. 12, 403–404.

Polvierkant, the edges perpendicular to the cells of a given Vierkant (analogous to supplementary trihedral angle), Schoute, I, 268.

$(Po)_k$, of k dimensions, *Polytop;* when the boundaries are not all linear $\overline{(Po)}_k$ is used, Schoute, II, 28, 292.

Polyschem, *polyhedroid*, see *-schem*.

Polysphäre, see *Sphere of n dimensions*.

Polytop, $(Po)_k$, a limited portion of any space, the boundaries $(Po)_{k-1}$; it is generally understood that the boundaries are linear, then it is a *polyhedroid;* Simplexpolytop, one bounded by simplexes, such in R_4 is the Tetraederpolytop or Vierflachzell; Schoute, II, 1, 28.

Prisma, $(Pr)_k$, of k dimensions, *prism*, *hyperprism*, etc.; — zweiter Stufe, with prisms for bases (Art. 136); — *s*-ter Stufe $(k + s)$-ter Dimension, $Pr[(Po)_k, RV(s)]$, the bases parallel $(Po)_k$, the lateral elements parallel Rs, Schoute, II, 37–39; pyramidales Prisma, hyperprism with pyramids for bases, Schoute, II, 41.

Prismenkeil, the *Huf* formed when a hyperprism is cut into two parts by a hyperplane (or by an R_{n-1}) which intersects a base, Schoute, II, 43.

Prismoid, *n*-dimensional polyhedroid bounded by two $(Po)_{n-1}$ in parallel R_{n-1}, and a Mantel of simplexes, $S(n)$, Schoute, II, 44.

Proper, see *Eigentlich*.

Punktwert of a space, the number of independent points in it (Art. 2); for R_d it is $d + 1$; Schoute, I, 12.

Pyramide, $(Py)_k$, of k dimensions, *pyramid*, *hyperpyramid*, etc.; — zweiter Stufe, *double pyramid;* *s*-ter Stufe $(k + s)$-ter Dimension, $Py[(Po)_k, S(s)]$, with a polyhedroid, $(Po)_k$, for base and a vertex-simplex, $S(s)$; Schoute, II, 35–36.

Pyramidenkeil, the *Huf* formed when a hyperpyramid is cut into two parts by a hyperplane (or by an R_{n-1}) which intersects the base, Schoute, II, 41.

Quadrièdre à quatre dimensions, tetraédroïde, *tetrahedroidal angle;* it has six "faces à deux dimensions," four "faces à trois dimensions," and four "trièdres de seconde espèce," Jouffret, 63.

Quasi-plane, R_{n-1} in R_n, Sylvester, 1863, 173; quasisphere, *sphere of any number of dimensions*, Clifford, 604, 605.

R_n, linear space of *n* dimensions; in Schoute R_n is usually the Operationsraum, R_d any space in R_n, $\bar{R}_{d+1} = R_d$, but R_w is used for $\bar{R}_w$, "w" referring to the Punktwert; Schoute, I, 4, 13.

$RV(s)$, the lateral elements, R_s, of a prism or cylinder "*s*-ter Stufe," Schoute, II, 39.

Raum, *space;* used alone for R_3, Schoute, I, 1; Basis-, Bild-, Cylinder-, Kegel-, Kugel-, Seiten-, etc., see these words.

Raumwinkel, *hyperplane angle*, Schenkelräume, its *cells*, Schoute, I, 268.

Region limitée, *restricted region*.

Restreint (Fr.), *restricted*, *region limitée*, *géométrie métrique differentielle*, Enrique, 48, 112.

Richtung, *Sinne*, *order*, Veronese, 381, 456, 498, 550.

Rotation, simple, double, Cole, 201, 209; Rotation von den $(p - 1)$-ten Potenz, when each point describes a K_p (see Art. 116, Th. 1, and Art. 147, Th. 2), Schoute, II, 297.

S_0, S_1, S_2, etc., *point, line, plane*, etc. (*Stern*), Veronese, 509.

$S(d)$, *simplex with d vertices*, Schoute, I, 10; $S_u(d)$, *improper simplex*, $S_g(d)$, *gemischtes Simplex*, Schoute, I, 28, 29.

$S_t(p, q)$, *Simplotop*.

Scheitel, *vertex*, Scheitelkant, *vertex-edge*, Schoute, I, 268.

Schein, *contour* of a figure as seen

from an outside point, Schoute, II, 17.

-schem, -hedroid, used by Schläfli with qualifying prefixes to denote various polyhedroids: Polyschem, 19; paralleloschem, hyperparallelopiped, 12; in space of four dimensions the six regular polyhedroids are, Pentaschem, Oktaschem, Hekkaidekaschem, Eikositetraschem, Hekatonkaieikosaschem, and Hexakosioschem, 46–52; a sphärisches Polyschem is a polyhedroid belonging to the geometry of the n-sphere; it is a Plagioschem when it has n boundaries, the same as simplex; the single parts of the boundary of a sphärisches Polyschem are Perrischeme, 58.

Schenkel (of an angle) side, Schenkelraum (of a hyperplane angle) cell, Schoute, I, 268.

Schief, oblique, Schoute, II, 293.

Sechshundertzell, Z_{600}, 600-hedroid; Schoute, II, 213.

Sechszehnzell, Z_{16}, 16-hedroid; Sechszehnzellnetz, Schoute, II, 202, 242.

Seiten (of a polyhedroidal angle), ebenen —, face angles, — von drei Dimensionen, trihedral angles, Veronese, 544; (of a pentahedroid) faces and cells, Veronese, 547.

Seitenraum, the R_{n-1} of a simplex $S(n + 1)$, Schoute, I, 142.

Semi-parallel, half-parallel.

Senkrecht, perpendicular; — kreuzen, — schneiden; — zugeordnet, polar, used of P_∞; halb —, in R_4 used of planes with one angle a right angle (see Art. 69); in space of more than four dimensions lower spaces may be "ein Viertel, zwei Viertel, or drei Viertel —," etc., Schoute, I, 40–49. Veronese uses senkrecht or "senkrecht von der ersten Art" for planes absolutely perpendicular in R_4, and "senkrecht von der zweiren Art" for planes half-perpendicular, 521.

Sense, order, Sime.

Simplex, triangle, tetrahedron, and in general a polyhedroid whose vertices are all independent (Art. 2). $S(d + 1)$ the simplex in R_d with $d + 1$ vertices, Schoute, I, 9–10, Simplicissimum, prime confine.

Simplex, sphärisch, spherical tetrahedron, etc. Schoute, II, 291.

Simplexpolytop, bounded by simplexes, Schoute, II, 28.

Simplicissimum, simplex, Sylvester, "Question 8242," Math. Questions from Educational Times, 47: 53.

Simplotop, $S_t(p, q)$, obtained by forming two simplexes $S(p + 1)$ and $S(q + 1)$ with one vertex in common from a set of $p + q + 1$ independent points (and so lying in a space R_{p+q}), and then letting each move parallel to itself over the other. A particular case is the doubly triangular prism (see Art. 143), Schoute, II, 44.

Sinne, sense, order, see Richtung.

Situs (Lat.), used by Gauss for direction of a plane, like Stellung, "Disquisitiones generales circa superficies curvas," Werke, IV, 219.

Space, 3-space, 4-space, etc., for R_3, R_4, etc.; the word space is used by Cayley for the highest space considered, like Schoute's Operationsraum, see Plane.

Sphere of n dimensions, hypersphere, n-sphere; called by Schläfli Polysphäre or n-sphäre, Disphäre, circle, Trisphäre, sphere, 58.

Sphärisch Cylinderraum, Kegelraum, Simplex, see these terms.

Spitze, vertex (point, line, or higher space), Veronese, 466, 557, 606.

Spread, surface, hypersurface, represented by an equation or by a system of equations, used with a number to denote the number of its dimensions as 2-spread, 3-spread, etc.; see articles in

Am. Jour. Math. by Carver, vol. 31, Sisam, 33, Eisenhart, 34, Eisland, 35.

Stellung, *direction of a plane, space,* etc., Schoute, I, 26, 75.

Stern, consists of all points collinear with the points of a space and a point outside of the space, used by Veronese to define the different spaces. — erster Art., R_3, — zweiter Art., R_4, etc., Veronese, 424, 507; Schoute, I, 190–192.

Strahl, *line,* Haupt —, Schoute, II, 161; Halb —, Schoute, I, 85.

Straight, *flat;* — vector, *line-vector, plane-vector,* etc.; straight 3-space, *Euclidean,* Lewis, "Four Dimensional Vector Analysis," *Proc. Am. Acad. Arts and Sci.,* v. 46: 166, 173.

Stumpf (of an angle), *obtuse;* (of a prism), *truncated,* etc., Schoute, II, 43, 127.

Subplane, subsurface, see *Plane.*

Superline, supercurve, see *Plane.*

Surface (Cayley), see *Plane.*

Teilweise parallel, orthogonal or senkrecht, see these terms.

Tessaract, *hypercube,* Hinton, *The Fourth Dimension,* London, 1904, 159. Tessaract belongs to a terminology in which the name of a figure designates the number of its axes: pentact, a figure with five axes, penta-tessaract, a regular 16-hedroid, T. Proctor Hall, *Am. Jour. Math.,* vol. 15: 179.

Tetrahedroidal angle, *quadrièdre à quatre dimensions, tetraèdroïde, Vierkant.*

Theme, *spread;* mono-, *line,* or *curve,* di-, *surface,* keno-, *system of points,* homaloid theme, *flat;* terms used by Sylvester in 1851.

Totalität, *hyperspace,* Schläfli, 6.

Trièdre de seconde espèce, *planotrihedral angle,* it has three "faces à deux dimensions," three "faces à trois dimensions," and three

"faces à quatre dimensions," Jouffret, 62.

U_{d-1}, the infinitely distant (uneigentlich) part of R_d, Schoute, I, 22.

$\overline{U}_k = U_{k-1}$ (see R_n), Schoute, I, 45.

Umkugel, see *Kugel.*

Unabhängig, *independent* (points), Veronese, 256.

Uneigentlich, *improper, ideal,* at infinity; — Punkt, *Fluchtpunkt;* also unendlich; Schoute, I, 2, 21.

Variety, *variété,* Enrique, 66; *Varietät,* Schoute, I, 209; *manifold.*

Vertex-edge, *droite-sommet, First, Scheitelkant.*

Vierflachzell, polyhedroid in R_4 bounded by tetrahedrons, *Tetraederpolytop,* Schoute, II, 28.

Vierkant, vierdimensionale —, *tetrahedroidal angle,* Schoute, I, 267.

Vierundzwanzigzell, Z_{24}, *24-hedroid;* — netz; Schoute, II, 203, 242.

Volumeinheit, *unit of volume, hypervolume,* etc., Schoute, II, 95.

Volum, *Inhalt,* Schoute, I, 156.

Weg, *line* or *curve,* Schläfli, 6.

Winkel, *angle,* Kanten-, Flachen-, Raum-, see these words; körperlich — von vier Kanten, *tetrahedroidal angle,* Veronese, 544.

Z_5, Z_8, Z_{16}, Z_{24}, Z_{120}, Z_{600}, the regular polyhedroids, Schoute, II, 203, 213.

Zell, *cell, polyhedroid,* Schoute, II, 196. Schoute uses the term Zell alone for polyhedroid of four dimensions, but with prefixes (Achtzell, Fünfzell, etc.) it seems to refer to the three-dimensional boundaries. See Jouffret, 96.

Zweiflach, used of a polygon in space regarded as having two faces, Schoute, II, 148, 182.

Zweiraum, *hyperplane angle,* Schoute, II, 8; used also of a polyhedron regarded as having two sides in R_4, Schoute, II, 186.

INDEX

Numbers refer to pages.

Absolutely independent points, 24.

Absolutely perpendicular planes, 81; see *Perpendicularity*.

Abstract geometry and different interpretations, 14; see *Geometries, examples of different kinds*.

Alembert, d', on time as the fourth dimension, 4.

Analogies, their assistance, 17; hyperplane angles and dihedral angles, 99; tetrahedroidal angles and trihedral angles, 129; plano-polyhedral angles and polyhedral angles, 133; isocline planes and parallel lines, 194; plano-prismatic hypersurfaces and polygons, 242.

Analytic development of the higher geometry, 6.

Analytical point, — locus, terms used by Cauchy, 6.

Angle, hyperplane, 95; see *Hyperplane angle*.

Angle of a half-line and a hyperplane, 80; of a half-plane and a hyperplane, 104; minimum between two planes, 116.

Angles at infinity, 232–234.

Angles, the two between two planes, 122; the associated rectangular system, the associated sense of rotation, 181.

Applications of the higher geometries: to a problem in probability (Clifford), 5; geometries with other elements, lines in space, spheres, etc., 10; in connection with complex variables, 11; to mechanics, 11; in proofs of theorems in three-dimensional geometry, 13.

Aristotle on the three dimensions of magnitudes, 1.

Axes of a hypercube and a 16-hedroid, 240, 292.

Axiom of Pasch, 30; of parallels, 221; see *Parallels, axiom of*.

Axioms of collinearity, restrictions in Elliptic Geometry, 25.

Axis of a sphere in a hypersphere, 211; of a regular polyhedroidal angle, 312.

Axis-element of a double pyramid, 204; of a double cone, 205.

Axis-plane of a rotation, 142, see *Rotation;* of a circle in a hypersphere, 211; of a plano-cylindrical hypersurface of revolution, 257.

Axis-planes of a conical hypersurface of double revolution, 206.

Base, prismatic, of a hyperprism with tetrahedral ends, 274.

Beginnings of geometry of more than three dimensions, synthetic, 4; analytic, 6.

Beltrami, Hyperbolic Geometry on certain surfaces, 7; kinematics, 13.

Bibliographies, Loria, Sommerville, 9.

Bôcher, our use of the term "infinity," 230.

Boundaries of a hypersolid are three-dimensional, 64.

Boundary-hypersurface of Hyperbolic Geometry, 95, 112.

Cauchy, applied the language of geometry to analysis, 6.

Cayley, early papers, 5; "Memoir on Abstract Geometry," 8.

Cell of a half-hyperspace, 62.

Cells of pentahedroid, 57; polyhedroid, 63; double pyramid, 67; hyperplane angle, 95; polyhedroidal angle, 126; plano-polyhedral angle, 133; prismoidal hypersurface, 235; plano-prismatic hypersurface, 242.

Centroid, 202; see *Gravity, centre of.*

Classes of points constitute figures, 19, 23.

Clifford, problem in probability, 5; "On the Classification of Loci," 8; kinematics, 13.

Closed sphere, passing out of, 79.

Collinear relation, 23; distinguished at first from "on a line," 19, 27; the two axioms, 19, 25.

Collinear with a segment, 25; triangle, 32; tetrahedron, 49; pentahedroid, 58.

Complex variables represented in space of four dimensions, 11, 219.

Cone, double, 70; see *Double cone.*

Configurations of points (Cayley, Veronese), 5, 8.

Conical hypersurface of double revolution inscribed in a hypersphere, intersecting it in the same surface as the inscribed cylinder of double revolution, 263.

Conical, sometimes used for hyperconical, 69.

Conjugate series of isocline planes, 183; see *Isocline planes.*

Continuity of points on a line, 28.

Coolidge, list of systems of geometry, 15.

Corresponding dihedral angles of parallel planes, 223.

Craig, kinematics of four dimensions, 13.

Curvature, Riemann, 7; of the hypersphere, constant, 218.

Cyclical order, 28.

Cylinder, double, 262; see *Double cylinder.*

Cylinder, prism, 259; see *Prism cylinder.*

Cylinders, the set in a prism cylinder, 258.

Cylindrical, sometimes used for hypercylindrical or for plano-cylindrical, 258, 266, 284.

Darboux, hesitated to use geometry of four dimensions, 9.

Dekagons, the seventy-two in a 600-hedroid, 323.

Density, of points on a line, 28.

Descartes, use of "sursolid," 2; knew the polyhedron formula, 300.

Descriptive geometry of four dimensions, 18.

"Determine," meaning in geometry, 19.

Diagrams only indicate relations, 18.

Dihedral angle, its plane angle the same at all points, proof independent of the axiom of parallels, 97; in a hypersphere, its volume, 209.

Dimensions, early references to the number, 1; differences in spaces of an even number and of an odd number, 14; of a rectangular hyperparallelopiped, 239; only three regular figures in a space of five dimensions, 317.

Diophantus, use of "square-square," etc., 2.

Directing-curve of a plano-conical hypersurface, 71; plano-cylindrical hypersurface, 256; similar directing-curves, 257.

Directing-polygon of a plano-polyhedral angle, 137; plano-prismatic hypersurface, 243; similar directing-polygons, 245.

Directing polyhedral angle of a plano-polyhedral angle, 135.

Directing-polyhedron of a polyhedroidal angle, 126; prismoidal hypersurface, 235.

Directing-surface of a hyperconical hypersurface, 69; hypercylindrical hypersurface, 253.

Direction on a line, opposite directions, 27.

Distance between a point and a hyperplane, 78; the minimum between two lines, 105; in a hypersphere, 208; at infinity, 232.

Distances between two great circles in a hypersphere, 217; two lines at infinity, 235.

Dodekahedrons, the net, four at a point, 324.

Double cone, 70; vertex-edge, base, elements, end-cones, 71; cut from a plano-conical hypersurface, 72; circular, axis-element, right, isosceles, generated by the rotation of a tetrahedron, 205.

Double cylinder, directing-curves, interior, right, generated by the directing-curves and their interiors, spread out in a hyperplane, 262; cylinder of double revolution, inscribed in a hypersphere, 263; relation to infinity, 264; volume, 267; hypervolume, 285; ratio to circumscribed and to inscribed hypersphere, 287.

Double Elliptic Geometry, 215; see *Elliptic Non-Euclidean Geometry*.

Double prism, the two sets of prisms, 246; right, regular, its cells spread out in a hyperplane, 248; interior, directing-polygons, 249; generated by the directing-polygons and their interiors, cut into two double prisms, 250; doubly triangular, 251; hyperprisms with prisms for bases as double prisms, relation to infinity, 252; volume, 265; doubly triangular double prisms cut into six equivalent pentahedroids, 280; hypervolume, 282.

Double pyramid, 66; vertex-edge, base, elements, end-pyramids, lateral faces, lateral cells, intersection with a plane, 67; with a hyperplane, 68; cut from a plano-polyhedral angle, 138; axis-element, right, isosceles, regular, 204; in a hyperplane, 318.

Double revolution, conical hypersurface of, 197; with plane elements, 206; its interior all connected, 207; cylinder of, 263, see *Double cylinder;* surface of, in a hypersphere, its importance in the theory of functions, 219; the intersection of the hypersphere with an inscribed cylinder of double revolution and with an inscribed conical hypersurface of double revolution, 263.

Double rotation, 145; in the hypersphere, 218.

Doubly triangular prism, 251.

Duality in the hypersphere, reciprocal figures, 212.

Edge Geometry, the elements half-planes with a common edge, 138; applied to the theory of motion with two points fixed, 173.

Edge of a polyhedron, how defined, 21; of a half-plane, 39; hemisphere, 209.

Edges of a tetrahedron, 45; pyramid, 55; pentahedroid, 57; polyhedroid, 63.

Elements, linear, of two planes, 61.

Elements of geometry, points, 19, 23; of Point Geometry, 113.

Elements of a double pyramid, 67; hyperconical hypersurface, hypercone, 69; plano-conical hypersurface, double cone, 71; polyhedroidal angle, 126; plano-polyhedral angle, 134; plano-prismatic hypersurface, 242; plano-cylindrical hypersurface, 256.

Elliptic Non-Euclidean Geometry: due to Riemann, 7; restrictions to the axioms of collinearity, 25; the points of a line are in cyclical order, 29; modification of proof of minimum distance between two lines, 105; lines with more than one common perpendicular line, 108; lines and planes with more than one common perpendicular line, planes with more than one common

z

perpendicular plane, 112; Edge Geometry is elliptic, 173; the most general motion in hyperspace, 174, 177; volume of a tetrahedron, 211; the geometry of the hypersphere is the Double Elliptic, 215, 217; difference between the Single Elliptic and the Double Elliptic, 215; poles of a hyperplane in four dimensions, 217; space of constant curvature, 218; the geometry at infinity is the Single Elliptic, 233; hypervolume of a pentahedroid, 287; the possible nets of polyhedrons in Elliptic Geometry, 306; a regular polyhedroid can be inscribed in a hypersphere, 309; the possible nets of polyhedroids, 316; see also *Non-Euclidean Geometry, Parallel axiom, Restrictions.*

Enriques, the foundations of geometry, 15; definition of segment, 21.

Euler's name usually associated with the polyhedron formula, 300.

Face angles of a polyhedroidal angle, 126.

Face of a half-hyperplane, 54; hyperplane angle, 95.

Faces of a tetrahedron, 45; pyramid, 55; pentahedroid, 57; polyhedroid, 63; plano-polyhedral angle, 133.

Figure is regarded as a class of points, 19, 23; belong to, lie in, 23.

Five dimensions, only three regular figures, 317.

Foundations, different systems, 15; definitions and intersections of elementary figures particularly considered, 17.

Four dimensions, space of, 24; our restriction to, 16, 59.

Fourth dimension as time, 4, 11; *The Fourth Dimension Simply Explained*, 9.

Gauss considered the higher space a possibility, 10.

Geometries of 1, 2, 3, . . . *n*, . . . dimensions, 24.

Geometries of different kinds, different interpretations of an abstract geometry, 14, 15; the geometry of half-hyperplanes with a common face, 99; Point Geometry, 113; Edge Geometry, 138; system of isocline planes, 197; the hypersphere, 212; system of parallel planes, 244.

Grassmann, *Ausdehnungslehre*, 7.

Gravity, centre of, memoir by Sylvester, 5; of a pentahedroid, 201; tetrahedron, triangle, 202.

Green, problem in attraction, 6.

Half-hyperplane, "half-hyperplane *ABC–D*," face, opposite half-hyperplanes, 54; half-hyperplanes with a common face form a one-dimensional geometry, 99.

Half-hyperspace, "half-hyperspace *ABCD–E*," cell, opposite half-hyperspaces, 62.

Half-hypersphere, 210.

Half-line, "half-line *AB*," "*AB* produced," opposite half-lines, 28.

Half-parallel planes, 224; see *Parallelism.*

Half-perpendicular planes, 85; see *Perpendicularity.*

Half-plane, "half-plane *AB–C*," edge, opposite half-planes, 39.

Halphen, geometry of *n* dimensions, 8.

Halsted, use of the terms "sect" and "straight," 25; proof that a line divides a plane, 37.

Hathaway, application of quaternions to geometry of four dimensions, 13.

Hatzidakis, kinematics of four dimensions, 13.

Hekatonikosahedroid, 326; see *120-hedroid.*

Hexadekahedroid, 291; see *16-hedroid.*

Hexakosioihedroid, 321; see *600-hedroid.*

Hilbert, definition of segment, 21.

Hyperbolic Non-Euclidean Geometry : planes with parallel elements, 95, 112; their common perpendicular plane, 112; boundary-hypersurfaces, 95, 112; translation along a line, 146, along boundary-curves, 146, 168; rotations in a hyperplane around parallel axes, 172; the most general motion in hyperspace, 174; rotations around parallel axis-planes, 178; pentahedroids which have no point equidistant from the five vertices, 199; the possible nets of polyhedrons, 306; a regular polyhedroid can be inscribed in a hypersphere, 309; the possible nets of polyhedroids, 316; see also *Non-Euclidean Geometry*.

Hypercone, 69; intersections, interior, with a cone for base, different ways of regarding it, 70; axis, generated by the rotation of a half-cone, 204; lateral volume, 266; lateral volume of a frustum, 267; hypervolume, 284; hypervolume of a frustum, 285.

Hyperconical hypersurface, directing-surface, elements, 69; of double revolution, 197; its plane elements, 206; its interior all connected, 207; intersection with a hypersphere, spherical directing-surface, 220.

Hypercube, the diagonal twice the edge, its cells spread out in a hyperplane, two forms of projection, 240; as a regular polyhedroid, reciprocal nets, 290; reciprocal relation to the 16-hedroid, 292; diagonals and axes form three rectangular systems, 293; the associated 24-hedroid, 295.

Hypercylinder, 254; lateral hypersurface, interior, spherical, axis, generated by a rectangle, by rotation of a half-cylinder, 255; with cylinders for bases, different ways of regarding it, 255, 261; lateral volume, 266; hypervolume, 284.

Hypercylindrical hypersurface, directing-surface, elements, 253; interior, sections, 254; relation to infinity, 256.

Hyperparallelopiped, its diagonals all bisect one another; rectangular, its dimensions, the square of the length of its diagonal equals the sum of the squares of its four dimensions, 239; as a double prism, 252; hypervolume when rectangular, 271, when oblique, 272.

Hyperplane, 24; "hyperplane *ABCD*," 50; figures which determine it, only one contains four given non-coplanar points, 51; ordinary space a hyperplane, 52; divided by a plane, 53; intersection with a plane, 60; intersection of two hyperplanes, 52, 60; opposite sides of a hyperplane, 62; at infinity, 231.

Hyperplane angle, face, cells, interior, divides the rest of hyperspace, 95; intersection with a hyperplane perpendicular to its face, 96; plane angle, 96, 98; two hyperplane angles are congruent when they have two equal plane angles, 96; the plane angle is the same at all points of the face, 97; as a magnitude, supplementary hyperplane angles, right hyperplane angles, the sum of two, 98; analogous to a dihedral angle, in the geometry of half-hyperplanes, measured by the plane angle, 99; the bisecting half-hyperplane, 100.

Hyperprism, lateral cells, etc., 237; its cells spread out in a hyperplane, 238; with prisms for bases, different ways of regarding it, 239, 252; lateral volume, 265; congruent and equivalent hyperprisms, 271; hypervolume when the bases are prisms, 273; when the bases are tetrahedrons, 274; hyperprism with tetrahedral ends, prismatic base and vertex edge, 274; hyper-volume of any hyperprism, 275.

Hyperpyramid, 63; base, interior, sections, 64; with a pyramid for base, different ways of regarding it, 66; cut from a polyhedroidal angle, 127; axis, regular, 203; lateral volume, of a frustum, 265; hy-pervolume, 276; frustum cut into pentahedroids, hypervolume, 278.

Hypersolid, the interior of a pentahe-droid as a hypersolid, 62; boun-daries are three-dimensional, 64; hypervolume, ratio of two, equiva-lent hypersolids, 270.

Hyperspace, term used to denote the space of four dimensions, 60; di-vided by a hyperplane, not di-vided by a plane, 62.

Hypersphere, great spheres and small spheres, 207; great circles and small circles, 208; distance in a hypersphere, tangent hyperplanes, 208; spherical dihedral angle, its volume, 209; tetrahedron, the sixteen associated tetrahedrons, their volumes, 210; axis and poles of a sphere, axis-plane and polar cir-cle of a circle, 211; their motion in a rotation of the hypersphere, 212; duality, reciprocal figures, 212; the geometry of the hypersphere as an independent three-dimensional geometry, 212; it is the Double Elliptic Non-Euclidean Geometry, 215; the Point Geometry at the centre, 216; the distances between two great circles, parallel great circles, 217; proof from Point Geometry that the geometry of the hypersphere is the Double Elliptic, 217; rotation, double rotation, screw motion, parallel motion, 218; curvature constant, 218; inter-section with a conical hypersurface of double revolution, 220; inter-section with an inscribed cylinder of double revolution a surface of

double revolution, 263; volume, 267; hypervolume, 285.

Hypersurface, 69; of a pentahedroid, 62.

Hypervolume, 270; of a rectangular hyperparallelopiped, 271; any hyperparallelopiped, 272; hyper-prism with prisms for bases, 273; with tetrahedral bases, 274; any hyperprism, 275; hyperpyramid, 276; frustum, 278; double prism, 280; cylindrical and conical hy-persurfaces, 284; hypersphere, 285; ratio of the hypersphere to inscribed and to circumscribed double cylinders, 287; pentahe-droid in elliptic hyperspace, 287.

Ideal points, lines, etc., at infinity, 230.

Ikosatetrahedroid, 296, see 24-he-droid.

Independent points, 24.

Infinity, sense in which the term is used, 230; points, lines, etc., at infinity, all points at infinity in a single hyperplane, 231; dis-tance, angle, 232; dihedral angle, 233; the geometry at infinity is the Single Elliptic, generalizations made possible by the use of these forms of expression, 233; dis-tances between two lines, 235; relation to infinity of the prismoidal hypersurface, 241; hyperparallelo-piped, 241, 253; plano-prismatic hypersurface, double prism, 252; hypercylindrical hypersurface, 256; plano-cylindrical hypersurface, prism cylinder, double cylinder, 264.

Interior of a figure as distinguished from the figure itself, 20; see Seg-ment, Triangle, Polygon, etc.

Intersect, intersection, 23.

Isoclinal angle (Stringham), 125.

Isocline planes, 123, 180; have an infinite number of common per-pendicular planes, 123, 182; series of isocline planes, 182; conjugate series, 183; the two senses in which planes can be isocline, 184; conjugate series isocline in opposite senses, 185; through any line pass two isocline to a given plane in opposite senses, 186; two intersecting planes are isocline to two pairs of planes, 187; when two planes are isocline to a given plane in the same sense the common perpendicular planes which they have with the given plane form a constant dihedral angle, 188; when two planes are isocline to a given plane in opposite senses, there is only one pair of common perpendicular planes, perpendicular to all three, 189; two planes isocline to a third in the same sense are isocline to each other in this sense also, 190; poles and polar series, all the planes of two conjugate series are isocline at an angle of 45° to a single pair of planes, 192; the converse also true, 193; in a system of planes isocline in a given sense any two series have a pair of planes in common, 193; if a plane intersects two isocline planes in lines the corresponding dihedral angles are equal, analogy to parallel lines, 194–196; a system of planes isocline in a given sense forms a two-dimensional geometry, 197; "ordinal" and "cardinal" system (Stringham), 198; a series cuts a hypersphere (with centre at O) in a surface of double revolution with equal radii, 220; projection from one upon the other of two isocline planes produces similar figures, 229.

Isocline rotation, every plane remains isocline to itself, 196.

Isosceles double pyramid, 204; double cone, 205.

Jacobi, generalizations of geometrical formulæ, 6.

Jordan, geometry of *n* dimensions, 8.
Jouffret, *Géométrie à quatre dimensions*, 9.

Kant, reference to the number of dimensions of space, 3.
Keyser, the four-dimensional geometry of spheres, 11; our intuition of hyperspace, 16; the angles of planes, 114; proof that two planes have a common perpendicular plane, 118.
Kinematics of four dimensions, articles by Clifford, Beltrami, Craig, Hatzidakis, 13.
Kwietnewski, complex variables represented in space of four dimensions, 11.

Lagrange, time as the fourth dimension, 4.
Lateral edges, faces, cells, hypersurface, etc., see *Pyramid, Hyperpyramid, Hypercone*, etc.
Layer, 241.
Left, right and left in a plane, 154.
Lewis, G. N., Wilson and Lewis on relativity, 12.
Line, 24; "line *AB*," only one line contains two given points, 26; properties of its points, order, 27; density and continuity, 28; opposite sides in a plane, 38; at infinity, 231.
Linear elements of two planes, 61.
Lobachevsky, *Pangeometry*, 221.
Loria, bibliography, 9.

McClintock, interpretations of Non-Euclidean Geometry, 10.
Methods of studying the higher geometries, 12.
Minkowski developed application to relativity, 12.
Möbius, symmetrical figures, 4.
Moore, E. H., definition of segment, 21.
Moore, R. L., properties of points on a line, 28; axioms of metrical geometry, 74.

More, Henry, spirits are four-dimensional, 3.

Motion in a plane does not change order in the plane, 160; in a hyperplane, does not change order in the hyperplane, 163; in hyperspace, does not change order in hyperspace, 166; in a plane with one point fixed, 167; the most general, 168; in a hyperplane, two equivalent if equivalent for three non-collinear points, motion with one point fixed, 169; every motion in a hyperplane equivalent to a motion of a plane on itself or to a screw motion, 170; in hyperspace, two equivalent if equivalent for four non-coplanar points, 172; motion with two points fixed, 173; with one point fixed, 174; every motion equivalent to a motion in which one plane remains fixed or moves only on itself, 174.

n dimensions, space of, 24.

N-hedroid and $5N$-hedroid, 311; the same as 120-hedroid and 600-hedroid, 321.

Nets of hypercubes, 290; 24-hedroids and 16-hedroids, 298; spherical polygons, 303; polyhedral angles, polyhedrons, 304; polyhedroidal angles, 313; polyhedroids, 314; net of twenty tetrahedrons at a point, 317; four dodekahedrons at a point, 324.

Non-Euclidean Geometry used in the theory of relativity, 12; not particularly considered in this text, 18; translations in, 146; nets of spherical polygons, 303; see also *Elliptic Geometry, Hyperbolic Geometry, Parallelism, Restrictions*.

Non-Euclidean Geometry by the author, 19.

Nöther, birational transformations, 8.

Object and plan of this book, 16, 73.

Octahedroid, regular, 290; see *Hypercube*.

Opposite directions on a line, 27; half-lines, 28; in cyclical order, 29; sides of a line in a plane, 38; half-planes, 39; sides of a plane in a hyperplane, half-hyperplanes, 54; sides of a hyperplane, half-hyperspaces, 62; elements of Point Geometry, 113; elements of Edge Geometry, 138; points in a hypersphere, 210, 213.

Order of points on a line, 27; "order AB," 153; Veblen's use of the term "order," 27; cyclical, 28; order in a plane, 153; two fundamental principles, right and left sides of lines through a point, 154; with respect to a triangle, "order ABC," 156; unchanged by any motion in the plane, 158; independent of any hyperplane, 162; order in a hyperplane, 161; with respect to a tetrahedron, "order $ABCD$," 162; unchanged by any motion in the hyperplane, 163; order in hyperspace, 164; with respect to a pentahedroid, "order $ABCDE$," unchanged by any motion, 165; order in Point Geometry, 179.

Ovidio, d', projective geometry, 12.

Ozanam, higher products imaginary, 3.

Paciuolo, use of "primo relato," etc., 2.

Pangeometry, term used by Lobachevsky, 221.

Parallel axiom, proofs which do not depend on it, 77, 97, 105, 128, 136, 202; restrictions due to its omission, 37, 78, 79, 103, 108, 112, 138, 139, 153, 160; see *Elliptic Geometry and Restrictions*.

Parallelism taken up after many other subjects, 19; parallel great circles in a hypersphere, 217; parallel motion in a hypersphere, 218; axiom of parallels, 221; parallel lines and planes, 221; half-parallel planes, their common perpendicular lines and planes, 224; their minimum distance, their linear elements, 225; lines and planes parallel to a hyperplane, parallel hyperplanes, 226.

Pasch, Axiom, 30.

Pentahedroid, edges, faces, cells, 57; intersection with a plane, 57, 60; interior, collinear with, 58; passing from cell to cell, 59; intersection with a line, 60; the five half-hyperspaces and the interior, 62; sections, 65; its cells or its edges spread out in a hyperplane, 68; the point equidistant from its vertices, 199; the point equidistant from its cells, 200; its centre of gravity, 201; pentahedroids with corresponding edges equal, 202; hypervolume in elliptic hyperspace, 287; regular, 203, 289; radii of circumscribed and inscribed hyperspheres, reciprocal pentahedroids, 289.

Perpendicularity : lines perpendicular to a line at a point, 74; perpendicular line and hyperplane, 75; planes perpendicular to a line at a point; two lines perpendicular to a hyperplane lie in a plane, 76; lines perpendicular to a plane at a point, 80; absolutely perpendicular planes, 81; if two planes intersect in a line, their absolutely perpendicular planes at any point of this line intersect in a line, 82; two planes absolutely perpendicular to a third lie in a hyperplane, 83; perpendicular planes, simply perpendicular, half-perpendicular, or perpendicular in a hyperplane; a plane perpendicular to one of two absolutely perpendicular planes at their point of intersection is perpendicular to the other, 85; a plane intersecting two absolutely perpendicular planes in lines is perpendicular to both, 86; the common perpendicular planes of two planes intersecting in a line, 87; perpendicular planes and hyperplanes, perpendicular along a line, 90; the planes perpendicular or absolutely perpendicular to planes lying in the hyperplanes, 91; lines lying in either and perpendicular to the other, 92; planes with linear elements all perpendicular to a hyperplane, 94; perpendicular hyperplanes, 98; lines or planes lying in one and perpendicular to the other, 101; the common perpendicular line of two lines not in one plane; lines with more than one common perpendicular line, 108; the common perpendicular line of a line and plane; the common perpendicular plane of two planes which have a common perpendicular hyperplane, 111; the common perpendicular planes of two planes which intersect only in a point, 118; planes with an infinite number of common perpendicular planes, 119, 182.

Plan and object of this book, 16, 73.

Plane, 24; "plane ABC," only one contains three given non-collinear points, 35; divided by a line, 37; two planes with only odd point in common, 51, 81; intersection of two in a hyperplane, 53; opposite sides of a plane in a hyperplane, 54; intersection with a hyperplane, 60; linear elements of two planes, 61; absolutely perpendicular planes, 81; perpendicular, 85; see *Perpendicularity;* if two not in a hyperplane have a common perpendicular line, they have a common perpendicular hyperplane, 94; isocline planes, 123; see *Isocline planes;* planes at infinity, 231.

Plane angle of a hyperplane angle, 96; see *Hyperplane angle.*

Plano-conical hypersurface, vertex-edge, directing-curve, elements,

intersection with a hyperplane, 71;
see *Double cone.*

Plano-cylindrical hypersurface, directing-curve, elements, 256; interior, right directing-curves, similar directing-curves, hypersurface of revolution, axis-plane, 257; intersection with plano-prismatic hypersurface, the set of cylinders, 258; intersection of two plano-cylindrical hypersurfaces, 261; the surface of intersection, 262; relation to infinity, 264; see *Prism cylinder* and *Double cylinder.*

Plano-polyhedral angle, faces, vertex-edge, cells, 133; elements, simple, convex, its hyperplane angles, 134; vertical plano-polyhedral angles, 134; directing polyhedral angles, polyhedral angles which are right sections, 135; theorems proved by means of them, 136; directing-polygons, 137; interior, 139, 140.

Plano-prismatic hypersurface, 241; faces, cells, elements, simple, convex, sections, 242; directing-polygons, 243; triangular, similar directing-polygons, 245; intersection of two plano-prismatic hypersurfaces, the two sets of prisms, 246; intersection with a plano-cylindrical hypersurface, 258; see *Double prism* and *Prism cylinder.*

Plano-trihedral angle, 134.

Plücker, the four coördinates of a line in space, 10.

Poincaré avoided use of geometry of four dimensions, 10; on analysis situs, 12; double integrals, 219.

Point, 23; independent and absolutely independent points, 24; at infinity, 231.

Point Geometry, 113; theorems in regard to perpendicular planes stated in the language of Point Geometry, 114; applied to the study of the angles of two planes, 114; plano-polyhedral angles and polyhedroidal angles, 136; Point

Geometry of a rectangular system, 179; in the theory of isocline planes, 180; the same as the geometry of the hypersphere, 216.

Poles and polar series of isocline planes, 193; poles of a sphere and polar circles in a hypersphere, 211; their motion in a rotation, 212; of a hyperplane in Elliptic Geometry of Four Dimensions, 217.

Polygon, sides, diagonals, cyclical order, 40; simple, convex, intersection with a line, 41; divided into two polygons, 42; interior, 44; the half-planes and interior, 45.

Polyhedral angle, 133; convex, can be cut in a convex polygon, 137; nets of polyhedral angles, 304.

Polyhedroid, edges, faces, cells, interior, 63; regular, definition, 289; can be inscribed in a hypersphere, the associated net of hyperspherical polyhedrons, 309; reciprocal polyhedroids, 310; its polyhedroidal angles are regular, 313; nets of polyhedroids, 314; list of possible nets, 315; the nets in each of the non-Euclidean geometries, 316.

Polyhedroid formula, 302; proved by Schläfli, 22; by Stringham, 302.

Polyhedroidal angle, elements, directing-polyhedron, face angles, polyhedral angles, cells, interior, 126; vertical polyhedroidal angles, 127; regular, axis, 312; the polyhedroidal angles of a regular polyhedroid are regular, net, reciprocal nets, 313.

Polyhedron, 63; regular, can be inscribed in a sphere; the associated net of spherical polygons; reciprocal polyhedrons, 303; nets, 304; list of possible nets, 305; the nets in each of the non-Euclidean geometries, 306.

Polyhedron formula, Descartes, Euler, 300.

Popular interest in the fourth dimension, 9.

Powers of a number in early algebra, 2.

Prism, the two sets of prisms in a double prism, 246; see *Double prism*.

Prism cylinder, the set of cylinders, right, regular, spread out in a hyperplane, 259; the directing-polygons and the directing-curves, generated by them and their interiors; cut into two prism cylinders, 260; triangular, hypercylinder with cylinders for bases as a prism cylinder, generated by the rotation of a prism, 261; volume, 267; hypervolume, 285.

Prismatic base of a hyperprism with tetrahedral ends, 274.

Prismoidal hypersurface, directing-polyhedron, edges, faces, cells, interior, sections, 235; with parallelopiped for directing-polyhedron, 236.

Projecting line, 78; plane, 84; factor for area, 229.

Projection upon a hyperplane, 78; of a line is a line or a part of a line, 79, 84; upon a plane, 81; a line and its projection upon a plane not coplanar, 84; of a plane upon a hyperplane, 103; from a plane upon an isocline plane produces similar figures, 229.

Projective geometry, points of a line in cyclical order, 29.

Ptolemy, the number of distances, 1.

Pyramid, base, edges, faces, intersection with a plane, 55; double pyramid, 66; see *Double pyramid*.

Quaternions applied to the study of geometry of four dimensions by Hathaway and Stringham, 13.

Ray or half-line, 28.

Reciprocal figures in a hypersphere, 212; pentahedroids, 289; hypercube and 16-hedroid, 293; 24-hedroids, 297; polyhedrons, 303; polyhedroids, 309; nets, see *Nets*.

Rectangular hyperparallelopiped, 239.

Rectangular system, 87, 89; as a tetrahedroidal angle, 128; ways in which it is congruent to itself, 179; the different arrangements, notation, used in studying the angles of two planes, 180; three belonging to the hypercube and 16-hedroid, 293.

Regular hyperpyramid, 203; pentahedroid, 203, 289; double pyramid, 204; hyperprism, 237; the hypercube is regular, 240, 289; regular double prism, 248; prism cylinder, 259; polyhedroid, 289; octahedroid (hypercube), 290; 16-hedroid, 291; 24-hedroid, 295; a regular polyhedroid can be inscribed in a hypersphere, the associated net of spherical polyhedrons, 309; regular polyhedroidal angle, 312; in space of five dimensions only three regular figures, 317; 600-hedroid, 317; 120-hedroid, 324.

Relativity and the fourth dimension, 11.

Restricted geometry, 19.

Restrictions to the second axiom of collinearity in Elliptic Geometry, 25; necessary in Edge Geometry, 138; a convex plano-polyhedral angle is restricted, 139; in Point Geometry a rectangular system is restricted, 179; restrictions due to omission of the axiom of parallels, see *Parallel axiom;* see also *Elliptic Geometry*.

Revolution, surface of double revolution in a hypersphere of importance in the theory of functions, 219; see *Double revolution*.

Riemann on the foundations of geometry, Elliptic Geometry due to him, 6.

Right and left in a plane, 154; see *Order*.

Rotation in a plane, in a hyperplane, figures remain invariable, 141;

in hyperspace, the axis-plane, 142; figures remain invariable, rotations around absolutely perpendicular planes commutative, 143; double rotation, 145; right and left in a plane, 154; when two rotations are equivalent to a single one in a hyperplane, 171, in hyperspace, 178; isocline, 196; of the hypersphere, the axis-circle and the circle of rotation, double rotation, screw motion, parallel motion, 218.

Rudolph, use of terms representing powers of a number, 2.

Schläfli, multiple integrals, 6; multiple continuity, 22.

Schotten, definitions of segment, 21.

Schoute, *Mehrdimensionale Geometrie*, 9; sections of a simplex, 14; descriptive geometry, 18; different kinds of perpendicularity, 85; the polyhedroid formula, 302.

Schubert, enumerative geometry, 12.

Screw motion, the translation and rotation are commutative, 146; in the hypersphere, 218.

Sect, used by Halsted for segment, 25.

Sections, study of a figure by them, 18; divide a figure into completely separated parts, 65, 245; of a pentahedroid, hyperpyramid, etc., see these terms; of a plano-polyhedral angle, 135.

Segment as defined by different writers, Hilbert, Enriques, E. H. Moore, Veblen, Schotten, 21; definition, "segment *AB*," collinear with, 25; interior, 28.

Segre, the use of geometry of four dimensions, 10, 13.

Semi-parallel, the same as half-parallel, 224.

Separate, of cyclical order, 29.

Series of isocline planes, 182; see *Isocline planes*.

Sides of a polygon, how defined, 21; triangle, 29; polygon, 40; of a line in a plane a property of the

plane, of a plane in a hyperplane a property of the hyperplane, 162.

Similar figures produced by projection from one upon the other of two isocline planes, 229; directing-polygons of a plano-prismatic hypersurface, 245; directing-curves of a plano-cylindrical hypersurface, 257.

Simplex, sections, 14.

Simplicius, reference to Aristotle and Ptolemy, 1.

Solid, the interior of a tetrahedron as a solid, 54.

Sommerville, bibliography, 9.

Space of 1, 2, 3, . . . *n*, . . . dimensions, 24; of four dimensions, 24, 59; ordinary space a hyperplane, 52.

Sphere, its geometry is elliptic, 25; closed, passing out of, 79; in a hypersphere, 207.

Spherical sometimes used for hyperspherical, spherical dihedral angle, tetrahedron, 209.

Stifel regards the higher powers as "against nature," 3.

Straight, used by Halsted for line, 25.

Stringham, application of quaternions to geometry of four dimensions, 13; on the angles of two planes, 114; use of the term "isoclinal angle," 125; "ordinal" and "cardinal systems," of isocline planes, 198; gave a proof of the polyhedroid formula, 302.

Strip, the portion of a plane between two parallel lines, 235.

Surface, the tetrahedron as a surface, 54; of double revolution in a hypersphere, 219; see *Double revolution*.

Sursolid in early algebra, sursolid loci, 2.

Sylvester, early papers, 5; defence of the use of geometry of four dimensions, 10.

Symmetrical figures congruent, Möbius, 4, 149; defined as those that can be placed in positions of symmetry with respect to a plane, 164.

Symmetry, 146; in a plane, in a hyperplane, 147, in hyperspace, 149; rotations which leave the symmetrical relation undisturbed in a plane, 147, in a hyperplane, 148, in hyperspace, 152; rotations which bring into coincidence figures symmetrical in a plane, 147, in a hyperplane, 148; symmetrical figures of ordinary geometry are really congruent, 148; symmetry in a hyperplane with respect to a point can be changed by rotation to symmetry with respect to a plane, 147; figures symmetrical in hyperspace with respect to a point or plane are congruent, 149; symmetry in hyperspace with respect to a line can be changed by rotation to symmetry with respect to a hyperplane, 150; in every kind of symmetry corresponding segments and angles are equal, 153; figures symmetrical in a plane cannot be made to coincide by any motion in the plane, 160; figures symmetrical in a hyperplane cannot be made to coincide by any motion in the hyperplane, 163; figures symmetrical in hyperspace cannot be made to coincide by any motion in hyperspace, 166.

Synthetic development of the higher geometry, 4; advantages of the synthetic method over the analytic, 14.

Tetrahedroidal angle, 127; two with corresponding face angles equal, 129; the bisecting half-hyperplanes of its hyperplane angles have a common half-line, 131.

Tetrahedron, edges, faces, intersection with a plane, 45; with a line, 48, 52; interior, collinear with, 49; the four half-hyperplanes and the interior, 54; correspondence of two, 128; spherical, its volume, 210; net of tetrahedrons, twenty at a point, 317.

Time as the fourth dimension, Lagrange, d'Alembert, 4; relativity, 11.

Translations along a line, figures remain invariable, 145; different kinds of translation in Non-Euclidean Geometry, 146.

Triangle, sides, cyclical order, 29; intersection with a line, 30, 37; interior, 30; collinear with, 32; the three half-planes and the interior, 39.

Use of studying the higher geometries, 13; see also *Applications*.

Veblen, definition of segment, 21; use of the term "order," 27; the properties of points on a line, 28; Axiom of Pasch, 29; axioms of metrical geometry, 74.

Vector analysis of Grassmann, 8.

Veronese, *Fondamenti*, 5, 8, 9; application of the higher geometry to theorems of ordinary geometry, 13; use of the elements at infinity, 230.

Vertex-edge of a double pyramid, 67; double cone, plano-conical hypersurface, 71; plano-polyhedral angle, 133; hyperprism with tetrahedral ends, 274.

Vertical polyhedroidal angles, 127; can be made to coincide, 167; plano-polyhedral angles, 134; cannot be made to coincide, 166.

Vieta, use of terms representing powers of a number, 2.

Volume of a spherical dihedral angle, 209; spherical tetrahedron, 210; at infinity, 233; lateral volume of a hyperprism, hyperpyramid, frustum of a hyperpyramid, 265; hypercylinder, hypercone, 266, frustum of a hypercone, 267; volume of a double prism, 265, 266, prism cylinder, double cylinder, 267; hypersphere, 267.

Wallis on the geometrical names of the higher powers, 3.

Wilson and Lewis, relativity, 12.

16-hedroid or hexadekahedroid, 291; axes, reciprocal relation to the hypercube, 292; diagonals of the hypercube and the 16-hedroid form three rectangular systems, 293; the associated 24-hedroid, 295; reciprocal nets of 16-hedroids and 24-hedroids, 298.

24-hedroid or ikosatetrahedroid, associated with a hypercube and a 16-hedroid, 295; reciprocal 24-hedroids, 297; reciprocal nets of 16-hedroids and 24-hedroids, 298.

120-hedroid or hekatonikosahedroid, construction, 324; table of its parts, 326.

600-hedroid, or hexakosioihedroid, construction of the first half, 317; completed, 321; its seventy-two dekagons, 323; table of its parts, 324.

THE following pages contain advertisements of a
few of the Macmillan books on kindred subjects

GEOMETRY

BY

WALTER BURTON FORD

Junior Professor of Mathematics, University of Michigan

And **CHARLES AMMERMAN**

The William McKinley High School, St. Louis

Edited by Earle Raymond Hedrick, Professor of Mathematics
in the University of Missouri

> *Plane and Solid Geometry, cloth, 12mo, 319 pp., $1.25 net*
> *Plane Geometry, cloth, 12mo, 213 pp., $0.80 net*
> *Solid Geometry, cloth, 12mo, 106 pp., $0.80 net*

STRONG POINTS

I. The authors and the editor are well qualified by training and experience to prepare a textbook on Geometry.

II. As treated in this book, geometry functions in the thought of the pupil. It means something because its practical applications are shown.

III. The logical as well as the practical side of the subject is emphasized.

IV. The arrangement of material is pedagogical.

V. Basal theorems are printed in black-face type.

VI. The book conforms to the recommendations of the National Committee on the Teaching of Geometry.

VII. Typography and binding are excellent. The latter is the reënforced tape binding that is characteristic of Macmillan textbooks.

" Geometry is likely to remain primarily a cultural, rather than an information subject," say the authors in the preface. " But the intimate connection of geometry with human activities is evident upon every hand, and constitutes fully as much an integral part of the subject as does its older logical and scholastic aspect." This connection with human activities, this application of geometry to real human needs, is emphasized in a great variety of problems and constructions, so that theory and application are inseparably connected throughout the book.

These illustrations and the many others contained in the book will be seen to cover a *wider range* than is usual, even in books that emphasize practical applications to a questionable extent. This results in a better appreciation of the significance of the subject on the part of the student, in that he gains a truer conception of the wide scope of its application.

The logical as well as the practical side of the subject is emphasized.

Definitions, arrangement, and method of treatment are logical. The definitions are particularly simple, clear, and accurate. The traditional manner of presentation in a logical system is preserved, with due regard for practical applications. Proofs, both formal and informal, are strictly logical.

THE MACMILLAN COMPANY

Publishers   64–66 Fifth Avenue   New York

THE CALCULUS

BY

ELLERY WILLIAMS DAVIS

PROFESSOR OF MATHEMATICS, THE UNIVERSITY OF NEBRASKA

Assisted by WILLIAM CHARLES BRENKE, Associate Professor of
Mathematics, the University of Nebraska

Edited by EARLE RAYMOND HEDRICK

*Cloth, semi-flexible, xxi + 383 pp. + Tables (63), 12mo, $2.00 net
Edition De Luxe, flexible leather binding, India paper, $2.40 net.*

This book presents as many and as varied applications of the Calculus
as it is possible to do without venturing into technical fields whose subject
matter is itself unknown and incomprehensible to the student, and without
abandoning an orderly presentation of fundamental principles.

The same general tendency has led to the treatment of topics with a view
toward bringing out their essential usefulness. Rigorous forms of demonstra-
tion are not insisted upon, especially where the precisely rigorous proofs
would be beyond the present grasp of the student. Rather the stress is laid
upon the student's certain comprehension of that which is done, and his con-
viction that the results obtained are both reasonable and useful. At the
same time, an effort has been made to avoid those grosser errors and actual
misstatements of fact which have often offended the teacher in texts otherwise
attractive and teachable.

Purely destructive criticism and abandonment of coherent arrangement
are just as dangerous as ultra-conservatism. This book attempts to preserve
the essential features of the Calculus, to give the student a thorough training
in mathematical reasoning, to create in him a sure mathematical imagination,
and to meet fairly the reasonable demand for enlivening and enriching the
subject through applications at the expense of purely formal work that contains no essential principle.

THE MACMILLAN COMPANY
Publishers   64-66 Fifth Avenue   New York

Analytic Geometry and Principles of Algebra

BY

ALEXANDER ZIWET

PROFESSOR OF MATHEMATICS, THE UNIVERSITY OF MICHIGAN

AND **LOUIS ALLEN HOPKINS**

INSTRUCTOR IN MATHEMATICS, THE UNIVERSITY OF MICHIGAN

Edited by **EARLE RAYMOND HEDRICK**

Cloth, viii + 369 pp., appendix, answers, index, 12mo, $1.60 net

This work combines with analytic geometry a number of topics traditionally treated in college algebra that depend upon or are closely associated with geometric sensation. Through this combination it becomes possible to show the student more directly the meaning and the usefulness of these subjects.

The idea of coördinates is so simple that it might (and perhaps should) be explained at the very beginning of the study of algebra and geometry. Real analytic geometry, however, begins only when the equation in two variables is interpreted as defining a locus. This idea must be introduced very gradually, as it is difficult for the beginner to grasp. The familiar loci, straight line and circle, are therefore treated at great length.

In the chapters on the conic sections only the most essential properties of these curves are given in the text; thus, poles and polars are discussed only in connection with the circle.

The treatment of solid analytic geometry follows the more usual lines. But, in view of the application to mechanics, the idea of the vector is given some prominence; and the representation of a function of two variables by contour lines as well as by a surface in space is explained and illustrated by practical examples.

The exercises have been selected with great care in order not only to furnish sufficient material for practice in algebraic work but also to stimulate independent thinking and to point out the applications of the theory to concrete problems. The number of exercises is sufficient to allow the instructor to make a choice.

To reduce the course presented in this book to about half its extent, the parts of the text in small type, the chapters on solid analytic geometry, and the more difficult problems throughout may be omitted.

THE MACMILLAN COMPANY

Publishers   64–66 Fifth Avenue   New York   4121-3

TRIGONOMETRY

BY

ALFRED MONROE KENYON

PROFESSOR OF MATHEMATICS, PURDUE UNIVERSITY

AND **LOUIS INGOLD**

ASSISTANT PROFESSOR OF MATHEMATICS, THE UNIVERSITY OF
MISSOURI

Edited by EARLE RAYMOND HEDRICK

Trigonometry, flexible cloth, pocket size, long 12mo (xi + 132 pp.) with Complete Tables (xviii + 124 pp.), $1.35 net

Trigonometry (xi + 132 pp.) with Brief Tables (xviii + 12 pp.), $1.00 net

Macmillan Logarithmic and Trigonometric Tables, flexible cloth, pocket size. long 12mo (xviii + 124 pp.), $0.60 net

FROM THE PREFACE

The book contains a minimum of purely theoretical matter. Its entire organization is intended to give a clear view of the meaning and the immediate usefulness of Trigonometry. The proofs, however, are in a form that will not require essential revision in the courses that follow. . . .

The number of exercises is very large, and the traditional monotony is broken by illustrations from a variety of topics. Here, as well as in the text, the attempt is often made to lead the student to think for himself by giving suggestions rather than completed solutions or demonstrations.

The text proper is short; what is there gained in space is used to make the tables very complete and usable. Attention is called particularly to the complete and handily arranged table of squares, square roots, cubes, etc.; by its use the Pythagorean theorem and the Cosine Law become practicable for actual computation. The use of the slide rule and of four-place tables is encouraged for problems that do not demand extreme accuracy.

Only a few fundamental definitions and relations in Trigonometry need be memorized; these are here emphasized. The great body of principles and processes depends upon these fundamentals; these are presented in this book, as they should be retained, rather by emphasizing and dwelling upon that dependence. Otherwise, the subject can have no real educational value, nor indeed any permanent practical value.

THE MACMILLAN COMPANY

Publishers   **64-66 Fifth Avenue**   **New York**